VERNON ♂
COLLECTORS' GUIDE
TO
ORDERS, MEDALS & DECORATIONS
(With Valuations)

Fourth (Revised) Edition

by
Sydney B. Vernon

Sydney B. Vernon
Box 890280, Temecula, CA 92589-0280, USA

Published by
Sydney B. Vernon
P.O. Box 890280, Temecula CA 92589-0280 ,U.S.A.

ISBN 0-9623575-4-5

CONTENTS

PREFACE

I have decided to write a preface to the IV edition to make clearer my purposes in writing this work, and to show how to use it most effectively.

This book is not a list of prices as so many are fond of suggesting, but rather a statement of values. A price is a fact. A certain amount of money changes hands after a seller and buyer come to an agreement, and an item is sold. However, a value is an opinion. Thus, on any given day an item will sell for whatever someone is willing to pay for it. When the value of an item to the buyer matches the value of an item to a seller, then a price is established. If they don't agree on value then the price is irrelevant, because the item won't be sold.

No one is required to buy or sell at the values listed herein. This is a value guide, and the operative word is "Guide." So this book is intended as an aid in helping the collector in making up his mind as to what he wants to collect and how much he wishes to spend. The dealer is of course interested in what the collector is willing to pay.

I am very complimented that some collectors have described it as their "bible," but I beg to differ. I will be most satisfied if collectors are guided by this work, not that they regard it some sacred writings to be adhered to blindly.

The basis principle behind *VERNON'S COLLECTORS' GUIDE . . .* is to provide a listing of values of Orders, Medals, and Decorations from the most commonly collected countries and/or topics. The values are in U.S. $ because the U.S.A. is the premium market for this whole field of collectibles. In most countries the awards collected are from that country, with few collecting those from other nations. In the U.S.A. because of our unique ethnic makeup there is a much wider range of interest. Some items may be higher or lower in value in the country of origin, than in the U.S.A.

Many factors may determine value; including rarity, beauty, popularity, as well as, not the least of all, currency fluctuation. Values have risen for many items in the last 25 years, but those of Germany in particular have soared in value because of the great increase in the value of the German Mark versus the consequent loss in that of the U.S. Dollar.

Rarity can be affected by political events as with the collapse of the U.S.S.R. and the subsequent flood of material into the international market. Values, and prices have plummeted. However, with newly imposed Russian restrictions some material has stabilized or even increased in value.

Another important feature of this work is the frequent warnings to the collector regarding the abundance of fakes/copies/reproductions now on the market. I have been in the forefront in the battle against this flood of spurious and dangerous material, and surprisingly enough have been criticised by some for being an alarmist, or acting to educate the collecting public. The argument being used that this is bad for business. Of course, I believe to the contrary that honesty and truth are the best protection for the hobby, and no one selling genuine material has anything to fear. The collector is entitled to the same consideration.

INTRODUCTION TO THE FOURTH EDITION

It makes me me delighted to write the Introduction to the Fourth Revised Edition of VERNON'S COLLECTORS TO ORDERS, MEDALS & DECORATIONS (with valuations.) The three earlier editions came out in 1986, 1990 and 1995 respectively. They have proved to be successful beyond expectations, and there is no doubt that this work has found a place in the hobby as a basic reference.

In this new edition, the word "revised" has an even more significant place. There has been an updating of the thousands of items listed and some other important changes have taken place. There are many new photos, which in combination with those in earlier editions gives greater scope for identification. Moreover, there has been a reorganization in the several of the major countries. Germany has undergone a reduction in the number of items listed, as some of these were too obscure to merit continued inclusion. Also in Germany, spacing has been added between the classes of many complicated Orders, so that the collector is not faced by a long stretch of type that might make it difficult to read. In Great Britain there has also been simplification with some of the entries so as to make things clearer to the collector. Finally, the U.S.A. has undergone some major changes, so that the campaign medals of the various armed services are grouped together in a more easily viewable format.

The chief purpose of these books is the promotion of knowledge. The more you learn, the more fulfilling collecting can be. Moreover, at a time when the collector is spending considerable amounts of money, protection from the dangers of ignorance is extremely important in order to avoid expensive mistakes.

In my introduction to the First Edition I indicated that its reason for being was to enable collectors of Orders, Medals & Decorations to have a work which served in several ways.

1. To provide a value catalogue both very broad in scope, and yet detailed enough to serve the specialized collector.

2. To bring together a variety of information which will be of benefit to the beginner. (I remember my own stumblings as a beginner in the early 1960's, with very little to guide me.)

3. To try and present in one work not just a vast array of material, but also be realistic in that it covers the interests of the overwhelming number of collectors. Therefore, if a country or an area is not covered it is because there is little collector interest in that material.

I appreciate that over the years users of these "Guides" have been commenting "Vernon says" concerning the values listed. However, again I should like to emphasize the basic principle of value. An Order, Medal or Decoration is worth what someone will pay on any given day. Thus, any person is free to disagree with the values listed herein. However, it should be pointed out that value guides do perform the very important function of providing a focus for discussion.

Collecting is very democratic. No one is forced to buy anything, and everyone is entitled to his or her own opinion. There is no right way to collect.

As with guides in other fields, values are statements of opinion based on an analysis of the market. I have used results of auction sales in N. America, Europe and elsewhere; other dealers' price lists; as well as conversations with other dealers and collectors. Finally, I have drawn on my experience as a collector since 1962, and as a dealer since 1967. Items listed as rare without values are not necessarily extremely valuable, but rather they seldom come up for sale. Some values listed are estimates based on an analysis of collector interest in that country's awards. For purposes of simplification, values listed herein are in U.S. Dollars, and are for the most recent or most common varieties, except as noted. Enameled awards should have little or no damage, and other items in VF to EF condition. A few very rare items in poor condition will still attract some interest.

It must be understood that rarity and value do not always coincide. Supply and demand are basic factors in this collector field as in any other.Thus, a rare Imperial German item will command a much higher price than an equally rare piece from Bulgaria or Rumania simply because the interest in German items prior to November 1918 is much higher than the other mentioned countries.

Since the publication of the earlier editions, the "Medal Market" has been a very active one, especially in the auctions, with much material advancing in price. In Great Britain, one of the important international markets, much consolidation has taken place, with retail dealers going out of business, and auction houses dominating the field. This should be viewed as a significant development, because auction results can differ wildly as a result of overly enthusiastic buyers competing for the "medal of their dreams"! Some value changes are also due to the volatility in the international currency market.

There have been many significant changes in values since the last edition, especially in the campaign medals of Great Britain, and the older medals of the U.S.A. The collapse of Soviet Russia has meant that there has been an unabated flood of Soviet awards, with a resultant severe decline in values except for the rarest items, which have actually gone up in value. More comments on this matter will be seen under the Russian section.

With the exception of the U.S.S.R., communist countries' awards have been omitted as there is very little collector interest in these items. Not every single item from the areas covered in this book is included. Some may have been left out due to their being very rare or obscure, some due to oversight on my part, and for simplification.

For most countries it was decided to end coverage with World War II, both in the interests of controlling the size of this work, and because collector interest in those countries lies in the pre-1945 material. Of course if items have been omitted, or if values are in dispute I would appreciate in hearing from readers of this book. I should like to emphasize the most important word in the title, "GUIDE" which should help many readers understand its purpose better. I should like to emphasize the considerable amount of comment which is interspersed through the listings which cast much light on many items.

Those of you who have earlier editions of this book will see significant changes. I have been fortunate have the assistance of my friend, and colleague, Adam Rohloff. He has advised and assisted me on the technical aspects, not least of which was coping with Word Perfect 6.1, besides helping to revise the military part of the United States section. The photos for this book were all taken by Adam Rohloff, and most are reproduced by the kindness of J. Robert Elliott, whose collection provided much of the material depicted. Steve Johnson was very helpful regarding sales and distribution.

Finally, despite all the efforts that I have made in these three editions, the results would not have been possible without the loving support of family members, and all my friends, inside and outside the collecting fraternity, as well as all my loyal clients who have said many kind things about these books. (And paid real money for them!)

It should be emphasized that the listings herein are not an offer to buy and sell at any particular price.

Acknowledgements:
An enterprise of this nature is interesting. The credit can go to many sources, but the responsibility to one. The author accepts responsibility for all errors and omissions, regardless of any assistance given by anyone else.

Technical Advisor:
Adam G. Rohloff

Photography:
Adam G. Rohloff

Marketing Advisor:
Steve Johnson

Photographic Sources:
J. Robert Elliott
Adam G. Rohloff
Sydney B. Vernon
Gordon Arnold
Steven Johnson

CHAPTER I
COLLECTING ORDERS, MEDALS & DECORATIONS

There have always been the few collectors who have been interested in awards granted by some monarch or government for heroism, long service, military campaigns and the like, but only recently have these items become the focus of a popular hobby. Since the early 1960's the collecting of these awards has grown steadily, and the value of many of them have grown accordingly.

The practice of making awards for gallantry, and various other distinctions for military and civilian service dates largely from the late 18th & early 19th centuries. Napoleon Bonaparte was keenly aware that some token of recognition from the nation could be motivation to achieve; the Legion of Honor was the result. Unlike prerevolutionary France where privilege, rank and class determined everything, it became possible for any Frenchman to aspire to this coveted award. Since its founding in 1802 the Legion of Honor has been bestowed on thousands of French citizens, military and civilian, as well as on many foreigners. Besides France, Great Britain, Austria and the German States awarded many such distinctions in the same time period and later. Strictly speaking the field can be broken down into three broad categories.

1.ORDERS-Orders originally date back to the days of knighthood in the Middle Ages, implying both an association with the noble class of society and a religious ideal. Some of the oldest of these Orders are: The Order of the Garter (Great Britain), Dannebrog (Denmark),and the Annunciation (Savoy-Italy). However, today they reflect mainly special distinctions conferred on citizens for some type of service in peace or war, both civil and military. Naturally, no communist country would accept the notion that its Orders had any noble or religious origins. Orders may come in any grouping of one to five classes, although some countries like Japan may have some with more. Class one, often referred to as the Grand Cross, will normally consist of a large metal and enameled breast star, worn on the left side of the chest, and a large, wide ribbon (sash) worn across the chest, over one shoulder, with a metal and enameled badge hanging from it. The term badge in this context will mean that part of an Order which hangs from a ribbon, and is usually enameled metal. Class two will normally consist of a smaller badge hanging from a ribbon worn around the neck, and a smaller breast star. This class goes by several names; Knight Commander (Great Britain), Grand Officer, Commander I Class, Commander with star. Class three is normally the neck badge alone, being referred to as Commander or Commander II Cl. Class four is worn on the left chest on a ribbon, and usually referred to as the Officer class. In some countries the fourth class may also have a ribbon device called a rosette. The Fifth class is usually similar in appearance as the fourth, but usually of a different metal, but worn in the same manner, and referred to as Knight (in Great Britain as member). The metals employed may range from gold, to silver, to bronze, with most badges enameled, while some are gold plated or gilt. Shapes of badges are frequently in cross form, while the breast star will have from four to eight points.

Many references use the term gold when they mean gold colored or gold plated, which may in turn mean silver/gilt or bronze/gilt. In Germany and Austria the word golden was often used in this manner. Where possible I have tried to indicate whether the item was actually gold or not. However, this was not always possible. Additionally, the term silver sometimes means silver color or silver plate. Obviously, the term "gold/gilt" should not be used, but something silver plate may be described as "silvered".

2.DECORATIONS-This is a common, all inclusive term frequently used to describe the whole field. However, the word more properly refers to an award, other than an Order, and given for some special distinction such as for heroism against the enemy in combat. Examples of these might be the British Victoria Cross, and the U.S.A.'s Medal of Honor, each their country's highest valor award. Some decorations may be made of gold or silver, some enameled. The Victoria Cross is made of bronze from captured Russian cannon taken in the Crimean War 1854-56. Some countries such as Imperial Russia, Great Britain, and Prussia may have had separate bravery awards for officers and enlisted men. The famous Prussian Pour Le Mérite was only for officers; enlisted men received the far less known Military Merit Cross.

3.MEDALS-This term is used more than any other to describe misleadingly the whole field. Most properly it should be applied to any award hanging from a ribbon, of gold, silver, bronze metal, etc., usually not enamelled, and issued to commemorate a whole range of military campaigns, long service, royal occasions, independence celebrations, and the like.

It should be pointed out that the terms "decorations" and "medals" are often used interchangeably, and a precise definition to please everyone does not exist.

For the new collector there seems to be a bewildering number of items available, a great lack of information, and the problem of how to proceed. How do you as the novice collector go about your hobby? Before you do anything else, buy or borrow a book or books, and you will soon begin to have some ideas on the subject. Of course you might wonder where do you find out about what books to obtain. Later in this book you will find an extensive bibliography which will give you an avenue of approach to the hobby. After you have read your book or books what do you do next? There are many possibilities. You decide which is the way to collect. There is no correct way. There are only different ways. Thus, whatever pleases you is correct, although considering some advice doesn't hurt, and may help you decide on your direction. Here are some possibilities:

1.You can decide to have a representative, worldwide collection. Thus, you will try to get an item from as many countries in the world that you can. The chief advantage is that you won't have to spend too much money. The chief disadvantages are that you won't have too much focus to your collection, and obtaining information on your items may be difficult.

2.You can collect Orders of the world, This is a variation of the above, but is more costly, as Orders are likely to be higher in price and rarer. However, since you will have a grouping of enameled awards there will be a more pleasing appearance to your collection.

3.Collecting gallantry awards from around the world can be very satisfying, but some of these are going to be expensive.

4.Collecting military campaign medals is a particularly interesting approach. The history of many countries can be seen in this way, and with the exception of some of the British items, the cost will not be too high.

5.Collecting lifesaving medals can be very interesting to those fascinated by non-combat heroism. These awards have been issued by many countries, and for more than a hundred years.

6.Red Cross awards have been made by many countries, and can form the basis for a very interesting collection.

7.Long Service Medals have been issued by many countries, and represent another possible avenue of approach.

8.Royal occasion awards such as weddings, jubilees, coronations have a great appeal also, and offer an international approach to collecting.

9.Collecting topically is also possible. You can choose from: a.Napoleonic era; b.Boxer Rebellion; c.World War I; d.World War II; e.Korean War; f.Independence Medals; etc.

10.Collecting by country seems to be the most common approach. The most popular countries for collector interest seem to be the U.S.A., Great Britain, Germany till 1945, Austria till 1918, and Imperial Russia. Since the awards of these countries are more popular they tend to be higher in price.

To concentrate their efforts more easily some collectors break down the country concept. Thus, a collector might collect only British Military Campaign Medals. This could be refined even further by staying with only one unit or regiment of the British army. Since most British campaign medals are named to the recipient it is possible to research the history of the man and the medal together.

The awards of the United States include an array of campaign and service medals from the Civil War right up to the present; as well as numerous ones for meritorious and long service, plus an extensive system of gallantry awards for the armed forces. The various departments of the Federal Government, as well as component and separate agencies have also issued many decorations. It might also be mentioned that there are many awards from the several states going back to the Mexican War of the 1840's, thus predating those of the Federal Government.

The awards system of Great Britain is not only comprehensive but awesome in its scope. Many collectors favor British items not only because of their beauty and integrity, but because so many of them have the recipient's name on them, which enables much research to be done. Literature on British awards is extensive and collectors are willing to exchange information gladly.

The German section of this book, covering from the 18th century until 1945, is the largest. The German states till 1918 issued many items covering major conflicts in history, which in themselves lend a topical approach to collecting. The III Reich section is also very extensive as this an area of great collector interest. However, it is also the most dangerous field of collecting due to the vast amount of fakes on the market.

The Orders, decorations, and medals of Imperial Russia are especially impressive. The Orders except for a brief period in World War I were genuine gold, with superb enamel work. The campaign medals are perhaps the oldest series stretching back to the days of Peter the Great in the early 18th century, to Nicholas II.

One of the major problems any collector must face is money. As with any other collectible field this comes into play very quickly. How much should you spend? How much is something worth? This guide is an attempt to answer the latter question. Only you can really decide how much you can afford to spend. Nevertheless, you can focus your collecting so that you can obtain the best value for what you spend. You will also have to decide whether you want a large number of items which are modest in cost or a few items which are expensive. You must bear in mind that cost or value is going to depend on a variety of factors. The dealer's cost; rarity; desirability (collector interest) should always be taken into consideration. There are rare items which do not command high prices because the collector interest in that country's awards is not very great. I would say therefore, whenever possible, that you buy the best piece that you can afford, in the best condition. If you pass up common items their price may increase somewhat, but they will be easily obtainable. However, if you pass up a rare piece not only may the price go up much more, but it will be difficult to obtain when you want it. Remember the higher the class of the award the higher the price. They were given more sparingly, and thus are more valuable. Gold items are going to be valuable because of intrinsic worth. A gold medal may weigh a lot but a gold order is likely to be hollow, and not nearly as valuable as you might think. Moreover, a badly damaged enameled order, unless it is very rare, can be worth a lot less than one in excellent, undamaged condition. The few very rare pieces are the exception.

I have been asked many times about investment possibilities in this field. The only way to answer this is to indicate that like any collectible field there are always possibilities of appreciation in value of the items you buy. However, this is a hobby which depends heavily on whim and changing interests. The best approach is to collect what you can afford, and what interests you. If there is appreciation in the value of the items you have bought over the years so much the better for you. If there have been no change or even a decline in value then you have the satisfaction of enjoying your hobby. During times of high international inflation many orders and decorations, like other collectibles, soar in value as speculators come into the field. However, days of reckoning come, and the British market in particular has suffered spectacular declines. Also the collector should understand that the great variations in the value of the U.S. dollar has caused great changes in values in both directions. Finally, I would point out that collector interest changes, so that some items can fall out of favor causing prices to decline, while others gain favor causing prices to rise.

There comes a time in the collector's life when selling all or part of a collection is contemplated. Should you wish to sell to a dealer you will have to consider the following. No dealer is going to give you retail value on your item(s). How would there be any profit involved? Depending on the items you are offering you can expect 25% to 50% of retail on common material, with perhaps 60% on better items, from a dealer. Of course you have the right to ask any price you desire, but there is no obligation on the dealers' part to pay it! If you sell a whole collection you must realize that the inclusion of much common material will cause the dealer to hedge his offer, in order to protect himself being stuck with a large number of pieces which are difficult to sell. You can also offer your items in an auction. This has the possible advantage of obtaining higher prices, but there are the auctioneers' fees to pay, and there is no guarantee that your item will be bought at a price that will please you, or even sold at all. Also settlement of your deal may take more time than you wish.

You as the collector can always try to sell the collection at retail, like a dealer. However, it is likely to be a piecemeal approach, with the best pieces going first. Moreover, you should bear in mind that if you try to get the highest possible prices for your items you may find considerable resistance on the part of other collectors. It is all very well for the seller to say that something is worth such and such. Nothing is worth anything more than someone is willing to pay. Unless the value you place on an item you are selling is acceptable to a buyer then there is no sale!

Therefore, it is my belief that collecting in this field as in any other should be based on how much enjoyment a person can get out of it, rather than worry about future value. If your collection increases in value, then the enjoyment is even greater. People who began their collectings before the mid-1960's saw for the most part their items go up in value enormously, but were,in many cases,unable to come to grips with the fact that if their items were worth more, then they could not expect to buy them at the bargain prices of the "good old days" when few people collected. Orders, medals and decorations were once cheap because hardly anyone was interested in them. Growth in the number of collectors has meant higher prices. However, when prices go too high then many collectors will be frozen out of the market. This happened, and in response prices came down, and more people returned to collecting again.

CHAPTER II
COPIES, FAKES & REPRODUCTIONS

In any collecting field a major problem faced by the collector, beginner or advanced, is whether the material being offered, or bought, is genuine. The term employed for an item which not original may depend on the intent of the maker with regard to how it is to be disposed of. If there were no intent to defraud then the term copy (or reproduction) is correct. However, if as is often the case the purpose was or is to deceive the collector then the proper term is fake. Throughout the value section I have tried to indicate special problems of copies and fakes, recognizing in the last analysis that the two terms are really the same I use the word copy for convenience. Also I have tried to indicate in the introduction to each country where some special problem may exist.

The greatest number of copies on the market today are those of III Reich awards. Without quoting an actual percentage it is likely that much of this material being offered is either not genuine or at least questionable. Some of it is very obvious, while much of it may be excellent in appearance, and difficult to decide about. One German dealer told me that copies were being made in Austria as early as 1946, and in Germany in 1947. Initially, old dies were used to restrike new items, and then new dies were made up. Thus, it is possible that the returned veteran who it seems is responsible for most of the III Reich material being over here may have picked up his items in the Army of Occupation after World War II. Nevertheless, none of this is meant to imply that the collector cannot find genuine Nazi awards, only that greater care must be taken.

Identifying genuine III Reich awards is not always easy. Some restrikes produced after World War II, from original dies, are virtually impossible to distinguish from original items. Many pieces may seem to be in poor condition because as the war ground on, the quality of the materials used and/or the workmanship deteriorated. Thus, it is quite possible that an original item can have a poor quality appearance, while that well made piece could be a copy. Much, but not all, III Reich material is hallmarked in some way. You may see numbers like 800 or 900 to indicate silver content. Letters such as R.K. or R.S., or names like Juncker, and Peekhaus refer to a manufacturer. "L" prefixed numbers such as L/11 will refer to a maker also, as will a plain number like 21. There is a controversy over the letters RS which indicate the maker Rudolf Souval of Vienna Austria. One may see two types of letters, one rounded, and one angular. There is a difference of opinion as to which is on genuine material. I must emphasize the mere appearance of a hallmark or number on a III Reich item is no guarantee of its being genuine; nor is the absence of such mean that you have a copy. III Reich medals are frequently marked on the ribbon ring, while badges may be marked on the reverse, or on top of or underneath the pin. On the badges you should examine the pin and catch carefully. If there is any sign of epoxy glue then the piece has either been repaired, or it is a fake, since epoxy did not exist in World War II. Some badges have been copied in lead. If you can bend it easily and write with it then you have a copy. If there are signs of bubbling and pitting, and the surface is not clearly struck, you may have a casting rather than a die struck item. Originals were rarely, or never produced in this manner. Of course, there are die struck copies.

Certainly, one of the most famous awards in the world is the Iron Cross, so named because of its main component. Thus, a test of a World War II Iron Cross (in all classes) should be as to whether it is magnetic or not. There are those who say that there were some late World War II pieces that weren't so made, but my feeling is that they are to be avoided. Another frequently copied piece is the so-called "Blue Max", the Prussian Officers' bravery award the Pour Le Mérite. Instituted in the 18th century, it has appeared in many types and styles, as well as in gold, silver/gilt and bronze/gilt. While there have been copies of the early items most collectors will come across the World War I period pieces, and it is these which pose the most problems. The fact that a piece is gold with a hallmark is no guarantee of its being genuine. What complicates the matter even further, is that some recipients, in order to protect this coveted award from wear, had wearing copies made by an official jeweler. These copies have an acceptable status in the collector world below that of the originals, but far above the host of low quality items made after World War II. There are also very nice quality copies made in Vienna between the wars which will also command a respectable place in a collection. Consulting reference materials is essential in this matter. A final note on III Reich hallmarks. It is generally accepted that the mark of L/58 is an indication of the item being a post-World War II copy, of high quality perhaps, but a copy nevertheless.

British awards present fewer, but different types of problems. There are copies of some British awards, made in France after World War I, namely, the Military Medal and the Distinguished Service Medal-George V type, but they are fairly obvious. They have no designer's name on obverse, they don't swivel at the suspension, and they are unnamed. Others such as the Edward VI Distinguished Conduct Medal, the George V Distinguished Service Order, and the George VI Distinguished Flying Cross are more of a problem. Fortunately for the collector these and other items are covered in Purves-**COLLECTING MEDALS & DECORATIONS** and in Abbott & Tamplin-**BRITISH GALLANTRY AWARDS**. Unnamed copies of the Victoria Cross are common. It can be said with reasonable assurance that an unnamed Victoria Cross is a copy since awarded ones were always named. However, there may be exceptions in the case of those presented to museums, or those awarded to the Unknown Soldiers of the First World War, from other countries. Despite this, the V.C. does not present a problem for most collectors as its price is very high. The Air Force Cross is a tricky item indeed. Care must be taken that the monarch's cipher is the same obverse and reverse, and that the designer's initials appear in the 7 o'clock position on the obverse centre.

The major problem which occurs with British awards is with the naming of the campaign medals, especially where the name of the original recipient has been ground off and replaced by someone else's. This renaming may have been done to deceive collectors, or simply by a recipient who lost his medal(s), and wanted to replace it (them). There are a few instances of medals being officially renamed, and in these verifiable cases the medals have the same value as an unaltered piece. Another, less prevalent, problem is that of fake bars to make relatively common medals into rarer ones. The naming of otherwise unnamed medals can also present a problem. Some years ago a number of unnamed medals from the Crimean War with the bar Balaklava were named up to members of units which took part in the classic "Charge of the Light Brigade". These pieces, seemingly named in the correct style, were at first accepted as genuine. Only the sharp eyes of a British dealer discovered minute differences in the naming which revealed that these pieces were fraudulent.

The faking of American medals involves several different problems. There have been three basic numbering systems used to number U.S. campaign medals, with several variations. There are genuine unnumbered medals which have faked numbering. The only real protection against this is experience, and being able to compare it with another, known, original piece. Further details on the numbering systems will be found in the U.S. section.

Several years ago a flood of U.S. Navy and Marine Corps Medals came on the market, presumably made somewhere in the Orient. They are identifiable by their dark appearance, fuzzy detail, and having a little knob instead of the normal ring. However, some of these have been seen with rings instead of knobs. Nevertheless, these pieces look poor and should not fool anyone if carefully examined.

Copies have been made in many countries, especially in France, Germany, and Austria, but also in the U.S.A., Britain, and in S.E. Asia. Much III Reich material has come from the U.S.A. as well as Europe. The chief sources for much of the other material seems to have been Paris and Vienna. The makers at one time may have been official suppliers of Orders etc to governments and royal houses, and continued to make them after the awarding authorities either no longer existed, or no longer had the undisputed right to continue awarding them. Many of these items are of good or even excellent quality, yet should be regarded as copies, or at best of doubtful parentage. Without being able to know when an item was made the collector can face a complicated problem. Here is where hallmarks can be of assistance. Consult **COURT JEWELERS OF THE WORLD** by Jeffrey Jacob.

An important step, previously referred to, is getting as much reference material as possible. The best protection a collector can have against the pitfalls of collecting is as many books as possible. There is no such thing as spending too much on research materials when you balance it against the high cost of ignorance. It is probable that you will find that references will have overlapping information. There is no one work which has everything in it. When you realize that collectors are prepared to spend large sums of money on pieces for a collection, yet hesitate to part with say $50.00 for a book which could save them many times its cost, it is not surprising that these same people are taken advantage of. Any collector should buy as many books as possible before going into this field in a serious way.

Study your references, ask questions of the seller, pick up items and examine them carefully with a powerful magnifier. In your collecting you need to be a wise consumer also. You as the buyer have no obligation to buy at a particular price, but sometimes a "bargain" is hard to resist. If you appear to know what you are doing then you will be prepared to impress the seller, who of course is under no obligation to sell to you at a particular price, just because you would like him to. Very often you will find that when you are buying from someone who does not normally handle this material there can be a great variation in price. You may be offered a rare item at a low price, and conversely a high price on a common item. A clear example of this the New York State Shooting Badge, once made by Tiffany & Co. of New York. Some antique dealers assume that since it is a Tiffany piece that it has a great deal of value, whereas in reality the badge is very common and commands about $15.00.

During the course of your collecting the question is going to arise concerning the purchasing of copies. My personal inclination is not to do so. However, this is a matter which you have to decide in relation to the type of collection that you want. If you are collecting gallantry awards you may well be satisfied with paying $25.00 for an excellent copy of a Victoria Cross rather than $25,000.00 for an original. I have known a collector pay $1000.00 for a copy set of the I Class of the Imperial Russian Order of St George, virtually unobtainable as an original, and certainly astronomical in cost. Copies run in all sorts of price ranges, and unless the item is extremely rare should be avoided. The more copies you have in your collection, the poorer impression you will make. You might even depreciate the value of the genuine pieces that you have which may be judged by the company they keep. There is enough original material around to be collected. However, you must be the final judge.

CHAPTER III
RIBBON STYLES

In the first edition of this work no mention was made of the ribbons or mountings that Orders, Medals & Decorations may have. Since this can be a means of identifying an item, or an aid in displaying them it was thought to be of interest to collectors that some reference be made of this matter.

As many collectors stay with the awards of one country they become familiar with them, their mountings, their ribbon types, etc. However, most collectors eventually come across awards from other countries which they may know nothing about and seek to find out some basic information. While it is not possible to provide information from every single country included in this book, it is possible to give some general guidelines which may help.

Most collectors readily understand that an award hangs from a ribbon. What collectors are not prepared for is the great variation in the styles of ribbons. Breast awards of Austria and Hungary are seen on a triangular ribbon, but so are the awards of Serbia, Montenegro, Yugoslavia, Bulgaria, and amazingly enough the Order of the Sacred Treasure of Japan in the classes of IV-VIII. The breast awards of Imperial Russia are seen on a unique five sided ribbon. British campaign medals are mainly worn with ribbons which pass through a horizontal suspension, unlike those of the U.S.A. which are gathered at the bottom to go through a ring. German awards can have several types of ribbons depending upon their time period. German and British awards are frequently found mounted in groups, again with various types of ribbon arrangements. These groups often will have some kind of pin on the back to facilitate wearing on the uniform.

What perplexes many collectors is how the "medal" is worn on the uniform. All awards from the U.S.A. come with a brooch on the ribbon for wearing. Most items from other countries do not appear to have such. This bothers American collectors a great deal. Many French awards come with a "U" shaped device with sharp points for sticking into the uniform. Frequently these stick into the fingers of the collector, although there is no evidence that any government planned this deliberately. Some collectors sew safety pins on the back of the ribbons for mounting. Some fasten a small piece of cardboard on the ribbon back and put a thumb tack through it onto the surface of the display case.

If you do decide to display your items in cases be very careful about keeping them out of the direct rays of sunlight which can cause enamel to crack or smash, and ribbons to fade. Ribbon material has also changed over the years. Originally many ribbons were silk, and then later cotton, but in recent years have been rayon and nylon. Some collectors want only original ribbons on their medal even if very tattered, even though no serving soldier or official would have been permitted to appear wearing such. For some ribbons a difference in color shade and intensity can be seen. In a few cases the ribbon may be rarer than the medal it hangs from. A good example of this is the French medal for Mexico 1862-63 which has an embroidered eagle and snake. Later editions of the ribbon are only printed.

Mention might be made on some of the devices that can be found on the ribbons of awards. Many countries use a rosette (a circular piece of cardboard covered with ribbon) on the ribbon of the fourth class of an Order to denote that class. This is a French origination, but can be found on the Austrian style ribbon of Bulgaria and on the Orders of Japan.

What sometimes confuses collectors that some awards have more than one ribbon, one for peacetime and one for wartime. Some may have the same ribbon for a military or civil award, while some may differentiate in a simple manner. The British Order of the Bath is a good example of how to confuse the collector. The ribbons are identical for the military and civil divisions. However, the military badges are completely different, while the breast stars, except for a wreath on the military, are the same. The British Empire Order went through a complete change in the 1930's, both with ribbon and design. Yet the type II ribbon could be worn with the type I design, although not the reverse. Also in both types the only difference between the military and civil awards is that a vertical stripe would be found in the centre of the ribbon. In the case of Rumania in the 1930's several of its Orders were changed in design, and the ribbons were also.

The actual wearing of awards varies from country to country. Usual practice is the highest class (referred to as the Grand Cross or I Class) being composed of a broad ribbon (sash) worn over one shoulder, across the chest, with a large metal and enameled badge hanging from it, with a large metal, commonly enameled, plaque or breast star of four to eight points worn on the left chest. Some of the Orders have with their highest class a Chain or Collar of precious metal and enamel, with the Order badge hanging from it. The second class usually consists of badge hanging from a narrower ribbon, referred to as a neck ribbon, cravat, or necklet, around the neck, with a smaller breast star also worn on the left chest. The III Class will be worn around the neck, while the fourth and lower classes will be worn on an even narrower ribbon on the left chest.

Some awards have the I Class worn around the neck only. Some have only one class altogether; and for some the term I Class may mean a pin back award as in the case of the Iron Cross I Class, worn pinback on the left chest without a ribbon!

A decision often faced by collectors is whether to buy medals that don't have ribbons, or have the wrong one. While this is a matter of individual choice I would point out that many collectors, including myself, have passed up items because there was no ribbon, and lost sight of the fact that replacement ribbons are obtainable, and that we are collecting medals primarily. The time to buy something is when you see it if you like it, want it and "need" it. What is reasonable to expect is that the seller should make a small adjustment in the price to make up for the lack of ribbon.

CHAPTER IV
BIBLIOGRAPHY

A Bibliography on a subject of collector interest is of necessity a matter of opinion, rather than being composed solely of sources of information. I do not pretend that it covers every book on the subject. However, it does include my selection based on books in my own collection, as well as works suggested by other authors. Where possible I have made comments pertinent to the work in question to help the collector choose. Nevertheless, the inclusion or exclusion of a reference from this bibliography is not to be taken as a statement as to the worth of said item.

Abbott, P. & Tamplin J. **BRITISH GALLANTRY AWARDS**-London 1982-Second Edition. A must book on the subject.

Angolia, J. **FOR FUHRER & FATHERLAND**-Volume I-The Military Awards of the III Reich; Volume II-The Political Awards of the III Reich-San Jose California-1976 & 1978.

Artuk, I. & Artuk, C. **THE OTTOMAN ORDERS**-Istanbul 1967-in Turkish & English.

Babin, L. **FOREIGN WAR MEDALS, ORDERS & DECORATIONS**-Rochester N.Y. c 1952.

Bascape, G. **THE ORDERS OF KNIGHTHOOD AND THE NOBILITY OF THE REPUBLIC OF SAN MARINO**-Delft, The Netherlands 1973.

Bax, W. **RIDDERORDEN, EERETEEKENEN, DRAAGTEEKENS EN PENNINGEN**- Maastrict, The Netherlands.

Belden, B. **UNITED STATES WAR MEDALS**-ANS NY 1916-reprinted by Norm Flayderman 1962.

Bell, C. **OFFICERS & MEN AT THE BATTLE OF MANILA BAY**-1972-a roll of recipients of the Manila Bay (Dewey) Medal.

Berghman, A. **NORDISKA ORDNER OCH DEKORATIONER**-Malmo, Sweden 1949.

Burke, Sir Bernard. **THE BOOK OF ORDERS OF KNIGHTHOOD AND DECORATIONS OF HONOUR**-London 1858.

Cardinale, H.E. **ORDERS OF KNIGHTHOOD, AWARDS, AND THE HOLY SEE**. Gerrards Cross, England 1983. The title is somewhat misleading, as it deals with Orders from several countries besides the Vatican State, but treats the subject from a religious viewpoint, which is apt since the whole matter in Europe stems from religious influence.

Castren, K. **LES ORDERS NATIONAUX DE LA FINLANDE**-Helsinki 1975.

Chalif, D. **MILITARY & AIRCREW BADGES OF THE WORLD**-Volume I-Albania to Hungary-San Jose, California 1982.

Cole, H. **CORONATION AND ROYAL COMMEMORATIVE MEDALS**-1877-1977- London 1977.

Davis, B. **BADGES & INSIGNIA OF THE THIRD REICH** 1933-1945- Poole, England 1983.

De la Bere, Sir Ivan. **THE QUEEN'S ORDERS OF CHIVALRY**-London 1961.

Delande, M. **DECORATIONS-FRANCE ET COLONIES**-Paris 1934. Especially useful to show variations of the Legion of Honor. Section on World War I items is spoiled by the fact that many pieces shown are copies.

de la Puente y Gomez, F. **CONDECORACIONES ESPANOLAS**-Madrid 1953.

Dimacopoulos, G. **GREEK ORDERS AND MEDALS**-Athens 1961-in Greek and English.

Dorling, T. **RIBBONS AND MEDALS**-revised by A. Purves, London 1983. Best comprehensive work available. Mainly British in content, but large foreign section including U.S.A.

Edkins, D. **THE PRUSSIAN ORDERN POUR LE MÉRITE**-The History of the Blue Max. Falls Church, Virginia 1981.

Elvin, C. **HANDBOOK OF THE ORDERS OF CHIVALRY**-London 1893.

Ercoli, E. **LE MEDAGILE, AL VALORE, AL MERITO E COMMEMORATIVO**-Military & Civil Awards of Sardinia & Italy (excluding Orders) 1793-1976-Milan 1976.

Feyver, W. editor **THE GEORGE MEDAL**-London 1980.

Forman, A. **FORMAN'S GUIDE TO THIRD REICH GERMAN AWARDS...AND THEIR VALUES**-1988-also gives values for documents and cases.

Gillingham, H. **ITALIAN ORDERS OF CHIVALRY AND MEDALS OF HONOR**- N.Y. 1922

...SPANISH ORDERS OF CHIVALRY AND MEDALS OF HONOR-N.Y. 1926.

Gleim, A. Planchet Press publications-Ft. Myer, Virginia-various dates-A series of scholarly works on many aspects of United States medals.

Gordon, L. **BRITISH BATTLES AND MEDALS**-6th edition-extensively revised by E.C. Joslin, A. Litherland & B. Simpkin-the major work on British Campaign Medals, and a must book for collectors of this series.

Gritzner, M. **HANDBUCH DER RITTER UND VERDIENSTORDERN**-Leipzig 1893; reprinted Graz, Austria 1962-an early compendium of Orders of the World.

BIBLIOGRAPHY

Hamelman, W. & Martin, D. **THE HISTORY OF THE PRUSSIAN POUR LE MÉRITE ORDER**-Volume I-1740-1812-Hamburg 1982.

Hamelman, W. **THE HISTORY OF THE PRUSSIAN POUR LE MÉRITE ORDER**-Volume II-1813-1888; Volume III 1888-1918-Dallas, Texas 1986

Hazleton, A. **THE RUSSIAN IMPERIAL ORDERS**-N.Y. 1932

Hieronymussen, P. **ORDERS, MEDALS & DECORATIONS OF BRITAIN & EUROPE**-London 1967. An extremely useful work on European awards after WWII. Hundreds of items in color, plus drawings. Originally published in Danish & German.

Jacob, J. **COURT JEWELERS OF THE WORLD**-Cherry Hill, N.J. 1978. Of the highest importance for collectors of Orders.

Jocelyn, A. **AWARDS OF HONOUR-THE ORDERS, DECORATIONS AND AWARDS OF GREAT BRITAIN AND COMMONWEALTH FROM EDWARD III TO ELIZABETH II**-London 1956.

Jorgensen, P. **DANISH ORDERS AND MEDALS**-Copenhagen 1964.

Joslin, E. **STANDARD CATALOGUE OF BRITISH ORDERS, DECORATIONS AND MEDALS**-London-several editions.

Kahl, R. **INSIGNIA, DECORATIONS AND BADGES OF THE THIRD REICH AND OCCUPIED COUNTRIES**-Kedichem, The Netherlands-c.1970.

Kerrigan, E. **AMERICAN WAR MEDALS AND DECORATIONS**-revised edition- 1990. A major work on U.S. awards.

Klenau, Arnhard Graf. **EUROPAISCHE ORDEN AB 1700-KATALOG OHNE DEUTSCHLAND**-1978.

Klietman, G. **DEUTSCHE AUSZEICHNEN**-Berlin 1971-an important work on German items from 1870-1945. Has separate photo section.

...**PHALERISTIK RUMANIEN**-Berlin 1975. This book on Rumanian Orders etc is in English & German, and is profusely illustrated.

...**POUR LE MÉRITE UND TAPFERKEITSMEDAILLE**-Berlin 1966. A softcovered book of the highest utility. Covers Germany and her allies in both World Wars-with handy black & white photo section.

Kraft, H. **DEUTSCHE LUFTFAHRTABZEICHEN BIS 1945**-Hamburg 1983.

Laslo, A. **THE INTERALLIED VICTORY MEDALS OF WORLD WAR I**-1st & 2nd editions-1986 & 1992. A book which has made available to collectors of this series a serious and comprehensive work.

Littlejohn, D. & Dodkins, C. **ORDERS, DECORATIONS, MEDALS AND BADGES OF THE THIRD REICH**-Mountain View, California-Volume I (including Danzig) 1968:Volume II 1973.

Littlejohn, D. **FOREIGN LEGIONS OF THE THIRD REICH**-IV Volumes- San Jose, California-1979 etc. Useful for lesser known awards of the Nazi puppet groups.

Lippe, Prince Ernst August zur. **ORDERN UND AUSZEICHNEN**-Munich 1958.

McDowell, C. **MILITARY AND NAVAL AWARDS OF THE UNITED STATES**-Springfield, Virgina 1984. The best book on the subject now available. Well written and illustrated. Covers the decorations.

Mayo, J. **MEDALS AND DECORATIONS OF THE BRITISH ARMY AND NAVY**-2 volumes-London 1897.

MEDALS YEARBOOK-value guide to British awards-London 1983 etc.

NATIONAL GEOGRAPHIC-December 1919 and October 1943-includes color illustrations of all U.S. awards to date.

Nimmergut, J. **ORDEN EUROPAS**-Munich 1981.

...**ORDEN & EHRENZEICHEN VON 1800-1945**-Munich 1983-several editions-priced catalogue of German awards.

Orders and Medals Research Society of Great Britain. **JOURNAL.**

Orders and Medals Society of America. **THE MEDAL COLLECTOR.**

O'Toole, E. **DECORATIONS AND MEDALS OF THE REPUBLIC OF IRELAND**-London 1972.

Paris Mint. **DECORATIONS OFFICIELLES FRANCAISE**-Paris 1954-comprehensive and useful. Many color plates.

Peterson, J. **ORDERS AND MEDALS OF JAPAN AND ASSOCIATED STATES**-Chicago, 1967. Monograph No. 1 of the Orders and Medals Society of America. An excellent reference in English on this subject, with precise details on all Japanese awards.

Pownall, H. **KOREAN CAMPAIGN MEDALS 1950-1953**-pamphlet London c. 1954.

Prowse, A. **THE IRON CROSS OF PRUSSIA AND GERMANY**-New Zealand 1971-an extremely useful aid to this decoration.

Purves, A. **COLLECTING MEDALS AND DECORATIONS**-London 1983 (several editions). One of the must books for the collector of British awards.

BIBLIOGRAPHY

...**THE MEDALS, DECORATIONS AND ORDERS OF THE GREAT WAR 1914-1918**. London 1975. The best book available on the subject in English. Many illustrations; pictures of U.S. and Japanese Victory Medals are of copies.

...**THE MEDALS, DECORATIONS AND ORDERS OF WORLD WAR II 1939-1945**. Similar in nature to the previous book, and extremely useful.

Quinot, H. **ORDERS DE CHEVALERIE ET DECORATIONS BELGES DE 1830 A 1963**. 1st Edition-Brussels, 1963.

Renault, J. **LA LEGION D'HONNEUR**-Paris, 1925. A massive and rare work which deals very thoroughly with subject. Also pictured are some early French awards.

Riley, D. **UNCOMMON VALOR**-Decorations, badges and service medals of the U.S. Navy and Marine Corps. USA 1980. A small, but handsome book showing all awards in color, with a general commentary for the reader.

Risk, J. **BRITISH ORDERS AND DECORATIONS**-N.Y. 1945. A useful discussion by a leading expert.

...**HISTORY OF THE ORDER OF THE BATH**-London, 1972. A thorough discussion of the subject.

Robles, P. **U.S. MILITARY MEDALS AND RIBBONS**-Rutland, Vermont 1971. Shows all U.S. military awards in color. Subject matter is general in nature.

Romanoff, Prince Dmitri. **THE ORDERS, MEDALS AND HISTORY OF THE KINGDOM OF BULGARIA**-Denmark 1982. An excellent presentation in English on an interesting country.

...**THE ORDERS, MEDALS AND HISTORY OF GREECE**-Denmark 1987-similar in nature to above.

...**THE ORDERS, MEDALS AND HISTORY OF MONTENEGRO**-II Edition-Denmark 1987-an interesting presentation in English on a country that no longer exists.

Roncetti, G. and Benby, E. **THE CANADIANS IN SOUTH AFRICA**-Toronto-an important reference regarding the Queen's South Africa Medal to Canadian recipients.

Rosigonli, G. **AIR FORCE BADGES AND INSIGNIA OF WORLD WAR II**-N.Y. 1977.

...**ARMY BADGES AND INSIGNIA OF WORLD WAR II**-Book I-Poole, England 1972; Book II 1975.

...**NAVAL AND MARINE BADGES AND INSIGNIA OF WORLD WAR II**-Poole, England 1980.

...RIBBONS OF ORDERS, DECORATIONS AND MEDALS-Poole, England 1976. Very useful for identifying many medals, although the colors are not always true. Discussion is very limited.

Schlaich de Bosse. **LES DISTINCTION HONORIFIQUES AU PAYS DE LUXEMBOURG 1430-1961**-Luxembourg, 1962.

Schreiber, G. **DIE BAYERISCHEN ORDEN UND EHRENZEICHEN**-Munich 1964.

Sculfort, V. **DECORATIONS, MEDAILLES, MONNAIES DU MUSSE DE L'ARMEE**-Paris 1912. French and foreign awards in the National Army Museum.

Smyth, Sir John. **THE STORY OF THE GEORGE CROSS**-London 1966.

...**THE STORY OF THE VICTORIA CROSS**-London 1963.

Strandberg, J. & Bender, R. **THE CALL OF DUTY**-San Jose, CA 1994

Tancred, G. **HISTORICAL RECORD OF MEDALS AND HONORARY DISTINCTIONS**-London 1891.

U.S. Senate Committee on Labor and Public Welfare. **MEDAL OF HONOR 1863-1968**-Washington D.C. 1968. Official U.S. Government publication on this decoration; with list of recipients, citations as well as pertinent information.

Vernon, S. **VERNON'S COLLECTORS' GUIDE TO ORDERS, MEDALS AND DECORATIONS (with valuations)**. Baldwin, NY 1986-1st edition; Wildomar, CA 1990 2nd edition.

...**SALES CATALOGUES** 1967-1994

Vietnam Council on Foreign Relations. **AWARDS AND DECORATIONS OF VIETNAM**-1972. All the awards of South Vietnam, civil and military, with explanation in English and Vietnamese.

von Hessenthal, W. and Schreiber, G. **DIE EHRENZEICHEN DES DEUTSCHEN REICHES**-Berlin 1940. The major work on the medals and decorations of Germany and States up to 1940, and Austria (then part of Germany), and a must book for the collector of German awards. Does not deal with Orders. Extremely rare.

von Heyden, H. **EHRENZEICHEN IN FRANKREICH UND BELGIEN**-Frankfurt am Main 1903.

von Prochazka, R. **OSTERREISCHISCHES ORDENS HANDBUCH**-3 volumes 1979-covers Austrian awards to date. Very comprehensive, with many clear illustrations.

WALDORF ASTORIA ALBUM-colored picture album of German Orders & Decorations. c.1930-280 items shown.

BIBLIOGRAPHY

Weaver, B., Gleim, A. and Farek, D. **THE WEST INDIES NAVAL CAMPAIGN OF 1898. THE SAMPSON MEDAL, THE SHIPS AND THE MEN.** - Arlington, Virginia 1986. An important book for the U.S. medal collector, which illustrates in complete detail the fascinating story of the "Sampson Medal". A must reference to verify and identify this series.

Werlich, R. **ORDERS AND DECORATIONS OF ALL NATIONS**-Military & Civil. II Edition-Washington D.C. 1964. An encyclopedia on the subject. Very useful on U.S. civilian awards. Shows only the highest class of Orders.

...**RUSSIAN ORDERS, DECORATIONS AND MEDALS**-Including Imperial Russia, Provisional Government, Civil War and the U.S.S.R.-II Edition Washington D.C. 1981. An important work for the collector-heavily illustrated. Does not show suspensions of medals.

Wrede, E. **FINLANDS UTMARKELSETECKEN**-Helsinki 1946. In Swedish, heavily illustrated.

Wyllie, R. **ORDERS, DECORATIONS AND INSIGNIA**-N.Y. 1927. U.S. and foreign awards.

CHAPTER V
GLOSSARY

The following terms are some that the collector is likely to come across while pursuing this hobby.

BADGE-refers usually to the part of an Order which hangs from a ribbon. It is most often enameled.

BAR or **CLASP**-refers to a device affixed to the medal, affixed to the ribbon, or slid over the ribbon, which will identify a campaign operation or commemorate some special activity in addition to that which is represented by the medal itself. In the case of some British items it is used to indicate a second or subsequent award.

BRONZE/GILT-refers to the practice of gold plating or coloring to enhance an item's appearance, or to indicate its class.

CASED-found in its original container, often made of wood with a leather or cloth covering. China and Japan also used lacquered cases for some of their awards.

CASTING-an item made from a mold rather than a die. Many copies are cast from an original. Through a magnifying glass the surface will appear pitted.

CIVIL-refers to an award which is awarded to non-military personnel or for non-combat operations.

CLASS-this refers to the level of, the grade of, or the precedence of an award. Sometimes classes are listed by number with the first being the highest. In Spain the I Class is the lowest of an Order. Other times classes are listed by name, such as: GRAND CROSS-consisting of a badge worn on a sash, and a breast star, and sometimes a collar or chain. GRAND OFFICER-consisting of a neck badge, and a breast star, COMMANDER WITH STAR, COMMANDER I CLASS, or KNIGHT COMMANDER (Great Britain)-see Grand Officer. COMMANDER-a neck badge. OFFICER-a breast badge worn on a ribbon (may be called Knight I Class), and usually in gold, silver/gilt or bronze/gilt metal. KNIGHT-a breast badge worn on a ribbon in silver or silvered metal. While many Orders have five classes, there are some that have only one, some three, and some eight.

COLLAR or **CHAIN**-worn with the highest class of some Orders, or with one class Orders around the neck, with the badge of the Order hanging from it. They can be of gold, silver/gilt, bronze/gilt, with some enameling. Very sparingly awarded.

COURT MOUNTED-refers to a style of mounting where the ribbon is extended below the award, as well as above it, with some material to stiffen the ribbon behind it. A pin is attached for fastening on the recipient's garment. So called because it was specially favored for royal court or formal wear.

CRAVAT-term used in the U.S.A. to denote a neck ribbon for an Order, or for the Medal of Honor.

DENAZIFIED-refers to the awards of the III Reich which can be worn in Germany only in a form with the swastika removed. This does not apply to those of the Nazi Party and its various auxiliaries which may not be worn at all. Thus, all permitted items have been redesigned to eliminate the swastika. In the case of the Iron Cross oakleaves appear on the obverse centre.

DIE STRUCK-refers to an item struck from a die, rather than a casting from a mold. While there are die struck copies, originals are almost always die struck. The features will usually be clear and precise, whereas a casting is likely to be blurred and pitted.

EDGE KNOCK-this term is employed by the British collector to refer to a dent in the edge of the medal. A badly knocked medal will be avoided by the collector unless it is rare or very cheap.

GLOSSARY

FIXED SUSPENDER-the suspension on top of the medal through which the ribbon (ring) will go, does not turn.

GILT-gold coloring or gold plating. Thus, the term gold/gilt should not be used.

GOLDEN(EN)-the use of this word does not always mean that the item concerned is made from the precious metal. It may be used to describe the appearance or class of the item, and be gilt on some other metal.

HALLMARK-a mark put on the item to indicate the manufacturer, and/or the metallic content. It may be a maker's initials, name, emblem, or a number, or a combination of these. See Jeffrey Jacob's COURT JEWELERS OF THE WORLD for further reference.

INSIGNIA-this term is used to indicate the various parts of an Order, such as badge, sash and breast star.

LAPEL BAR or **LAPEL PIN**-in the U.S.A. refers to a small metal and enamel bar worn on the lapel of civilian clothes to indicate the award of some decoration.

MILITARY-when applied to an award indicates that it is either specifically a military one, or that it becomes a military award by the addition of a device like swords, or by the wearing of a special ribbon as in the case of the British Empire Order. The British Order of the Bath has two distinct sets of insignia for its military and civil classifications.

MINIATURE-a small replica of a Order, Medal or Decoration which is wor

PRECIOUS METAL CONTENT-many items may have been made from precious metals, such as gold and silver. An Austrian gold mark might be 750 indicating 18 karat gold. A Russian gold mark might be 56. Silver marks might be 800, 900, or even 925, 938, or even 958. American silver items are usually marked sterling. Some pieces appearing gold will be marked 1/20 10KGF, or one twentieth 10 karat goldfilled.

RENAMED-the name of the original recipient has been removed and replaced by another. Usually, renamed medals have considerably less value, unless the renaming was officially done, as was the case with some British campaign medals.

RESTRIKE-the reissue of an item, either from original or newly made dies. This may indicate an unauthorized issue.

REVERSE-the back of an Order, Medal or Decoration.

RIBBON BAR-a narrow piece of ribbon mounted on a bar for wearing on a uniform in place of an original award.

RIBBON BAR DEVICES-small emblems worn on the ribbon bar to indicate some special distinction, such as combat service etc.

SUSPENSION-refers to the attachment at the top of the medal so that a ribbon can be worn with the item.

SWIVEL SUSPENSION-the suspension at the top of the medal turns, so that you can display either the obverse or reverse as you wish. Many British campaign medals swivel.

TINSEL STAR-A breast star made of metallic thread on a cloth backing. Frequently covered with sequins. In use till mid 19th century when replaced by metal stars. (See breast star.)

WAR DECORATION-or Kriegs Dekoration-is a wreath which is placed on some Austro-Hungarian awards to indicate a military or wartime award.

WITH SWORDS-the addition of swords makes an award into a military or wartime one. The swords may be fastened between the arms of a cross, or fastened at the top, or on both at the same time. When swords are worn on the ring of an Order badge the breast star has them above the device, or badge centered on it.

ALBANIA

The awards of this country are colorful and interesting, and more sought after by collectors, since the first edition of this book appeared; especially for the World War II issues from the Italian Occupation. The rarity of some of the awards is hard to determine, since it appears that at one time King Zog was not averse to selling awards to raise a little extra revenue.

Material is generally of good quality, and there does not seem to be a problem of copies.

Order of the Black Eagle-1914

1.Grand Cross badge	650.00
2.Grand Cross breast star	600.00
3.Grand Officer neck badge	650.00
4.Grand Officer breast star	600.00
5.Commander-neck badge	650.00
6.Officer-breast badge	450.00
7.Knight	400.00
8.Merit Medal-I Class-gilt	250.00
9.Merit Medal-II Class-silver	150.00

Order of Scanderbeg-1925-44

10.Grand Cross badge	700.00
11.Grand Cross breast star	650.00
12.Commander	550.00
13.Officer	300.00
14.Knight	250.00

(This Order was issued in modified form during the Italian Occupation 1939-44. Values similar to above.)

Order of Fidelity-(B.E.S.A.)-1926-44

15.Grand Cross badge	550.00
16.Grand Cross breast star	500.00
17.Grand Officer-neck badge	400.00
18.Grand Officer-breast star	400.00
19.Commander	400.00
20.Officer	250.00
21.Knight	200.00

(This Order was issued in modified form during the Italian Occupation of 1939-44. Values similar to above.)

22.Honor Collar of Albania-1925	rare

Bravery Order-1928-1940

23.First Class-neck badge & breast star	rare
24.Second Class-neck badge	1200.00
25.Third Class-medal	550.00

26.Accession Medal-Prince William of Wied-1914	250.00

21 12 7

Type I

11
Type II

AUSTRIA

Holy Roman Empire (Austria) till 1806
Austrian Empire 1806-1867
Austro-Hungarian Empire (Austria-Hungary) 1867-1918
Austrian Republic 1918-1938
Annexed Territory of Germany 1938-45
Austrian Republic 1945

Austria was one of the first countries to award decorations to its people. The oldest award, the Order of the Golden Fleece, dates back to the Middle Ages, but other than that campaign medals were given out in the 1790's for the early stages of the French Revolutionary period.

The awards of this country encompass all of the possible combinations of gallantry, merit, long service etc.; especially Orders for gallant or meritorious service to the state. Thus, the history of the country is well reflected in the development of its parade of orders, medals, and decorations.

The Orders of Austria (used as a general term for all periods) present a handsome appearance, and were made by some of the most famous jewelers in Europe. Unfortunately, it is in the Orders section that the collector has the most problems. It is reasonably safe to say that any Austrian Order not hallmarked in some way, either by the maker's name, a metal content such as 750 (18 karat) for gold, or a * indicating bronze/gilt for postwar exchange, is not genuine. This is very important in dealing with the Maria Theresa Order which may be found in unhallmarked gold copies. Also there are silver/gilt and bronze/gilt copies with the maker's name. I have also seen unhallmarked copies of the Orders of Franz Joseph, and St Stephen. I have also had in my possession copies of the Order of Elizabeth, and the Starry Cross Order. Copies of the Franz Joseph bravery medals exist without the designer's name, but there are also some made of "pot metal" which may be late war issues, but also do not have the designer's name.

Another major problem the collector may encounter is the difficulty in obtaining the trifold or triangular style of ribbon used by this country.

Nevertheless, the Austrian field of collecting is very interesting and rewarding for the collector, especially when you consider that prices have been quite stable over the years. Moreover, for those who find that the pre-1918 German states are too expensive for their taste will often collect this country because of its Germanic relationships.

Reference should be made to an unusual feature of Austrian Orders, namely, the practice of wearing a device on the ribbon of a lower class of an Order to signify a higher grade, without wearing the higher grade, the KLEINE DEKORATION.

Another interesting feature is how the awards of Austria were mounted for wearing. Unlike the awards of other countries, which may have differed in size, there was no attempt made to have them all hang at the same level as with British or German items. The very distinctive trifold ribbon made this virtually impossible.

Austria-Monarchy

Order of the Golden Fleece-1429-1918
1.Collar with badge-gold   rare
2.Collar with badge-early 20th century-silver/gilt   rare
3.Neck badge on ribbon-gold   14,000.00
4.Neck badge on ribbon-silver/gilt   10,000.00
(So many variations exist of this Order due to its long existence. Values will vary
accordingly. Beware of copies in many different qualities. Values for gold items.
See also Spain.)

Order of Maria Theresa-Military-1757-1918
5.Grand Cross badge   rare
6.Grand Cross breast star   10,000.00
7.Commander-neck badge   rare
8.Knight-breast badge   8000.00
(All grades are rare. Insignia were also awarded with diamonds. A tinsel breast
star exists. Gold, silver/gilt, and bronze/gilt copies have been made. Gold badges
should be hallmarked on suspension with maker's name and/or gold mark of 750
[18 karat].)

Order of Leopold-1808-1918
9.Collar (gold)   20,000.00
10.Collar-silver/gilt   10,000.00
11.Collar-bronze/gilt   7000.00
12.Grand Cross badge   4000.00
13.Grand Cross breast star   3500.00
14.First Class badge   2500.00
15.First Class breast star   4000.00
16.Commander-neck badge-gold   2500.00
17.Knight-breast badge-gold   750.00
18.Kleine dekoration of the Grand Cross   850.00
19.Kleine dekoration of the 1st class   600.00
20.Kleine dekoration of the Commander Cross   550.00
(This is a complicated Order with many variations. With war decoration (wreath)
add 20%; with war decoration and swords add 40%. World War I badges are
generally bronze/gilt with hallmark of asterisk (*) to indicate eventual replacement
by gold insignia after the war was won; values 60-75% of above. Copies of this
Order exist, hallmarks missing.)

Order of the Iron Crown-1815-1918
21.Collar-gold   20,000.00
22.First class badge   3000.00
23.First class breast star   2000.00
24.Second Class-neck badge   1750.00
25.Third Class-breast badge   750.00
26.Kleine dekoration of the First class   800.00
27.Kleine dekoration of the Second class   450.00

(With war decoration add 20%; with war decoration and swords add 40%. World War I issues are bronze/gilt with values 60-75% of above. Copies exist without hallmarks. See also the Order of the Crown of Italy. Several variations of this Order exist.)

Franz Joseph Order-1848-1916

28.Grand Cross badge	1600.00
29.Grand Cross breast star	1600.00
30.Commander Cross I Class-neck badge	1200.00
31.Commander Cross I Class-breast star	1500.00
32.Commander Cross-neck badge	1200.00
33.Officer-pin back badge (World War I)-gold	700.00
34. Officer- pin back badge (World War I)-silver/gilt	550.00
35.Knight-breast badge	400.00

(On many of the gold badges, which should be hallmarked, the reverse opens like a locket. With war decoration add 20%; with war decoration and swords add 40%. World War I issues are silver/gilt or bronze/gilt, and worth 60-75% of above values. For kleine dekoration on the Knight's badge ribbon add $250.00 to $800.00. Copies exist without hallmarks. Because this Order is dated 1849 confusion exists with the Merit Crosses in gold and silver also dated 1849 with the initials FJ.)

36.Order of the Starry Cross-1886-1918	2500.00

(Awarded to ladies on a bow ribbon. Many variations exist. Also awarded with diamonds to ladies of the Imperial & Royal House. Copies exist without hallmarks.)

Order of Elizabeth-1898-1918

37.Grand Cross badge	3500.00
38.Grand Cross breast star	4000.00
39.First Class badge-gold on bow	2500.00
40.First Class breast star	3000.00
41.Second Class badge	1500.00
42.Elizabeth Cross-silver	unique
43.Elizabeth Medal-silver	700.00

(This was also a ladies' Order; copies exist.)

44.Order of Elizabeth Theresa-1750-1918	3000.00

(Several variations of this Order exist.)

Military Merit Cross-1849-1918

45.First Class-large pin back breast cross	5000.00
46.Second Class-neck badge	1200.00
47.Third Class-breast badge	75.00
48.Kleine dekoration of the First Class	350.00
49.Kleine dekoration of the Second Class	250.00

(With war decoration add 10%; with swords add 20% to I & II Classes. Extra award bars are worn on the ribbon of the III Class. There are many variations of this award.)

Order of St Stephen-see Hungary

Honor Decoration of the Red Cross-1914-18
50.Merit Cross-large pin back breast badge	2200.00
51.First class-neck badge	800.00
52.Officer-pin back badge	250.00
53.Second Class-silver/gilt/enamels-breast badge	95.00
54.Second Class-silver/enamels	85.00
55.Merit Medal-I Class-silver/gilt	85.00
56.Merit Medal-II Class-silver	65.00
57.Merit Medal-III Class-bronze	45.00

(With and without war decoration.) When awarded to ladies is on bow ribbon. Reverse dated 1864-1914.)

58.Honor Decoration for Arts & Letters-1887-1918	2500.00

Merit Cross for Military Chaplains-1801-1918
59.Golden Merit Cross 1801-1859	rare
60.Silver Merit Cross 1801-1878	rare
61.Golden Merit Cross-(I Class)-1911	2000.00
62.Golden Merit Cross-(I Class)-1916-with swords	rare
63.Silver Merit Cross-(II Class)-1911	500.00
64.Silver Merit Cross-(II Class)-1916-with swords	rare

(This decoration may be found on the peace ribbon, white, or the war ribbon, white/red.)

Cross of Merit-1849-1918
Type I-1849-1860-30mm x 30mm-crown without enamel
65.Golden Merit Cross-with crown-gold	500.00
66.Golden Merit Cross-gold	450.00
67.Silver Merit Cross-with crown	225.00
68.Silver Merit Cross	200.00
Type II-size 28mm x 28mm-crown with enamel	
69.Golden Merit Cross-with crown	95.00
70.Golden Merit Cross	75.00
71.Silver Merit Cross-with crown	60.00
72.Silver Merit Cross	50.00

(The Golden Merit Cross may be gold, silver/gilt, or bronze/gilt World War I issue; and is found on the peace or war ribbon. With swords on ribbon add $5.00 (World War I). See also the Iron Merit Cross of 1916 of similar design. Do not confuse with the Franz Joseph Order which also bears date 1849 and the initials FJ.)

Iron Merit Cross-1916-18
73.Iron Merit Cross with crown	30.00
74.Iron Merit Cross	25.00

(With swords on ribbon add $5.00.)

AUSTRIA

Bravery Medals-1789-1918
(On reverse till 1916 "Der Tapferkeit"; then for Karl the Latin "Fortitudini".)
Joseph II-1789-1792

75.Golden Medal-I.N. Wirt engraver	rare
76.Silver Medal	1500.00
77.Silver Medal-no engraver	1000.00

Franz II-1792-1804

78.Golden Medal	rare
79.Silver Medal	800.00

Franz I-1804(new title as Emperor of Austria)

80.Golden Medal	rare
81.Silver Medal	800.00

Franz I-1804-1839

82.Golden Medal	rare
83.Silver Medal	800.00

Ferdinand-1835-1848

84.Golden Medal	3000.00
85.Silver Medal-large	550.00
86.Silver Medal-small	350.00

Franz Joseph-1848-1859-portrait facing left

87.Golden Medal	2500.00
88.Large Silver-engraver's name	500.00
89.Large Silver-no engraver's name	400.00
90.Small Silver-engraver's name	300.00
91.Small Silver-no engraver's name	250.00

(Obverse legend-Franz Joseph I Kaiser von Österreich.)
Franz Joseph-1859-1866-portrait facing left

92.Golden Medal	2500.00
93.Large Silver-engraver's name	375.00
94.Large Silver-no engraver's name	250.00
95.Small Silver-engraver's name	175.00
96.Small Silver-no engraver's name	125.00

(Obverse legend-Franz Joseph I V.G.G. Kaiser V. Österreich)
Franz Joseph-1866-1917-by Tautenhayn or Leisek-facing right.

97.Golden Medal-gold	1200.00
98.Golden Medal-bronze/gilt-World War I	350.00
99.Large Silver Medal	75.00
100.Small Silver Medal	40.00
101.Bronze Medal-1915-17	30.00
102.Coin Metal-no engraver-small	25.00
103.Pot Metal-no engraver	35.00

(Also found with additional award bars on ribbon. Copies exist of the gold & large silver of this type which have no engraver's name, are thick, and have a frosted appearance.)
Karl-1917-18-engraver Kautsch

104.Golden Medal-gold	1250.00
105.Golden Medal-bronze/gilt	550.00

(Copies exist in excellent striking with Kautsch very clear. However, on rim about 1 o'clock appears UNECHT [not genuine]).

106.Large Silver Medal 75.00
107.Small Silver Medal 35.00
108.Bronze Medal 25.00
109.Pot Metal-no engraver 25.00
(Also found with large K on ribbon for officers, and with additional award bars.)

Military Merit Medal-1890-1918 (Commonly known as "Signum Laudis")
Franz Joseph 1890-1916
110.Large Military Merit Medal 200.00
111.Silver Military Merit Medal-1911 35.00
112.Bronze Military Merit Medal-gilt 35.00
Karl-1916-1918
113.Large Military Merit Medal 225.00
114.Silver Military Merit Medal 35.00
115.Bronze Military Merit Medal 35.00
(This decoration also found with extra award bars, and swords on the ribbon-add
$5.00.)

Civil Merit Medal-1804(reverse IVSTITIA REGNORVM FUNDAMENTVM)
1804 issue-43mm
116.Golden Merit Medal rare
117.Silver Merit Medal rare
1835 issue-36mm
118.Golden Merit Medal rare
119.Golden Merit Medal-bronze/gilt rare
120.Silver Merit Medal 700.00
1835 issue(reverse MERITIS)
121.Golden Merit Medal I Class-48mm rare
122.Silver Merit Medal I Class rare
123.Golden Merit Medal II Class-39mm rare
124.Silver Merit Medal II Class 800.00
125.Golden Merit Medal III Class-33mm rare
126.Golden Merit Medal III Class-bronze/gilt rare
127.Silver Merit Medal III Class 600.00
128.Bronze Merit Medal 175.00
Franz Joseph issue 1848
129.Golden Merit Medal I Class-48mm rare
130.Silver Merit Medal I Class 800.00
131.Golden Merit Medal II Class-39mm rare
132.Silver Merit Medal II Class 600.00
133.Golden Merit Medal III Class-33mm 200.00
134.Silver Merit Medal III Class 400.00
Karl-1917
135.Silver Merit Medal 500.00

War Cross for Civil Merit-pin back-1916
136.First Class-64mm-silver/gilt/enamel 1000.00
137.Second Class-44mm-silver/gilt/enamel 95.00

AUSTRIA

138.Third Class-44mm-silver/enamel	85.00
139.Fourth Class-mm-bronze/gilt	65.00

(These items should be profusely hallmarked on the reverse.)

Military Long Service Decorations for Officers-1849-1918
1849-1890

140.For 50 years-golden eagle	175.00
141.For 25 years-silver eagle	75.00

1890-1918

142.I Class for 50 years	125.00
143.II Class for 40 & 35 Years(after 7 August 1913)	65.00
144.III Class for 25 years	55.00

Military Long Service Decorations for N.C.O.'s-1849-1918
1849-1890

145.For 16 years-1849-67-numeral XVI	35.00
146.For 18 years-1867-69-numeral XVIII	40.00
147.For 24 years-1869-90-numeral XXIV	55.00
148.For 8 years-1849-67-numeral VIII	25.00
149.For 12 years-1867-90-numeral XII	20.00

1890-1918

150.I Class for 24 years-1890-1913-numeral XXIV	35.00
151.I Class for 20 years-1913-1918-numeral XX	25.00
152.II Class for 12 years-1890-1913-numeral XII	20.00
143.II Class for 10 years-1913-1918-numeral X	15.00
154.II Class for 6 years 1913-1918-numeral VI	15.00
155.II Class for 6 years 1916-1918-war metal-numeral VI 15.00	

Landsturm (Home Guard) Meritorious Service-1908

156.Bronze Medal-40 years-Octo Lustra	200.00
157.Bronze Medal-25 years-Quinque Lustra	75.00

Jubilee Medals-Franz Joseph-Fiftieth Jubilee-1898

158.Honor Medal for 40 years faithful service	20.00

Armed Forces and Police Jubilee

159.Gold Medal-double eagle suspender	850.00
160.Gold Medal-bronze/gilt	175.00
161.Bronze Medal-no double eagle suspender	10.00

Court Officials Jubilee issues-bar 1848-1898

162.Military-gold-trifold ribbon	rare
163.Civil-gold-straight ribbon	rare
164.Military-silver-trifold ribbon	200.00
165.Civil-silver-straight ribbon	200.00
166.Military-bronze-trifold ribbon	100.00
167.Civil-bronze-straight ribbon	100.00
168.Ladies'-bronze-on bow ribbon	100.00

Jubilee Commanders' Medal-large gold oval medal 108mm x 88mm awarded to regiments of the Austro-Hungarian Army which Franz Joseph had commanded for

50 years. For the infantry it was worn on the regimental flags; for the cavalry on special trumpet banners.

169.1st Tirolian Infantry Regiment	1700.00
170.4th Tirolian Infantry Regiment	1700.00
171.1st Dragoon Regiment	1700.00
172.2nd Dragoon Regiment	1700.00
173.1st Hussar Regiment	1700.00
174.1st Uhlan Regiment	1700.00
175.6th Uhlan Regiment	1700.00
176.8th Corps Artillery Regiment	1700.00

Jubilee Commemorative Medal for the Imperial Russian Kexholm Regiment of the Imperial Guard Franz Joseph

177.Golden Medal for the regimental flag-92mm	rare
178.Silver Medal-for officers-34mm	1000.00
179.Bronze Medal-forEnsigns,Sgt Majors & Flag Bearers	900.00

180.Commemorative Badge of His Imperial & Royal Highness the Archduke Albert-1899-pin back-silver-34 awarded   6500.00

Commemorative Medal for the Royal Prussian Grenadier Guard Regiment Nr. 2-1899

181.Golden Medal for the regimental flag	rare
182.same-bronze/gilt	rare
183.Silver Medal-34mm-for officers	275.00
184.Bronze Medal-34mm-for enlisted men	95.00

Commemorative Medal of the Royal Bavarian Infantry Regiment Nr.13- 1899

185.Golden Medal for the regimental flag-92mm	rare
186.same-bronze/gilt	rare
187.Silver Medal-34mm-for officers	800.00
188.Bronze Medal-for N.C.O.'s	700.00

189.Fire Service Medal for 25 Years-1906   25.00

190.Mayors of Lower Austria-Badge of Office-1907   275.00

Jubilee Decorations 1908-60th Jubilee of Franz Joseph

191.Jubilee Cross with diamonds	rare
192.Jubilee Cross-military ribbon	15.00
193.Jubilee Cross-civil ribbon	15.00
194.Jubilee Cross-court ribbon	15.00

Commander's Jubilee Medal for Foreigners (awarded to members of eleven foreign regiments of which Franz Joseph was honorary commander.) -1908

195.Gold Medal for royalty & generals	1400.00
196.Silver Medal-officers	250.00
197.Bronze Medal-N.C.O.'s	125.00

AUSTRIA

Franz Joseph Commemorative Cross-1918
198.1st grade-golden metal   250.00
199.2nd grade-silver metal   150.00

Campaign Medals & Miscellaneous Awards
Commemorative, Honor & Merit Medal-Joseph II(reverse VIRTUTE ET
EXEMPLO)
Obverse: IOSEPHVS II D.G. ROM. REX-1764-65
200.Golden Medal   3500.00
201.Large silver medal-50mm   450.00
202.Small silver medal-46mm   400.00
203.Bronze medal   95.00
Obverse: IOSEPHUS II D.G. R. IMP.-1765-1780
204.Golden Medal   3500.00
205.Large silver medal-50mm   450.00
206.Small silver medal-46mm   400.00
Obverse: IOS. II D.G. R. IMP.-1780
207.Golden medal   3500.00
208.Large silver medal-50mm   450.00
209.Small silver medal-46mm   375.00
Obverse: IOSEPHUS AUGUSTUS
210.Golden medal   2500.00
211.Large silver medal-50mm   350.00
212.Medium silver medal-46mm   300.00
213.Small silver medal-29mm   250.00

Academy of Military Surgeons-Vienna-1785
214.Golden Medal-60mm   2500.00
215.Silver Medal-60mm   800.00

Military Surgeon's Merit Medal-1785-1790
216.Large silver medal-50mm   700.00
217.Medium silver medal-43mm   500.00
218.Small silver medal-35mm   450.00

Commemoration Medal-Limburg Volunteers-Leopold II-1790-93
219.Large gold medal-34mm   2500.00
220.Small gold medal-32mm   2000.00
221.Silver medal-29mm   550.00

222.Silver Merit Medal for the Netherlands-1790   500.00

Coronation Medal-Leopold II-1790
223.Large gold medal-49mm   1800.00
224.Medium gold medal-43mm   1100.00
225.Small gold medal-36mm   800.00
226.Large silver medal-49mm   575.00
227.Medium silver medal-43mm   450.00
228.Small silver medal-36mm   350.00

Coronation Medal-Leopold II-1790-for Hungary & Bohemia
229.Large gold medal-49mm   2500.00
230.Small gold medal-36mm   950.00
231.Large silver medal-49mm   500.00
232.Small silver medal-36mm   350.00

Coronation Medal-Franz II-1792
233.Large gold medal-49mm   1800.00
234.Medium gold medal-43mm   1200.00
235.Small gold medal-36mm   750.00
236.Large silver medal-49mm   475.00
237.Medium silver medal-43mm   450.00
238.Small silver medal-36mm   350.00

Coronation Medal-Franz II-1792-for Hungary & Bohemia
239.Large gold medal-49mm   2000.00
240.Small gold medal-36mm   1100.00
241.Large silver medal-49mm   500.00
242.Small silver medal-36mm   350.00

Netherlands Campaigns-1792-94
243.Silver medal-Duke Carl Alexander of Lorraine   rare
244.Gold medal-Franz II-1792   2000.00
245.Silver medal   650.00
246.White metal medal   200.00
247.Golden medal-Franz II-1793   1800.00
248.Golden medal-Franz II-1794   1800.00
249.Silver medal   650.00

Gold Medal for Eight British Officers-1794
250.Gold medal-on a neck chain   rare
251.Restrike in alloy   575.00

252.Silver Medal for Olmutz-1796   750.00

Tirolian Commemorative Medal-1796
253.Large silver medal-40mm   350.00
254.Small silver medal-34mm   125.00

Brave Defenders of the Fatherland-1797
255.Large gold medal-39mm   rare
256.Small gold medal-35mm   850.00
257.Silver medal-39mm   175.00

Lower Austria Merit Medal-1797
258.Golden medal-Senior officers   1500.00
259.Silver medal-Junior officers-41mm   350.00
260.Silver medal-N.C.O.'s-39mm   250.00
261.Silver medal-enlisted men-37mm   150.00

AUSTRIA

262.Silver Medal for Dalmatia   285.00

Commemorative Medal for the Creation of the Austrian Empire-1804
Type I-Franciscus Austriae Imperator
263.Golden medal-50mm   1800.00
264.Silver medal-50mm   400.00
Type II-Franc. I AVST
265.Golden medal-50mm   1800.00
266.Silver medal-50mm   400.00

267.Army Cross-1813-14(also known as the "Cannon Cross")   150.00

Civil Honor Cross-1813-14
268.Golden honor cross   rare
269.Silver honor cross   3000.00
(Since the appearance of the Civil Cross of 1813-14 is similar to that of the Army
Cross, except for the wreath between the arms of the latter, the collector should
be alert for fake civil crosses made by removing the wreath from between the arms
of the Army Cross.)

270.Gold Cross for Bohemian Nobles-1808   rare

Tirolian Homage Medal-1838
271.Silver medal   rare
272.Bronze medal   rare

273.Tirol Commemorative Medal-1848-Franz Joseph   150.00

War with Denmark-1864-bronze
274.Rim inscription "Aus Erobetem Geschutz"
  (From captured cannon)   75.00
275.same-but without inscription   100.00
(Obverse FJ on left & W on right-compare with Prussian issue where the initials
are reversed.)

Defense of the Tirol-1866
276.Dated medal   95.00
277.Undated medal   125.00

278.Prague Citizens Medal-1866-silver   375.00

279.General Campaign Medal-1873-gilt/bronze   25.00
(There are several variations or strikings of this medal which generally do not
affect valuation. Among the campaigns this was awarded for was the Boxer
Rebellion-China 1900, for which Austria, alone among the participants did not
issue a special medal.)

280.Cruiser Empress Elizabeth-S. Pacific and Far Eastern Cruise-
1892-93-bronze   900.00

281.50th Anniversary Medal for the Loyal Defenders of the Tirol-
1859-1909-silver   550.00

282.Bosnia-Herzegovina Annexation Medal-1909   75.00

283.Cruiser Franz Joseph I-Far Eastern Cruise-1910-12   1500.00

Balkan Wars' Mobilization Cross-1912-1913-gilt/bronze
284.Impressed date   45.00
285.Engraved date   45.00

286.Franz Joseph Cross-1916   rare

287.Troop Cross (Truppen Kreuz)-Karl-1916   15.00
(Since this award was made from zinc it is not often found with its details sharply
defined.)

Wound Medal-Karl
288.Medal for invalids-gray ribbon-red edges   20.00
289.Medal for war wounded-1 wound-ribbon as above-1 stripe   20.00
290.same-2 wounds-2 stripes   25.00
291.same-3 wounds-3 stripes   30.00
292.same-4 wounds-4 stripes   35.00
293.same-5 wounds-5 stripes   50.00

Flying Badges-1912-1918
294.Golden pilot's badge-1912   550.00
295.Field pilot's badge-1913   550.00
296.same-but for Karl-1916-17   650.00
297.same-1917-combined crowns of Austria & Hungary   650.00
298.Air Crew badge-1917-L for Luftfahrer(Air Crew)   600.00
299.General aircrew badge-1917   600.00
300.Naval flying badge-1913   750.00
(Note: Numerous copies of these badges exist. However, many legitimate
variations also exist. For further reference: Don Chalif-MILITARY PILOT &
AIRCREW BADGES OF THE WORLD-Vol I.)

Austria-REPUBLIC 1919-1934; FEDERAL REPUBLIC 1934-1938

Honor Decoration for Merit of the Republic-1922
Austrian Merit Order-1934-38

301.Badge-black enamel   rare
302.Breast star-irregular shape-81mm x 77mm-1922   rare
303.Breast star-8 pointed-gilt-90mm-1934-38   rare

AUSTRIA

Grand Cross I Class-with eagle-red enamel-1935-38
304.Badge-on sash   1000.00
305.Breast star   1000.00
306.Kleine dekoration-Knight I Class   200.00

Grand Golden Honor Decoration-1929-34
Grand Cross I Class of the Merit Order-1934-red enamel
307.Badge-on sash   450.00
308.Breast star-similar 298   rare
309.Breast star-similar 299   400.00
310.Kleine dekoration-Knight I Class   200.00

Grand Cross of the Merit Order-white enamel-1934
311.Badge-on sash   350.00
312.Breast star-similar 299   300.00
313.Kleine dekoration-Knight   200.00

Golden Honor Decoration with Star-red enamel-1922
314.Neck badge   350.00
315.Breast star   300.00
316.Kleine dekoration-Knight I Class-1934-38   125.00

Grand Honor Decoration with Star-white enamel-1922(Commander Cross with Star
of the Merit Order-1934)
317.Neck badge   300.00
318.Breast star   300.00
319.Kleine dekoration-Knight   125.00

Grand Golden Honor Decoration-red enamel-1922(Commander Cross of the Merit
Order-1934)
320.Neck badge   350.00
321.Kleine dekoration-1934-38-Knight   125.00

Grand Honor Decoration-white enamel-1922(Commander Cross of the Merit
Order-1934)
322.Neck badge   300.00
323.Kleine dekoration-1934-Knight   125.00

Grand Silver Honor Decoration-1922(Merit Order-Officer-1934)
324.Five Armed badge-1922-red enamel   250.00
325.Four Armed badge-1926-white enamel   85.00
326.Kleine dekoration   75.00

Golden Honor Decoration-1922(Knight I Class Merit Order-1934)
327.Red enameled badge on breast ribbon   100.00

Silver Honor Decoration-1922(Knight Merit Order-1934)
328.White enameled cross on breast ribbon   75.00

Merit Decoration-1927 & 1934
329.Golden Merit Cross-gilt 75.00
330.Silver Merit Cross-silvered 50.00

Merit Medal-1922 & 1934
331.Golden medal-1922 type 50.00
332.Golden medal-1934 type 50.00
333.Large silver medal-1922-45mm 45.00
334.Large silver medal-1934-45mm 45.00
335.Silver medal-1922-36mm 35.00
336.Silver medal-1934-36mm 35.00
337.Bronze medal-1930 25.00
338.Bronze medal-1934 25.00

Military Merit Cross-1935-38
339.First class-large pin back cross 68mm x 70mm one awarded
340.Second class-neck badge nine awarded
341.Third class-breast badge - 167 awarded 700.00

Military Long Service Decoration-1934
342.I Class-officers-35 years - 32 awarded rare
343.II Class-officers-25 years - 643 awarded 150.00
344.I Class-N.C.O.'s-35 years two awarded
345.II Class-N.C.O.'s-25 years - 487 awarded 150.00
346.I Class-enlisted men-12 years 25.00
347.II Class-enlisted men-5 years 20.00

348.Military Merit Medal for Officers-1935-38 - 112 awarded 600.00

Order of Arts & Science-1934-38
349.Merit Cross I Class-pin back cross 350.00
350.Merit Cross II Class-on ribbon 250.00
351.Merit Medal-oval-on ribbon 200.00

Honor Decoration of the Red Cross-1923
352.Merit Star-pin back 850.00
353.Honor Decoration-I Class-neck badge-57mm x 48mm 275.00
354.Honor Decoration-Officer-pin back badge 175.00
355.Honor Decoration-II Class-on ribbon 125.00
356.Honor Medal-I Class-gilt 75.00
357.Honor Medal-II Class-silver 65.00
358.Honor Medal-III Class-bronze 45.00
(Note: Ribboned awards to ladies are found on bow ribbons.)

Commemorative Medals-1914-18(1932)
359.Combat-with swords on ribbon 35.00
360.Noncombat-without swords 25.00
361.Defense of the Tirol 1914-18 25.00

AUSTRIA

362.Jubilee Medal-10th Anniversary of the Republic	50.00
363.Military Chaplain's Decoration-neck badge	350.00

Fire Service & Lifesaving Medal-1922
364.40 Years-silvered medal	35.00
365.25 Years-bronze medal	25.00

Faithful Service Medal for 40 Years
366.Type I-1927	35.00
367.Type II-1934	50.00

Flying Badges of the Republic
368.Oval-green wreath-pin back-various types	500.00

(Beware of copies.)

STATE DECORATIONS

Carinthia
369.Bravery Cross-I Class-1919-pin back	250.00
370.Merit Cross-I Class	550.00
371.Bravery Cross-II Class-on ribbon	60.00
372.Merit Cross-II Class	75.00

Styria
373.Bravery and Merit Medal-1919-20	225.00
374.Honor Plaque 1924-for the Iron Corps 1914-18	225.00

Unofficial Awards
375.Cross of the Austrian Honor Legion-1914-18	50.00
376."Für Der Heimat"-Cross for World War II	75.00
377.Iron Cross-I Cl 1939-45-no device or date on obverse	150.00
378.Iron Cross-II Cl-no device or date on obverse	75.00

17   13   7
Hungary

136   137 & 138

25 39 35

36

45

47

46

47

51 50 51

53 & 54 53 & 54

69 & 71   73   70 & 72

161   192-194

274 & 275   267   276 & 277

141 & 143   140 & 142   144

339

340

341

AUSTRIA

314 & 320

355   317 & 322

BELGIUM

Kingdom since 1830.

The Orders and decorations of Belgium reflect very well the history of the country. The Orders of Leopold and Leopold II commemorate the role played by these monarchs in their country's development. The Orders are handsome in appearance, and there is an extensive grouping of awards for both world wars. Additionally, because of the colonial empire in Africa (principally the Belgian Congo) there is a much larger selection of items to collect than a small country would seem to indicate.

Belgian awards are not especially rare, because of the circumstances of their presentation. With certain exceptions, most awards of this country are made by document only. The recipient must then go to a store, of which there are several, operated by a jeweler/manufacturer, and buy the designated award. However, it is also possible for the non-awardee to go and buy these items. Thus, the number awarded has no relation to those actually made and sold.

Other than some very obvious cast copies of the very common Belgian awards, the only copy I have come across was a 1914-18 Croix de Guerre stamped FRANCE.

Therefore, the collector finds that Belgium offers reasonable prices and very little fear of copies!

Order of Leopold-1832

1.Collar	3000.00
2.Grand cross badge	500.00
3.Grand cross badge-with swords	550.00
4.Grand cross badge-with anchors	1000.00
5.Grand cross breast star	450.00
6.Grand cross breast star-with swords	550.00
7.Grand cross breast star-with anchors	750.00
8.Grand officer breast star(awarded without badge)	400.00
9.Grand officer breast star-with swords	450.00
10.Grand officer breast star-with anchors	650.00
11.Commander-neck badge	250.00
12.Commander-with swords	300.00
13.Commander-with anchors	600.00
14.Officer	100.00
15.Officer-with swords	150.00
16.Officer-with anchors	300.00
17.Knight	75.00
18.Knight-with swords	150.00
19.Knight-with anchors	300.00

(The values for the Order of Leopold are for type I-French language insignia in silver/gilt. For gold insignia add 25%. For type II-French/Flemish languages deduct 10%. This Order can also be worn with gold and silver palms, and swords on ribbons of the Officer and Knight classes. This Order is unique in that it is the only one which has its awards to naval personnel distinguished from those of other awards by use of anchors instead of swords.)

Order of the Crown-1897

20.Grand Cross badge	450.00
21.Grand Cross breast star	400.00
22.Grand Officer breast star-no badge awarded	300.00
23.Commander-neck badge	200.00
24.Officer	85.00
25.Knight	60.00
26.Medal-I Class-gilt-type I-French language	35.00
27.same-type II-French/Flemish languages	25.00
28.Medal-II Class-silver-type I	25.00
29.same-type II	20.00
30.Medal-III Class-bronze-type I	15.00
31.same-type II	10.00

(Crossed swords may be worn on the ribbon of the Officer & Knight badges of this Order.)

Order of Leopold II-1900
Type I-French language;Type II-French/Flemish languages

32.Grand Cross badge-type I	350.00
33.Grand Cross badge-type II	300.00
34.Grand Cross breast star-type I	350.00
35.Grand Cross breast star-type II	300.00
36.Grand Officer cross(same as Officer)-type I	85.00
37.Grand Officer cross-type II	75.00
38.Grand Officer breast star-type I	275.00
39.Grand Officer breast star-type II	250.00
40.Commander-neck badge-type I	175.00
41.Commander-type II	150.00
42.Officer-breast badge-type I	85.00
43.Officer-type II	75.00
44.Knight-breast badge-type I	50.00
45.Knight-type II	40.00
46.Merit Medal-I Class-gilt-type I	25.00
47.same-type II	20.00
48.Merit Medal-II Class-silver-type I	20.00
49.same-type II	15.00
50.Merit Medal-III Class-bronze-type I	15.00
51.same-type II	10.00

(Gilt and silver palms may be worn on the ribbons of the Officer and Knight badges, as well as crossed swords; add $5.00 per item.)

Order of the Lion-Belgian Congo-1881-1960

52.Collar	rare
53.Grand Cross badge	650.00

54.Grand Cross breast star	600.00
55.Grand Officer breast star-no badge awarded	450.00
56.Commander-neck badge	450.00
57.Officer-breast badge	250.00
58.Knight-breast badge	200.00
59.Merit Medal-I Class-gilt	50.00
60.Merit Medal-II Class-silver	40.00
61.Merit Medal-III Class-bronze	35.00

Order of the Star of Africa-Belgian Congo-1888-1960

62.Collar	rare
63.Grand cross badge	450.00
64.Grand cross breast star	450.00
65.Grand officer breast star-no badge awarded	300.00
66.Commander-neck badge	250.00
67.Officer-breast badge	150.00
68.Knight-breast badge	125.00
69.Merit Medal-I Class-gilt	50.00
70.Merit Medal-II Class-silver	40.00
71.Merit Medal-III Class-bronze	30.00

Croix de Guerre (War Crosses)

72.Type I-1914-18-reverse "A"	30.00
73.Type II-1940-45-reverse "L"	65.00
74.Type II-1954-reverse "coat of arms"	75.00

(On the ribbon of this award various devices could be worn such as bronze, silver, or silver/gilt palms or lions. Add $5-10.00 per device.)

Various Military and Civilian Campaign Awards

75.1870-71 Commemorative Medal-for mobilization during the Franco-Prussian War 1870-71	25.00
76.Yser Medal 1914-18 (1918)	25.00
77.Yser Cross 1914-18 (1934)-replaced previous award	45.00
78.Frontline Service Cross 1914-18 (1934)	25.00
79.Maritime Decoration 1914-18-cross-(1918)	40.00
80.Maritime Decoration-medal	35.00

Civic Decoration-1914-15;1914-1918

81.Cross-I Class-with swords-silver/gilt	35.00
82.Cross-II Class-with swords-silver	25.00
83.Medal-III Class-with swords-silver	20.00
84.King Albert Medal-National Gratitude-1919	20.00
85.Queen Elizabeth Medal-1914-16	35.00
86.same-but with Red Cross in suspension	45.00
87.Combat Volunteers Medal 1914-18 (1930)	20.00

88.Victory Medal 1914-18 (1919)	20.00
89.Political Prisoners Medal 1914-18 (1930)	20.00
90.Cross for Deportees 1914-18 (1922)	25.00

Commemorative Medal for Aid & Food Supplies-1914-18

91.I Class-bronze/gilt-rosette on ribbon	35.00
92.II Class-bronze/gilt	30.00
93.III Class-silvered bronze	25.00
94.IV Class-bronze	20.00

National Restoration Medal-1914-18 (1928)

95.I Class-gilt	35.00
96.II Class-silver	25.00
97.III Class-bronze	15.00

98.Liege Medal 1914 (1920)-unofficial	25.00
99.Commemorative War Medal-1914-18 (1919)	15.00

(Although seemingly a simple medal of modest value it was really very complicated. This medal could be worn with the following devices on the ribbon: a.Gilt crown for volunteers. b.Service bars-1st for 12 months, others for 6 months-in silver;1 gilt replaced 5 silver. c.Small enameled red cross for wound. d.Silver crown for Intelligence Officers holding a Belgian Order. e.Silver lion-Belgian Intelligence service. f.Bronze anchor for Merchant Navy. g.Bars 1916-R-1917 & 1916-R-1918-Belgian Expeditionary Corps in Russia. h.Two crossed anchors for Marines. i.Black enamel bars for P.O.W. Except for the Russian bars add $5.00 to value; Russian bars rare. Add $5.00 to $50.00 depending on device.)

100.Armed Resistance Medal 1940-45 (1946)	20.00
101.Volunteers Medal 1940-45 (1946)	20.00
102.Maritime Medal 1940-45 (1941)	25.00

Civic Decoration-1940-45

103.I Class-gilt-white enameled cross	35.00
104.II Class-silver-white enameled cross	30.00
105.III Class-gilt medal	25.00
106.IV Class-silver medal	20.00
107.V Class-bronze medal	15.00

(On the crosses there are crossed torches through the arms;on the medals there are crossed torches as part of the suspension. Ribbon device states 1940-45.)

108.Political Prisoners' Cross-silver/enamel	75.00

(A silver bar with star could be worn for each 6 months in a German Concentration Camp-add $10.00.)

109.Prisoner of War Medal-1940-45 (1947)	25.00
110.Civil Resistance Medal-1940-45 (1952)	15.00
111.Acts of Rebellion Medal-1940-45 (1951)	20.00

Belgian Recognition Medal-1940-45 (1945)
I Class-gilt	25.00
112.same-with red cross	30.00
113.II Class-silvered	20.00
114.same-with red cross	25.00
115.III Class-bronze	15.00
116.same-with red cross	20.00

117.War Commemorative Medal-1940-45 (1946)   25.00
(Like its World War I counterpart this medal could be worn with various devices
on its ribbon. Add $5.00 per device. Copies of this medal exist, made in the USA
for veterans.
a.Two crossed sabres for the campaigns of 1940. b.Red enamel cross with chevron
for the wounded. c.Lion-for a citation not rewarded by the Croix de Guerre.
d.Bronze crown for volunteers. e.Cross lightning bolts for intelligence service.
f.Bronze bar for war prisoners. g.Crossed anchors for Merchant Marine. Add
$5.00 to $20.00 depending on device.)

Korean War-1950-54
118.Volunteers Medal-similar to 101	35.00
119.same-with bar Pugnator	50.00
120.Korean Service Medal-bar Coree-Korea	100.00
121.United Nations Service-with slipover bar Coree-Korea rather than standard type	100.00

(See also item 74-Croix de Guerre 1954)

Other Belgian Awards

Order of the Star of Honor-Commemorating the Revolution of 1830 and Belgium's
independence-1831
122.I Class-gold neck badge	rare
123.II Class-gold breast badge	rare
124.II Class-silver breast badge	rare

Iron Cross & Medal-1833-replaced previous award
125.Iron Cross	rare
126.Iron Medal	rare
127.Volunteers Commemorative Cross 1830 (1878)	85.00

25th Anniversary Decoration of Leopold I-1830-55 (1856)
128.I Class-Army & Civic Guard Officers-silver/enamel	50.00
129.II Class-enlisted men-unenameled medal	25.00

Medal of Honor for Acts of Devotion During Mining Accidents-1840
130.I Class-gold-1840	60.00
131.II Class-silver	35.00
132.I Class-gold-1844	60.00
133.II Class-silver	35.00

BELGIUM

134. Medal for Vaccination-bronze-1833   75.00

Cholera Epidemics Medals
135. I Class-gold-1832   75.00
136. II Class-silver   45.00
137. III Class-bronze   35.00
138. I Class-gold-1849   60.00
139. II Class-silver   45.00
140. III Class-bronze   35.00

Epidemics Medals
Non-wearable type-1846
141. I Class-gold   75.00
142. II Class-silver   50.00
143. III Class-bronze   25.00
Wearable type-1860
144. I Class-gold   75.00
145. II Class-silver   45.00
146. III Class-bronze   35.00
147. Animal Disease Epidemics Medal-to veterinarians-1866   75.00

Prison Medal of Honor-1857-1863
Type I-Leopold I-1857-1865
148. I Class-gold   75.00
149. II Class-silver   45.00
Type II-Leopold II-1866-1909
150. I Class-gold   75.00
151. II Class-silver   45.00
Type III-Albert-1910-1934
152. I Class-gold   75.00
153. II Class-silver   45.00
Type IV-Leopold III-1934-1950
154. I Class-gold   75.00
155. II Class-silver   45.00
Type V-Baudoin-1951
156. I Class-gold   60.00
157. II Class-silver   25.00

Civic Decoration-1867
158. I Class-gold/enameled cross   35.00
159. II Class-silver/enameled cross   25.00
160. III Class-gold medal   25.00
161. IV Class-silver medal   20.00
162. V Class-bronze medal   15.00
(For government employees, Civic Guard & Firemen [1896].)

Industrial & Agricultural Awards
163. Decoration for Workers & Artisans-1847-63   45.00
164. Decoration for Industry & Agriculture-I Class-1863   45.00

165.Decoration for Industry & Agriculture-II Class — 40.00
166.Decoration for Labor-bilingual-I Class-similar to 165 — 35.00
167.Decoration for Labor-II Class — 30.00

50th Anniversary of the Belgian Railways-1884
168.I Class-enameled cross-silver — 65.00
169.II Class-bronze medal — 25.00

Commemorative Decorations for the Belgian Telegraph System
170.I Class-silver/gilt/enamels-1896-50th Anniversary — 75.00
171.II Class-silver/gilt — 50.00
172.75th Anniversary-1921 — 35.00
173.100th Anniversary-1946 — 35.00

Postal Service Commemorative Medals
174.75th Anniversary-1924 — 25.00
175.100th Anniversary-1949 — 20.00

Commemorative Decoration-Ferry Boats-Ostend-Dover
176.I Class-silver/gilt/enamels-50th Anniversary-1896 — 45.00
177.II Class-silver — 25.00
178.100th Anniversary-1946 — 40.00

Military Cross-Officers' Long Service-1885
179.I Class-25 years-rosette on ribbon — 95.00
180.II Class-same-no rosette-includes N.C.O. service — 85.00
(This decoration was evidently the basis for the design of the Croix de Guerre 1914-18 & 1940-45; except that this award is silver/gilt and black enamel.)

Military Decoration-1846;1952;1955
181.I Class-for gallantry — 75.00
182.II Class-Long Service-N.C.O.'s-15 years — 60.00
183.II Class for gallantry — 60.00
184.II Class for Long Service-Enlisted Men-10 years — 35.00

Leopold II Commemorative Medal-1905 & 1909
185.Type I-dates-1865-1905 — 20.00
186.Type II-dates 1865-1909 — 25.00
187.Type III-dates 1885-1909 — 35.00
(Awarded for Long Service-civil, military & Belgian Congo.)

188.Commemorative Medal of Albert-dated 1909-1934 — 15.00

189.VII Olympic Games Commemorative Medal-Antwerp-1920 — 750.00
(450 awarded 1922-24; 28 to Belgian athletes, and the others to notables.)

190.Independence Commemorative-1930-silvered — 25.00

BELGIUM

Decorations for Physical Education & Sports-1935 & 1939
191.I Class-gold	45.00
192.II Class-silver	35.00
193.III Class-bronze	20.00
194.Cross for Sporting Merit(1939)-replaced 191-193	35.00

Medal for Agricultural Merit-1958
195.I Class-gold	40.00
196.II Class-silver	25.00
197.III Class-bronze	15.00

Lifesaving Medals-silver & silver/gilt & usually named on reverse
198.Leopold I	250.00
199.Leopold II	175.00
200.Albert	175.00
201.Leopold III	175.00
202.Baudoin	175.00

Royal Household Medals
Leopold II-1889-Employees of the Royal Household
203.I Class-gilt	75.00
204.II Class-silver	50.00
205.III Class-bronze	35.00

Leopold II-Employees of Foreign Courts
206.I Class-gold	95.00
207.II Class-silver	60.00
208.III Class-bronze	45.00

Albert-1910-For Servants of the Royal Household
209.I Class-gold-35 years	75.00
210.II Class-silver-25 years	50.00
211.III Class-bronze-15 years	35.00

Albert-Special award for Servants of the Royal Household
212.I Class-gold	85.00
213.II Class-silver	60.00

(For specially meritorious service. Could also be awarded to N.C.O.'s of the Belgian Army under certain circumstances.)

Albert-Employees of Foreign Courts
214.I Class-gold	95.00
215.II Class-silver	60.00
216.III Class-bronze	45.00
217.Visit of King Albert & Queen Elizabeth to Brazil-1920	75.00
218.King Albert Commemorative Cross-dated 1874-1934- awarded to former members of Royal Household staff	95.00

Leopold III-Employees of the Royal Household
219.I Class-gold-35 years	75.00
220.II Class-silver-25 years	50.00
221.III Class-bronze-15 years	35.00

Leopold III-Special Service Medal
222.I Class-gold	85.00
223.II Class-silver	60.00

Leopold III-Medal for Foreigners
224.I Class-gold	85.00
225.II Class-silver	60.00
226.III Class-bronze	45.00

Baudoin-Employees of the Royal Household
227.I Class-gold-35 years	75.00
228.II Class-silver-25 years	60.00
229.III Class-bronze-15 years	25.00

Baudoin-Special Medal
230.I Class-gold	85.00
231.II Class-silver	65.00

Baudoin-Medals for Foreigners
232.I Class-gold	75.00
233.II Class-silver	65.00
234.III Class-bronze	35.00

235.Merit Cross for Military Chaplains	300.00

Belgian Red Cross Awards
236.Cross of Merit-I Class-gold	200.00
237.Cross of Merit-II Class-silver	95.00
238.Cross of Honor-gold-1940-45	125.00
239.Bronze Palms 1940-45-pin back	50.00

Other Awards of the Belgian Congo (see also the Orders of the Lion and the Star of Africa.)

Service Star-1889-1960
240.Type I-I Class-silver/gilt-1889	85.00
241.II Class-silver	65.00
242.Type II-I Class-silver/gilt-1910	75.00
243.II Class-silver	50.00
244.Type III-I Class-silver/gilt-1936	65.00
245.II Class-silver	45.00
246.Type IV-I Class-silver/gilt-1956	50.00
247.II Class-silver	35.00

Service Medal-for Natives
248.Type I-Leopold II	75.00
249.Type II-Albert	65.00
250.Type III-Leopold III	65.00
251.Type IV-Baudoin	50.00

Merit Medals for Native Chiefs-1889
252.Type I-Leopold II-1889	200.00
253.Type II-Leopold II-1908	300.00

BELGIUM

254.Type III-Leopold II-1908-1910	250.00
255.Type IV-Albert-1910-34	200.00
256.Type V-Leopold III-1934-53	250.00
257.Type VI-Baudoin-1953-55	250.00
258.Type VII-Baudoin-1955-60	250.00

259.Arab Campaign Medal-1892-94(1895)-issued by Leopold II
for the suppression of the Slave Trade — 200.00

World War I Medals
Africa Service Medal-1914-16(1917;1921;1931)

260.Silver-for Europeans	150.00
261.same-bar Mahenge	200.00
262.Bronze-for natives	100.00
263.same-bar Mahenge	175.00
264.Colonial Commemorative Medal-1914-18-non-military-1935	45.00

World War II Medals
Abyssinia Campaign-1941(1947)

265.bar Abyssinie	25.00
266.same-without bar	20.00

Africa Service Medal-1940-45(1947)

267.without campaign bar	20.00
268.bar Nigerie	25.00
269.bar Moyen Orient	25.00
270.bar Madagascar	25.00
271.bar Birmanie	25.00

(This was a military award.)

272.Colonial War Medal-1940-45(1947)-civilian	20.00
273.Congo Commemorative Medal-1929	35.00
274.Congo Commemorative Medal-1958-50th Anniversary	25.00

275.Family Merit Medal-1956-to mothers of large native
families in the Congo & Ruanda-Urundi — 35.00

Lifesaving Medals (similar to Belgian awards)

276.Leopold II	225.00
277.Albert	125.00
278.Leopold III	125.00
279.Baudoin	95.00

12

11

13

14   58   25

68

179   72

81   182

75   260 & 262

77   99

108

268

272

265

BOXER REBELLION-CHINA 1900

The medals of this series are very popular with collectors, as they represent an opportunity to collect around a theme. As an episode in history which aroused a brief period of collaboration among rival powers it has long held fascination for the variety of awards available.

As indicated by values, some of the British and American pieces are the most highly prized, especially those actually engaged in the defense of the Western Legations against the Chinese. Copies are mainly a problem with U.S. medals, and occasionally the German combat medal. The Italian is much rarer than its value would indicate. Austria-Hungary alone did not create a new medal, but instead gave the standard 1873 Campaign Medal.

1.Austria-Hungary	25.00
2.France-silver medal-bar 1900-Chine-1901	200.00
3.Germany-bronze-combattents	85.00

(various campaign bars are sometimes seen on the ribbon of this medal, i.e. Admiral Seymour Expedition-add $75.00-$200.00 each.)

4.Germany-steel-non-combattents	60.00

Great Britain

5.no bar-silver-British recipient	165.00
6.no bar-silver-native	85.00
7.no bar-bronze-native	125.00
8.bar Relief of Pekin-British-Royal Navy-silver	300.00
9.bar Relief of Pekin-British-Royal Welsh Fusiliers	350.00
10.Relief of Pekin-native-silver	200.00
11.bar Relief of Pekin-native-bronze	250.00
12.bar Taku Forts-Royal Navy	500.00
13.bars Taku Forts & Relief of Pekin-Royal Navy	700.00
14.bar Defence of Legations	6500.00
15.Transport Medal-bar China 1900	600.00
16.Transport Medal-bars S.Africa 1899,China 1900	800.00

17.Italy-reverse CINA-dated	1000.00
18.Italy-reverse CINA-undated (occupation forces)	800.00
19.Japan	500.00
20.Russia-silver	450.00
21.Russia-bronze	300.00

United States of America

21.Army-numbered No.	1000.00
22.Army-numbered M.No.	500.00
23.Army-plain numbered	800.00
24.Army-early unnumbered	125.00
25.Navy-1900 date-numbered	950.00
26.Navy-1901 date-numbered	1200.00
27.Navy-early unnumbered	100.00
28.Marine Corps-numbered	1500.00
29.Marine Corps-early unnumbered	200.00

BRAZIL

Empire
Republic

The Empire of Brazil was established as a consequence of the Napoleonic Wars. The Portuguese royal family fled to their colony in the New World, as a result of the French conquest of the mother country. Subsequently, Brazil became a monarchy in its own right, when the King of Portugal returned after the downfall of Napoleon, until the late 19th century. Thus, there are two forms of the Order of the Southern Cross, royal and republican. Other than some of the Brazilian orders, I have catalogued some of the Brazilian decorations which collectors run across, which relate to the two world wars.

EMPIRE

Order of the Rose-1829-1891
1.Grand Cross badge	3000.00
2.Grand Cross breast star	2000.00
3.Commander-neck badge	2500.00
4.Knight-breast badge	1800.00

(Werlich states there are two other classes, which lack the crown suspension. However, I have never seen such. Since I have seen all the other classes I would assume that they should be classed as rare.)

Order of Pedro I-1828-1891
5.Grand Cross badge	rare
6.Grand Cross breast star	rare
7.Commander	rare
8.Knight	2500.00

Order of the Southern Cross
Type I-1822-1891
9.Grand Collar	rare
10.Grand Cross badge	rare
11.Grand Cross breast star	rare
12.Grand Officer badge	rare
13.Grand Officer breast star	rare
14.Commander	rare
15.Officer	rare
16.Knight	1800.00

REPUBLIC

Order of the Southern Cross
Type II-1932
17.Grand Collar	rare
18.Grand Cross badge	600.00
19.Grand Cross breast star	500.00

BRAZIL

20. Grand Officer badge	350.00
21. Grand Officer breast star	500.00
22. Commander	350.00
23. Officer	150.00
24. Knight	95.00

Order of Naval Merit-1934
25. Grand Cross badge	500.00
26. Grand Cross breast star	450.00
27. Grand Officer badge	250.00
28. Grand Officer breast star	400.00
29. Commander	250.00
30. Officer	150.00
31. Knight	95.00

Order of Military Merit-1934
32. Grand Cross badge	500.00
33. Grand Cross breast star	450.00
34. Grand Officer badge	250.00
35. Grand Officer breast star	400.00
36. Commander	250.00
37. Officer	150.00
38. Knight	95.00

Order of Aeronautical Merit-1934
39. Grand Cross badge	600.00
40. Grand Cross breast star	550.00
41. Grand Officer badge	300.00
42. Grand Officer breast star	500.00
43. Commander	300.00
44. Officer	200.00
45. Knight	150.00

46. Naval Distinguished Service Cross	200.00

47. War Cross 1917-1918 (copies exist)	350.00
48. World War I Victory Medal-copies exist	2500.00

49. Expeditionary Cross-World War II-I Class	75.00
50. Expeditionary Cross-World War II-II Class	50.00
51. South Atlantic Anti-Submarine Patrol Medal	50.00

30 & 31   24

46   47

BULGARIA

Principality 1879-1908
Kingdom 1908-1946

The Orders and decorations of Bulgaria show the influence of several countries, Imperial Russia, Germany, France, and Austria-Hungary. Since the Bulgarian language is so similar to Russian, and the Cyrillic alphabet was used, many people confuse the early awards of this country with those of Russia. Also some of the early awards were Russian made, and were so hallmarked. The Soldiers' Cross for Bravery in four classes was modeled on that of the Imperial Russian St George Cross. The Austrian influence may be seen in the use of the trifold ribbon, while the multiple classes employed for the Orders seem German in origin. Moreover, the French influence can be noted by the use of rosettes to distinguish the IV or Officer classes of Orders.

Except for the early Russian made pieces, most of the Bulgarian Order insignia appear to be of Austrian manufacture, and are of two types, bearing a princely crown, till 1908, and then a royal crown of very distinctive appearance.

With the exception of the flying badges of both World Wars, the awards of this country do not seem to present problems regarding copies. Since prices have remained stable, and the items are reasonably priced, and handsome in appearance, there is an opportunity for the collector with modest means.

Military Order for Bravery-1880-1944
Type I-dated 1879(1880-1914)

1.Grand Cross badge-for princes	rare
2.Grand Cross breast star	rare
3.I Class badge	2500.00
4.I Class breast star	2500.00
5.II Class badge	1500.00
6.III Class breast badge-gold-with crown	850.00
7.IV Class breast badge-silver-without crown	450.00
8.IV Class-without swords	550.00
9.Bravery Cross-I Class-gilt-bow on ribbon	300.00
10.Bravery Cross-II Class-gilt-trifold ribbon	175.00
11.Bravery Cross-III Class-silvered-bow on ribbon	150.00
12.Bravery Cross-IV Class-trifold ribbon	100.00

(Items 9-12 were awarded to enlisted men, and patterned after the Imperial Russian St George Cross.)
Type II-with date 1915

13.Grand Cross badge	rare
14.Grand Cross breast star	rare
15.I Class badge	2500.00
16.I Class breast star	2500.00
17.II Class badge	1250.00
18.III Class badge-grade 1-pin back-white enamel	850.00
19.III Class badge-grade 2-on ribbon	550.00
20.IV Class badge-grade 1-pin back-red enamel	350.00

21.IV Class badge-grade 1-without swords	550.00
22.IV Class badge-grade 2-on ribbon	300.00
23.IV Class badge-grade 2-without swords	350.00
24.Bravery Cross-I Class-gilt	150.00
25.Bravery Cross-II Class-gilt	125.00
26.Bravery Cross-III Class-silvered	75.00
27.Bravery Cross-IV Class-silvered	50.00
Type III-dated 1941	
28.III Class-grade 1	850.00
29.II Class-grade 2	750.00
30.IV Class-grade 1	550.00
31.IV Class-grade 1-without swords	850.00
32.IV Class-grade 2	400.00
33.IV Class-grade 2-without swords	650.00

(Some varieties of type III were awarded to members of the German Armed Forces in World War II.)

Order of St Alexander-1887-1944
Type I-princely crown-1887-1908

34.Grand Cross badge	1000.00
35.Grand Cross badge-with swords	1200.00
36.Grand Cross badge-with swords on ring	1350.00
37.Grand Cross breast star	750.00
38.Grand Cross breast star-with swords	700.00
39.Grand Cross breast star-with swords above	750.00
40.Grand Officer Cross-neck badge	600.00
41.Grand Officer Cross-with swords	650.00
42.Grand Officer Cross-with swords on ring	700.00
43.Grand Officer breast star	600.00
44.Grand Officer breast star-with swords	650.00
45.Grand Officer breast star-with swords above	700.00
46.Commander-neck badge	600.00
47.Commander-with swords	650.00
48.Commander-with swords on ring	700.00
49.Officer-rosette	400.00
50.Officer-with swords	450.00
51.Officer-with swords on ring	450.00
52.Knight	400.00
53.Knight-with swords	450.00
54.Knight-with swords on ring	400.00
55.Silver Merit Cross	300.00
56.Silver Merit Cross-with swords	325.00
57.Silver Merit Cross-with swords on ring	350.00

Type II-royal crown-1908-44

58.Large collar	rare
59.Small collar	rare
60.Grand Cross badge-with diamonds	rare
61.Grand Cross badge-with swords & diamonds	rare

62.Grand Cross badge	700.00
63.Grand Cross badge-with swords	750.00
64.Grand Cross badge-with swords on ring	800.00
65.Grand Cross breast star-with diamonds	rare
66.Grand Cross breast star-with swords & diamonds	rare
67.Grand Cross breast star	850.00
68.Grand Cross breast star-with swords	800.00
69.Grand Cross breast star-with swords above	850.00
70.I Class badge-with diamonds-green enamel	rare
71.I Class badge-with swords & diamonds	rare
72.I Class badge	650.00
73.I Class badge-with swords	700.00
74.I Class badge-with swords on ring	750.00
75.I Class breast star-with diamonds	rare
76.I Class breast star-with swords & diamonds	rare
77.I Class breast star	650.00
78.I Class breast star-with swords	750.00
79.I Class breast star-with swords above	900.00
80.Grand Officer-neck badge-with diamonds	rare
81.Grand Officer	450.00
82.Grand Officer-with swords	500.00
83.Grand Officer-with swords on ring	600.00
84.Grand Officer breast star-with diamonds	rare
85.Grand Officer breast star	550.00
86.Grand Officer breast star-with swords	575.00
87.Grand Officer breast star-with swords above	650.00
88.Commander-neck badge	450.00
89.Commander-with swords	500.00
90.Commander-with swords on ring	550.00
91.Officer	350.00
92.Officer-with swords	375.00
93.Officer-with swords on ring	425.00
94.Knight-with crown	300.00
95.Knight-with crown & swords	325.00
96.Knight-with crown & swords on ring	350.00
97.Merit Cross-with crown	250.00
98.Merit Cross-with crown & swords	275.00
99.Merit Cross-with crown & swords on ring	300.00
100.Merit Cross-without crown	100.00
101.Merit Cross-with swords	125.00
102.Merit Cross-with swords on ring	150.00

Order of Merit-1883-1944
Type I--head of Prince Alexander-1883-86

103.I Class	400.00
104.II Class	300.00

Type II-younger head of Prince Ferdinand-1887-1908

105.I Class	300.00

106.II Class	250.00
Type III-older head of King Ferdinand-1908-1918	
107.I Class	250.00
108.II Class	200.00
Type IV-head of King Boris-1918-43	
109.I Class	500.00
110.II Class	400.00

Civil Merit Order-1891-1944
Type I-princely crown

111.Grand Cross badge	900.00
112.Grand Cross breast star	700.00
113.Grand Officer-neck badge	700.00
114.Grand Officer breast star	600.00
115.Commander-neck badge	700.00
116.Officer-rosette	500.00
117.Knight-with crown	350.00
118.Knight-without crown	350.00
119.Silver Merit Cross-with crown	250.00
120.Silver Merit Cross-without crown	225.00

Type II-royal crown-1908-1944

121.Grand Cross badge-with diamonds	rare
122.Grand Cross badge	650.00
123.Grand Cross breast star-with diamonds	rare
124.Grand Cross breast star	650.00
125.I Class badge-with diamonds	rare
126.I Class badge	600.00
127.I Class breast star-with diamonds	rare
128.I Class breast star	600.00
129.Grand Officer-neck badge-with diamonds	rare
130.Grand Officer	500.00
131.Grand Officer breast star-with diamonds	rare
132.Grand Officer breast star	500.00
133.Commander-neck badge-with diamonds	rare
134.Commander	500.00
135.Officer-rosette	300.00
136.Knight-with crown	250.00
137.Knight-without crown	200.00
138.Merit Cross-with crown	150.00
139.Merit Cross-without crown	125.00

Military Merit Order-1900-1944
Type I-princely crown-1900-1908

140.Grand Cross badge	700.00
141.Grand Cross badge-with war decoration(wreath)	750.00
142.Grand Cross breast star	650.00
143.Grand Cross breast star-with war decoration	700.00
144.Grand Officer-neck badge	500.00

BULGARIA

145.Grand Officer-with war decoration	550.00
146.Grand Officer breast star	400.00
147.Grand Officer breast star-with war decoration	425.00
148.Commander-neck badge	450.00
149.Commander-with war decoration	500.00
150.Officer	300.00
151.Officer-with war decoration	325.00
152.Knight-with crown	250.00
153.Knight-with crown & war decoration	300.00
154.Knight-without crown	225.00
155.Knight-with war decoration	225.00
156.Silver Merit Cross-with crown	95.00
157.Silver Merit Cross-without crown	75.00

Type II-royal crown-1908-1944

158.Grand Cross badge-with diamonds	rare
159.Grand Cross badge-with war decoration & diamonds	rare
160.Grand Cross badge	600.00
161.Grand Cross badge-with war decoration	650.00
162.Grand Cross breast star-with diamonds	rare
163.Grand Cross breast star-with war decoration & diamonds	rare
164.Grand Cross breast star	575.00
165.Grand Cross breast star-with war decoration	600.00
166.Grand Officer-neck badge-with diamonds	rare
167.Grand Officer-with war decoration & diamonds	rare
168.Grand Officer	450.00
169.Grand Officer-with war decoration	475.00
170.Grand Officer breast star-with diamonds	rare
171.Grand Officer breast star-with war decoration & diamonds	rare
172.Grand Officer breast star	350.00
173.Grand Officer breast star-with war decoration	400.00
174.Commander-neck badge-with diamonds	rare
175.Commander-with war decoration & diamonds	rare
176.Commander	400.00
177.Commander-with war decoration	350.00
178.Officer	300.00
179.Officer-with war decoration	325.00
180.Knight-with crown	200.00
181.Knight-with crown & war decoration	225.00
182.Knight-without crown	125.00
183.Knight-with war decoration	110.00
184.Merit Cross-with crown	75.00
185.Merit Cross-without crown	50.00

(Note:All insignia of this Order are with swords.)

Royal Order of Sts Cyril & Methodius-1908-1944

186.Large collar	rare
187.Small collar	rare
188.Badge of the Order	5000.00

189.Breast Star of the Order   4000.00
(Note:This was the Kingdom's highest Order.)

Red Cross Order-1908-1944
190.I Class-gentlemen	500.00
191.I Class-ladies	500.00
192.I Class breast star	550.00
193.II Class-gentlemen	400.00
194.II Class-ladies	400.00
195.III Class-centre enameled	300.00
196.IV Class-centre not enameled	250.00
197.Red Cross Medal	125.00

Miscellaneous Medals & Decorations

198.Election of Prince Alexander-silver-1880	500.00
199.War of Liberation-1880	85.00

Medal of Merit-1883-1944
Type I-Alexander-Prince of Bulgaria-1883
200.Gold Medal-silver/gilt	150.00
201.Silver Medal	100.00
202.Bronze Medal	60.00

Type II-Fredinand-Prince of Bulgaria-1887
203.Gold Medal-silver/gilt	150.00
204.Silver Medal	100.00
205.Bronze Medal	60.00

Type III-Ferdinand-Prince of Bulgaria-1891
206.Gold Medal-with crown	150.00
207.Gold Medal-without crown	100.00
208.Silver Medal-with crown	75.00
209.Silver Medal-without crown	65.00
210.Bronze Medal-with crown	40.00
211.Bronze Medal-without crown	25.00

Type IV-Ferdinand-Prince of Bulgaria-without beard-1900
212.Gold Medal-with crown	150.00
213.Gold Medal-without crown	100.00
214.Silver Medal-with crown	75.00
215.Silver Medal-without crown	65.00
216.Bronze Medal-with crown	40.00
217.Bronze Medal-without crown	25.00

Type V-Tsar(King) Ferdinand of Bulgaria-new crown-1908
218.Gold Medal-with crown	150.00
219.Gold Medal-without crown	100.00
220.Silver Medal-with crown	75.00
221.Silver Medal-without crown	65.00
222.Bronze Medal-with crown	40.00
223.Bronze Medal-without crown	25.00

BULGARIA

Type VI-King Boris of Bulgaria-1918-1944
224.Gold Medal-with crown	175.00
225.Gold Medal-without crown	125.00
226.Silver Medal-with crown	100.00
227.Silver Medal-without crown	75.00
228.Bronze Medal-with crown	50.00
229.Bronze Medal-without crown	35.00

Medal for Arts & Science
Type I-Prince Alexander-1883
230. & 231. Gold & Silver Medals	rare

Type II-Prince Ferdinand-1887
232.Gold Medal	rare
233.Silver Medal	550.00

Type III-Tsar Ferdinand-1908
234.Gold Medal-with crown	rare
235.Gold Medal-without crown	rare
236.Silver Medal-with crown	550.00
237.Silver Medal-without crown	350.00

Type IV-King Boris-1918
238.Gold Medal-with crown	500.00
239.Gold Medal-without crown	350.00
240.Silver Medal-with crown	300.00
241.Silver Medal-without crown	150.00

Serbian War Medal-1886
242.Silver Medal	75.00
243.Bronze Medal	50.00

Cross for the Election of Prince Ferdinand-1887
244.I Class-silver/gilt/enamel	450.00
245.II Class-silver/enamel	350.00
246.III Class-silver/gilt & centre enameled	275.00
247.IV Class-silver	125.00
248.V Class-bronze	75.00

(When awarded to ladies it was worn on a bow ribbon.)

Long Service Cross-1887-1944
Type I-Ferdinand
249.I Class-XX Years-for officers-enameled	250.00
250.I Class-X Years-for officers-enameled	195.00
251.II Class-XX Years-NCO's & enlisted men	125.00
252.II Class-X Years-NCO's & enlisted men	75.00

Type II-Boris
253.I Class-XX Years-for officers-enameled	250.00
254.I Class-X Years-for officers-enameled	185.00
255.II Class-XX Years-for NCO's & enlisted men	150.00
256.II Class-X Years-for NCO's & enlisted men	85.00

Prince Ferdinand's Wedding Medal-1883
257.Gold Medal-silver/gilt-with crown   300.00
258.Gold Medal-without crown   275.00
259.Silver Medal-with crown   225.00
260.Silver Medal-without crown   125.00
261.Bronze Medal-with crown   75.00
262.Bronze Medal-without crown   50.00

263.25th Anniversary of 1876 Revolt-1901   125.00

Cross for the Proclamation of the Kingdom-1908
264.Type I-horizontal crowns on arms   125.00
265.Type II-crowns on arms facing centre   125.00

RED CROSS AWARDS

Red Cross Medal-1908
266.Gold Medal-silver/gilt   125.00
267.Silver Medal   75.00
268.Bronze Medal   50.00
268A.World War I issue 1915   75.00

Red Cross Decoration-Ferdinand-1917
269.I Class-neck badge   450.00
270.I Class-breast star   400.00
271.II Class-neck badge (as 269-but worn without star)   450.00
272.III Class-breast badge   250.00
273.IV Class-unenameled arms   175.00

Red Cross Decoration-Boris-undated
274.I Class-neck badge   350.00
275.I Class-breast star   350.00
276.II Class-neck badge(as 274-but worn without star)   350.00
277.III Class-breast badge   125.00
278.IV Class-unenameled arms   75.00
(Note: When awarded to ladies the insignia were worn on a bow ribbon, of course
this did not apply to the breast star.)

Lifesaving Medals
Type I-Ferdinand-1908-18
279.Gold Medal-silver/gilt   350.00
280.Silver Medal   250.00
281.Bronze Medal   175.00
Type II-Boris-1918-44
282.Gold Medal-silver/gilt   350.00
283.Silver Medal   250.00
284.Bronze Medal   175.00

BULGARIA

285.Silver Jubilee-Ferdinand-1912   rare

Balkan Wars Commemorative Medal-1912-13-on three ribbons
286.Combat ribbon   125.00
287.non-combat ribbon   125.00
288.next of kin ribbon   125.00

World War I-Commemorative Medals-1915-18:-1933
289.Combat ribbon   25.00
290.non-combat ribbon   30.00
(When awarded to women these medals are worn on a bow ribbon.)

Flying Badges
291.Pilot's Badge-1915-1918-silver & gilt-pin back   650.00
293.Observer's Badge-1915-18-as above   600.00
294.Tourist Sport Pilot Wings-bronze-curved   300.00
295.Tourist Sport Pilot-with special merit-silvered   325.00
(Note:gilt versions of 294 & 295 are German copies.)
296.Pilot's Badge-1935-44-silver/gilt/enamels   450.00
297.Observers's Badge-1935-44-as above   400.00
(Note: specimens of 296 & 297 were made in Germany during World
War II. It is up to the collector to decide as to their place.)

67   130 & 134

190   5

195 10 & 12 19
25 & 27

180 116

242 & 243   286

268A   289

CHINA

Monarchy till 1911
Republic 1911-1949

During the monarchy China had only one Order, the Order of the Double Dragon, sometimes known as the Coral Button. The term "Republic" is actually misleading, as after the downfall of the Empire China became the arena for a constant struggle for power among a variety of military adventurers, who are lumped together by historians as the "Warlords". One of them, Chiang Kai-Shek, associated with Sun Yat-Sen, leader of the Kuomintang or Nationalist Party, succeeded in fastening his rule over most of the country by 1931. At that time the Japanese began a major intrusion into Chinese affairs by their conquest of Manchuria. (See Japan for puppet state awards of Manchukuo.) In 1937 a fullscale invasion of China took place.

Since the warlord period is very confusing no attempt is being made at this time to cover its awards. As far as the Nationalist government is concerned some of the more commonly found Orders are being listed. However, no awards of the Nationalist government on Taiwan are being included, as collector interest seems to be very limited.

Since the field of Chinese awards is very confusing I must emphasize that the values listed below are more tentative than those from other countries, nevertheless, they can be useful.

Empire

Order of the Double Dragon-1882-1911

1. Type I-1882-1900	rare
Type II-1900-1911	
2. I Class badge-grade I	rare
3. I Class badge-grade II	rare
4. I Class badge-grade III	rare
5. I Class breast star-grade I-gold	rare
6. I Class breast star-grade II	rare
7. I Class breast star-grade III	rare
8. II Class badge-grade I	1300.00
9. II Class badge-grade II	900.00
10. II Class badge-grade III	800.00
11. II Class breast star-grade I-silver	750.00
12. II Class breast star-grade II	700.00
13. II Class breast star-grade III	650.00
14. III Class-neck badge	550.00
15. IV Class	450.00
16. V Class	400.00

Republic
Order of the Striped Tiger-1921-1928

17. I Class badge	rare
18. I Class breast star	1200.00

19. II Class badge	1200.00
20. II Class breast star	900.00
21. II Class badge	900.00
22. III Class-neck badge	650.00
23. IV Class-breast badge	550.00
24. V Class	500.00
25. VI Class	450.00
26. VII Class	400.00
27. VIII Class	230.00
28. IX Class	250.00

Order of the Precious Golden Grain-1912

29. I Class badge	rare
30. I Class breast star	rare
31. II Class badge	rare
32. II Class breast star	rare
33. III Class neck badge	900.00
34. IV Class-breast badge	700.00
35. V Class	600.00

Order of the Golden Grain-1912-1929

36. I Class badge	1500.00
37. I Class breast star	900.00
38. II Class badge	900.00
39. II Class breast star	700.00
40. III Class-neck badge	600.00
41. IV Class-breast badge	500.00
42. V Class	450.00
43. VI Class	400.00
44. VII Class	350.00
45. VIII Class	250.00
46. IX Class	200.00

Order of the Cloud and Banner-1935

47. I Class badge	rare
48. I Class breast star	rare
49. II Class badge	rare
50. II Class breast star	rare
51. III Class badge	rare
52. III Class breast star	rare
53. IV Class	900.00
54. V Class	800.00
55. VI Class	700.00
56. VII Class	550.00
57. VIII Class	450.00
58. IX Class	350.00

(This Order was also awarded to members of the American Volunteer Group, Flying Tigers.)

CHINA

59.Order of Victory-1945   600.00

Decoration for American Troops who served in China during World
War II
60.Type I-numbered on reverse   85.00
61.Type II-unnumbered issues   50.00
62.Type III-U.S. made copy   15.00
(This award was issued by the Nationalist government on Taiwan, but was included
since a number have shown up in the U.S.A. in recent years.)

For further details on the awards of this country see Robert Werlich-ORDERS &
DECORATIONS OF ALL NATIONS-Military & Civil. The ribbons for the
various classes are described.

CZECHOSLOVAKIA

Republic 1918-1938;1945-1949; People's Republic 1949

SLOVAKIA
Puppet state of the III Reich-1938-1945

The Orders and decorations of Czechoslovakia, although new in time, reflect the symbols of the state which echo the early Bohemian monarchy; the Lion and the Linden Leaves. The heroes of the past,like Charles IV and Jan Ziska gave their names to awards of merit and bravery. Items of this country are handsome in appearance, and reasonable in price. Except for the World War I Victory Medal there does not seem to be a problem with copies. There is confusion between the Order of the White Lion established 1922, and the Military Order of the White Lion of 1945. The former has swords also, just to complicate matters. However, since the 1945 award is seldom seen the confusion is likely to be less of a problem than one might imagine.

The awards of Slovakia, as a briefly existing state are quite scarce or even rare. Many were made in Germany, and also presented to German military serving in Eastern Europe. However, care should be taken in buying the rarer items of this country, particularly the Grand Cross breast star of the Order of Prince Pribina.

Czechoslovakia

Order of the White Lion-type I-1922-39
1.Collar	rare
2.Grand Cross badge-civil	750.00
3.Grand Cross badge-military	850.00
4.Grand Cross breast star-civil	650.00
5.Grand Cross breast star-military	650.00
6.Commander-neck badge-civil	600.00
7.Commander-military	650.00
8.Officer-breast badge-civil	450.00
9.Officer-military	500.00
10.Knight-civil	400.00
11.Knight-military	425.00
12.Merit Medal-I Class-silver/gilt	250.00
13.Merit Medal-II Class-silver	175.00

(Note: The type II of this Order of the Communist government differs in appearance only by the Lion being uncrowned.)

Order of the Falcon (Sokol)-1918-1919
14.Badge without swords	350.00
15.Badge with swords	400.00

(Note: Although awarded for a short period it seems to have been given liberally enough that it not a rare item.)

CZECHOSLOVAKIA

Order of Charles IV-For the National Guard-1935-39
16.Grand Cross badge	600.00
17.Grand Cross breast star	600.00
18.Commander-neck badge	500.00
19.Commander-with swords	550.00
20.Officer	275.00
21.Officer-with swords	325.00
22.Knight	150.00
23.Knight-with swords	125.00
24.Merit Medal-for long service	100.00

Military Order of the White Lion-1945
25.I Class-breast star-with gold swords	2000.00
26.II Class-breast star-with silver swords	1200.00
27.III Class-breast badge	750.00
28.Merit Medal-I Class-gold	500.00
29.Merit Medal-II Class-silver	400.00

Officer's Order of Jan Ziska-1945
30.I Class-gold breast star	2000.00
31.II Class-silver breast star	1100.00
32.III Class-silver medal	500.00

Military Order for Liberty-1946
33.I Class-gold breast star	rare
34.II Class-silver medal	500.00
35.III Class-bronze medal	350.00

36.Bravery Medal-bronze-1939	150.00

Merit Medal
37.I Class-silvered	45.00
38.II Class-bronze	35.00

Campaign Medals
39.War Cross 1918-(looks like 4 circles joined)	75.00
40.Revolutionary Cross-1918	50.00
41.Revolutionary Cross-with campaign bar	75.00
42.Revolutionary Cross-with Russian Civil War bar	300.00
43.World War I Victory Medal-designer Spaniel obverse	125.00
44.World War I Victory Medal-without designer's name	85.00
45.Naval Commemorative Medal-1914-18	200.00
46.Slovak Commemorative Medal-1918-38	50.00
47.War Cross-1939	45.00
48.Campaign Medal-1939-45	25.00
49.Campaign Medal-1939-45-with campaign bar	35.00
50.Cross for Political Prisoners-1939-45	75.00

SLOVAKIA-Nazi puppet state 1938-45

Order of Prince Pribina-1940-45

51.Collar	rare
52.Special Class of the Grand Cross-badge	rare
53.Special Class of the Grand Cross-breast star	rare
54.Grand Cross badge	1500.00
55.Grand Cross badge-with swords	1600.00
56.Grand Cross breast star	1100.00
57.Grand Cross breast star-with swords	1500.00
58.Grand Officer Cross	800.00
59.Grand Officer Cross-with swords	900.00
60.Grand Officer breast star	800.00
61.Grand Officer breast star-with swords	1100.00
62.Commander	800.00
63.Commander-with swords	900.00
64.Officer	650.00
65.Officer-with swords	700.00
66.Knight	550.00
67.Knight-with swords	600.00

Order of the Slovak Cross-1940-45

68.Collar	rare
69.Grand Cross badge	1750.00
70.Grand Cross badge-with swords	1950.00
71.Grand Cross breast star	1600.00
72.Grand Cross breast star-with swords	1800.00
73.Grand Officer	1150.00
74.Grand Officer-with swords	1300.00
75.Grand Officer breast star	1150.00
76.Grand Officer breast star-with swords	1400.00
77.Commander	1150.00
78.Commander-with swords	1300.00
79.Officer	850.00
80.Officer-with swords	950.00
81.Knight	700.00
82.Knight-with swords	800.00

Order of the War Victory Cross-1939-45
Type I-enameled on one side-1939-40

83.I Class badge-red enamel	1500.00
84.I Class breast star	1500.00
85.II Class-blue enamel	750.00
86.III Class-brown enamel	650.00
Type II-both sides enameled-1940-45	
87.Collar	rare
88.Grand Cross badge	1150.00
89.Grand Cross badge-with swords	1300.00
90.Grand Cross breast star	1150.00

CZECHOSLOVAKIA

91. Grand Cross breast star-with swords	1300.00
92. I Class neck badge-red enamel	850.00
93. I Class breast star	1100.00
94. II Class neck badge-red enamel	750.00
95. III Class badge-blue enamel	550.00
96. IV Class badge-brown enamel	500.00
97. IV Class badge-with swords-white enamel	600.00
98. V Class-gilt medal	150.00
99. V Class-gilt medal-with swords	200.00
100. VI Class-silver medal	125.00
101. VI Class-silver medal-with swords	175.00
102. VII Class-bronze medal	110.00
103. VII Class-bronze medal-with swords	150.00

Bravery Medal-1939-45
104. I Class-gilt	200.00
105. II Class-silver	125.00
106. III Class-bronze	75.00

Merit Cross for Defense of the State-1939
107. I Class-silver-white enamel	rare
108. II Class-bronze	rare

Defense of Slovakia Medal-1939
109. Type I-dated	150.00
110. Type II-undated	125.00

Suppression of the National Uprising-1944
111. Large gold medal-36mm	500.00
112. Large silver medal-36mm	300.00
113. Large bronze medal-36mm	200.00
114. Small gold medal-30mm	350.00
115. Small silver medal-30mm	150.00
116. Small bronze medal	85.00

Various Badges(copies exist)
117. Eastern Front Honor Badge-silver-combat	300.00
118. Eastern Front-bronze-non-combat	150.00
119. Crimean Service Badge-1943-44	300.00
120. Tank Service Badge	225.00
121. Military Sport Badge	300.00
122. Pilot/Observer Badge	500.00
123. Air Gunner Badge	rare
124. Flight Engineer Badge	300.00

REPLACEMENT DECORATIONS-new awards replacing earlier non-Slovak decorations, excepting those from the Allies of World War I.

Commemorative Cross-for pre-1914 awards-all rare
125.I Class-brown ribbon-3 yellow stripes
126.II Class-2 yellow stripes
127.III Class-1 yellow stripe

Great War Commemorative Cross-for 1914-18 awards-all rare
128.I Class-gilt-white ribbon-3 black stripes
129.II Class-2 black stripes
130.III Class-1 black stripe

Revolutionary Cross-1918-21-Siberia & Independence-all rare
131.I Class-violet ribbon-3 green stripes
132.II Class-2 stripes
133.III Class-1 stripe
134.IV Class-no stripes

27 25 & 26 10

15 30 & 31 23

36   39   40

45   48

111-113   95   98, 100, 102

56

DENMARK

The Orders, decorations, and medals of this country offer a special challenge. Since most awards have to be returned on the death of the recipient it is difficult to state how many items are available for collectors. The Order of the Elephant is a case in point. When President Eisenhower died the Elephant Order in the Eisenhower museum had to be returned to be replaced by one marked copy! In 1987 a London dealer offered a copy set of the Elephant for about the equivalent of $3500.00! Other than the Korean War Red Cross decoration there does not seem to be a problem with copies.

The Order of the Dannebrog does turn up because it has been bestowed on foreigners who were not necessarily required to return it. As one of the few Orders which continued to be awarded in genuine gold, after most others were discontinued, it is particularly striking in its appearance. Also, because this Order changed monarch's cyphers with each new reign it is possible to assemble a collection around the Dannebrog.

Order of the Elephant-1463
1.Collar	rare
2.Badge of the Order	rare
3.Breast Star of the Order	4500.00

(This Order is normally returned on the death of the recipient.)

Order of the Dannebrog-1219
Type I-till 1808
4.Collar	rare
5.Badge of the Order	rare
6.Breast Star of the Order	rare

Type II-Frederik VI-1808-1839
7.Collar	5000.00
8.Grand Cross badge-with diamonds	rare
9.Grand Cross badge	3500.00
10.Grand Cross breast star	2500.00
11.Commander-neck badge-I Class	2200.00
12.Commander-breast star	2000.00
13.Commander	1500.00
14.Knight	700.00
15.Silver Merit Cross	375.00

Type III-Christian VIII-1839-1848
16.Grand Cross badge	2000.00
17.Grand Cross breast star	1500.00
18.Commander-neck badge-I Class	1250.00
19.Commander breast star	950.00
20.Commander	1250.00
21.Knight	700.00
22.Silver Merit Cross	250.00

Type IV-Frederik VII-1848-1863
23.Grand Cross badge	2000.00
24.Grand Cross breast star	1500.00

DENMARK

25.Commander-neck badge-I Class	950.00
26.Commander breast star	800.00
27.Commander	950.00
28.Knight	600.00
29.Silver Merit Cross	250.00
Type V-Christian IX-1863-1906	
30.Grand Cross badge	1500.00
31.Grand Cross breast star	1250.00
32.Commander-neck badge-I Class	900.00
33.Commander breast star	950.00
34.Commander	900.00
35.Knight	500.00
36.Silver Merit Cross	250.00
Type VI-Frederik VIII-1906-1912	
37.Grand Cross badge	1500.00
38.Grand Cross breast star	1200.00
39.Commander-neck badge-I Class	900.00
40.Commander breast star	950.00
41.Commander	900.00
42.Knight	475.00
43.Silver Merit Cross	125.00
Type VII-Christian X-1912-1947	
44.Grand Cross badge	1250.00
45.Grand Cross breast star	1250.00
46.Commander-neck badge-I Class	900.00
47.Commander breast star	750.00
48.Commander	900.00
49.Knight	450.00
50.Silver Merit Cross	125.00
Type VIII-Frederik IX-1947-1972	
51.Grand Cross badge	1250.00
52.Grand Cross breast star	1250.00
53.Commander-neck badge-I Class	950.00
54.Commander breast star	700.00
55.Commander	950.00
56.Knight	450.00
57.Silver Merit Cross	125.00
Type IX-Queen Margarethe-1972	
58.Grand Cross badge	1500.00
59.Grand Cross breast star	1500.00
60.Commander-neck badge-I Class	900.00
61.Commander breast star	750.00
62.Commander	900.00
63.Knight	400.00
64.Silver Merit Cross	125.00
Medal of Merit-1845	
65.Christian VIII-gold	rare
66.Christian VIII-silver	rare

67.Frederik VII-gold	rare
68.Frederik VII-silver	rare
69.Christian IX-gold	rare
70.Christian IX-silver	550.00
71.Frederik VIII-gold	rare
72.Frederik VIII-silver	550.00
73.Christian X-gold	rare
74.Christian X-silver	450.00
75.Frederik IX-gold	rare
76.Frederik IX-silver	125.00

(Note: A number of bars have been awarded with this medal for various activities, especially for polar expeditions; all rare.)

Medal for Heroic Deeds

77.Christian VII-gold	rare
78.Christian VII-silver	rare
79.Frederik VI-gold	rare
80.Frederik VII-silver	rare
81.Christian VIII-silver (no gold awarded)	rare
82.Frederik VII-gold	rare
83.Frederik VII-silver	rare
84.Christian IX-gold	rare
85.Christian IX-silver	550.00
86.Frederik VIII-silver	rare
87.Christian X-silver	rare
88.Frederik IX-silver	rare

Medal for Saving Life from Drowning-1812

89.Frederik VI-type I-silver	rare
90.Frederik VI-types II,III,IV-gold	rare
91.Frederik VI-types II,III,IV-silver	rare
92.Christian VIII-silver	550.00
93.Frederik VII-gold	rare
94.Frederik VII-silver	550.00
95.Christian IX-silver	550.00
96.Frederik VIII-silver	550.00
97.Christian X-silver	rare
98.Frederik IX-silver	rare
99.Margarethe	rare

Ingenio et Arti Medal-1841-all issues	rare

King's Medal of Recompense-1865

100.Christian IX-gold	rare
101.Christian IX-silver	250.00
102.Frederik VIII-silver/gilt-with crown	350.00
103.Frederik VIII-silver/gilt	275.00
104.Frederik VIII-silver-with crown	225.00
105.Frederik VIII-silver	125.00

DENMARK

106.Christian X-silver/gilt-with crown	350.00
107.Christian X-silver/gilt	275.00
108.Christian X-silver-with crown	200.00
109.Christian X-silver	125.00
110.Frederik IX-silver/gilt-with crown	350.00
111.Frederik IX-silver/gilt	275.00
112.Frederik IX-silver-with crown	200.00
113.Frederik IX-silver	125.00

Royal Household Medal-1889

114.Gold Medal	rare
115.Silver Medal	350.00

Campaign Medals

116.Medal of Merit in Gold for Battle of Copenhagen-1801	rare
117.Medal of Merit In Silver for Battle of Copenhagen	rare
(See also Great Britain-Naval General Service Medal-bar Copenhagen)	
118.Commemorative War Medal-1848-50	75.00
119.Commemorative War Medal-1864	65.00
120.Combined Commemorative War Medal for 1848-50 & 1864	95.00
121.Christian X's War Participation Medal 1940-45	350.00

Long Service and Good Conduct Medals

122.Navy-type I-1801-1814	rare
123.Navy-type II-1814-1843	rare
124.Navy-type III-since 1843	75.00
125.Army-since 1945	65.00
126.Defense Department-for civilians-1953	75.00
127.Air Force-1959	95.00
128.Police-1959	65.00
129.Civil Defense-1963	rare
130.Home Guard-1959	95.00
131.Distinguished Flying Medal-1962	rare
132.N.C.O.'s 8 Year Long Service Cross	75.00
133.N.C.O.'S 16 Year Long Service Cross	95.00

Other Awards

134.Christian IX's Centenary-1918	350.00
135.Slesvig Medal-1920	95.00
136.Frederik VIII's Centenary-1943	450.00
137.Pro Dania Medal(Christian X's Liberation Commemorative Medal for World War II.)	250.00
138.Galathea Medal-1954	450.00
139.Korea Medal-Jutlandia Hospital Ship	750.00

Red Cross Awards

140.Badge of Honor-1916		450.00
141.Medal-1927		125.00
142.Prisoner of War Aid-1914-1919		375.00
143.Aid to Sick & Wounded-Finland 1939-40		rare
144.Relief Work 1939-45		125.00
145.Prisoner of War Exchange-Korean War(9 awarded)		rare

(Care must be taken on this last item, as it is similar to earlier awards. Thus it has been easy to erase previous details on the reverse and engrave those for the Korean War award.)

28   24   29

46 & 48

ESTONIA (ESTHONIA)

Republic 1919-1940

This country was formerly part of the Russian Empire before the Revolution of 1917. After the downfall of Imperial Russia, and the critical years of the Russian Civil War, Estonia emerged as independent country only to be submerged again in the Soviet Union in 1940. The awards of this country are of a high quality, and their rarity is such not only because of the brevity of the country's independence, and the number of awards made, but also because many awards were likely to have been destroyed since their mere possession might have rendered their owners liable to danger under the Soviet regime. There are copies known to exist. The following values are for pre-1941 issues only.

Order of the Cross of Liberty-1919-1940
1.I Class-Grade 1-gold-white enamel	2500.00
2.I Class-Grade 2-silver-white enamel	1250.00
3.I Class-Grade 3-blackened-white enamel	700.00
4.II Class-Grade 1-gold-red enamel	1200.00
5.II Class-Grade 2-silver-red enamel	900.00
6.II Class-Grade 3-blackened-red enamel	750.00
7.III Class-Grade 1-gold-blue enamel	1200.00
8.III Class-Grade 2-silver-blue enamel	750.00
9.III Class-Grade 3-blackened-blue enamel	600.00

Order of the Coat of Arms of Esthonia-1936-1940
10.Collar & Gold breast star	President of the Republic
11.Grand Cross badge	2200.00
12.Grand Cross breast star-gold	2000.00
13.I Class badge	1500.00
14.I Class breast star-silver	1500.00
15.II Class neck badge	1250.00
16.II Class breast star	1250.00
17.III Class neck badge	1250.00
18.IV Class breast badge-rosette	750.00
19.V Class breast badge	650.00
20.Medal I Class-gold-large-neck ribbon	900.00
21.Medal II Class-gold-large-breast ribbon	750.00
22.Medal III Class-gold-small-breast ribbon	600.00
23.Medal IV Class-silver-large-breast ribbon	500.00
24.Medal V Class-small-breast ribbon	400.00

Order of the White Star-1936-40 (Werlich says 1928)
25.Collar	rare
26.Golden breast star of the collar	3500.00
27.Grand Cross badge	3500.00
28.Grand Cross breast star-golden	3000.00
29.I Class badge	1200.00
30.I Class breast star-silver	950.00
31.II Class neck badge	700.00

ESTONIA

32.II Class breast star	700.00
33.III Class neck badge	700.00
34.IV Class breast badge-rosette	450.00
35.V Class	350.00
36.Medal I Class-gold	300.00
37.Medal II Class-silver	250.00
38.Medal III Class-bronze	200.00

Order of the Eagle Cross-1928-40

39.I Class badge	1250.00
40.I Class badge with swords	1500.00
41.I Class breast star	1000.00
42.I Class breast star with swords	1250.00
43.II Class neck badge	650.00
44.II Class neck badge with swords	700.00
45.II Class breast star	650.00
46.II Class breast star with swords	700.00
47.III Class neck badge	700.00
48.III Class neck badge with swords	750.00
49.IV Class breast badge-rosette	500.00
50.IV Class breast badge with swords	550.00
51.V Class breast badge	400.00
52.V Class breast badge with swords	450.00

Honor Decoration of the Home Defense Corps-1919-1928

53.I Class	950.00
54.II Class	750.00
55.III Class	550.00

Red Cross Order-1919-1940

56.I Class badge	1000.00
57.I Class breast star	900.00
58.II Class neck badge	650.00
59.II Class breast star	750.00
60.III Class neck badge	650.00
61.IV Class breast badge-rosette	550.00
62.V Class breast badge	450.00
63.Medal I Class-gold	450.00
64.Medal II Class-silver	400.00
65.Medal III Class-bronze	350.00

Commemorative Decoration of the New Constitution-1937

66.I Class neck medal	rare
67.II Class breast medal	950.00

68.Independence Medal-1918-21	350.00

51

53-55

9

62

FINLAND

Grand Duchy of the Russian Empire 1809-1917
Republic 1918

The Orders and decorations of this country, while distinctively Finnish, also bear the mark of its associations with Imperial Russia. Its awards are of high quality, and the use of white enamel on the St George type crosses of the Orders bears this out very well. The Order of the Cross of Liberty is extremely complicated as the listings show, and may well present a puzzle to the collector.

Regarding copies there seems to be no problem at all. However, some collectors are suprised with the appearance of the swastika on a number of Finnish items. This has nothing to do with an association with Nazi Germany in World War II. Finland used the swastika before it took on any negative implications. Nevertheless, the collar of the White Rose Order which had swastikas figured prominently in it was redesigned to avoid any misunderstandings after World War II.

Mannerheim Cross of the Liberty Cross Order-1940-1945
1.I Class-neck badge-unique award to Field Marshal Mannerheim	
2.II Class-pin back cross	rare
3.II Class-with Marshal's batons	rare

Order of the Liberty Cross-1918-1960
Type I-dated 1918-War of Independence and Civil War
4.Grand Cross badge-with swords & diamonds-white enamel	rare
5.Grand Cross badge	750.00
6.Grand Cross badge-with swords	800.00
7.Grand Cross breast star-with swords & diamonds	rare
8.Grand Cross breast star	1500.00
9.Grand Cross breast star-with swords	1600.00
10.I Class neck badge-with swords & diamonds	rare
11.I Class neck badge	600.00
12.I Class neck badge-with swords	700.00
13.I Class breast star-with swords & diamonds	rare
14.I Class breast star	850.00
15.I Class breast star-with swords	750.00
16.II Class-breast badge-white enamel	350.00
17.II Class-with swords	375.00
18.III Class-gilt-blue enamel	350.00
19.III Class-with red cross	375.00
20.III Class-with swords-black enamel	300.00
21.IV Class-silver-blue enamel	200.00
22.IV Class-with red cross-black enamel	300.00
23.IV Class-with swords-black enamel	150.00
24.Liberty Medal-I Class-silver	75.00
25.Liberty Medal-I Class-with red cross	200.00
26.Liberty Medal-II Class-bronze	60.00
27.Liberty Medal-II Class-with red cross	150.00

Type II-dated 1939-War with U.S.S.R.-1939-40

28.	Grand Cross badge-with diamonds	rare
29.	Grand Cross badge-with swords & diamonds	rare
30.	Grand Cross badge	700.00
31.	Grand Cross badge-with swords	800.00
32.	Grand Cross breast star-with diamonds	rare
33.	Grand Cross breast star-with swords & diamonds	rare
34.	Grand Cross breast star	1350.00
35.	Grand Cross breast star-with swords	1600.00
36.	I Class neck badge	575.00
37.	I Class neck badge-with swords	650.00
38.	I Class breast star	750.00
39.	I Class breast star-with swords	850.00
40.	II Class breast badge-white enamel	300.00
41.	II Class breast badge-with swords	275.00
42.	II Class badge-with red cross	550.00
43.	II Class badge-with red cross & swords	rare
44.	III Class badge-gilt-blue enamel	200.00
45.	III Class badge-with swords-black enamel	250.00
46.	III Class badge-with red cross-black enamel	500.00
47.	IV Class badge-blue enamel	300.00
48.	IV Class badge-with swords-black enamel	175.00
49.	IV Class badge-with red cross-black enamel	400.00
50.	Liberty Medal-I Class-silver	75.00
51.	Liberty Medal-I Class-with red cross	200.00
52.	Liberty Medal-II Class-bronze	50.00
53.	Liberty Medal-II Class-with red cross	175.00
54.	Merit Medal-I Class-gilt	50.00
55.	Merit Medal-II Class-silver	40.00
56.	Merit Medal-III Class-bronze	25.00

Type III-dated 1941-War with the U.S.S.R. 1941-1944

57.	Grand Cross badge	rare
58.	Grand Cross badge-with swords	rare
59.	Grand Cross breast star	rare
60.	Grand Cross breast star-with swords	rare
61.	I Class neck badge	750.00
62.	I Class neck badge-with swords	800.00
63.	I Class neck badge-with oakleaves & swords	850.00
64.	I Class breast star	800.00
65.	I Class breast star-with swords	850.00
66.	I Class breast star-with oakleaves & swords	1200.00
67.	II Class breast badge-white enamel	300.00
68.	II Class breast badge-with swords	325.00
69.	II Class breast badge-with oakleaves & swords	350.00
70.	III Class badge-gilt-blue enamel	250.00
71.	III Class badge-with swords-black & gilt	275.00
72.	III Class badge-with red cross-black & gilt	450.00

73.III Class badge-with oakleaves & swords-black & gilt	250.00
74.IV Class badge-blue & silver	275.00
75.IV Class badge-with swords-black & silver	150.00
76.IV Class badge-with red cross-black & silver	450.00
77.IV Class badge-with oakleaves & swords-black & silver	300.00
78.IV Class badge-black next of kin ribbon-black/silver	150.00
79.Liberty Medal-I Class-silver	65.00
80.Liberty Medal-I Class-with red cross	250.00
81.Liberty Medal-II Class-bronze	50.00
82.Liberty Medal-II Class-with red cross	200.00
83.Merit Medal-I Class-gilt	75.00
84.Merit Medal-I Class-black next of kin ribbon	60.00
85.Merit Medal-II Class-silver	40.00
86.Merit Medal-III Class-bronze	30.00

Type IV-undated-post World War II

87.Grand Cross badge	rare
88.Grand Cross breast star	rare
89.I Class neck badge	500.00
90.I Class breast star	600.00
91.II Class breast badge	400.00
92.III Class breast badge	225.00
93.III Class badge-with red cross	350.00
94.IV Class breast badge	175.00
95.IV Class badge-with red cross	275.00
96.Liberty Medal-I Class-silver	60.00
97.Liberty Medal-I Class-with red cross	150.00
98.Liberty Medal-II Class-bronze	40.00
99.Liberty Medal-II Class-with red cross	125.00
100.Merit Medal-I Class-gilt	60.00
101.Merit Medal-II Class-silver	45.00
102.Merit Medal-III Class-bronze	30.00

Order of the White Rose-1919

103.Collar-type I-with swastikas	rare
104.Collar-type II-without swastikas	rare
105.Grand Cross badge	700.00
106.Grand Cross badge-with swords	750.00
107.Grand Cross breast star	700.00
108.Grand Cross breast star-with swords	750.00
109.Commander-I Class neck badge	300.00
110.Commander-I Class neck badge-with swords	325.00
111.Commander-I Class breast star	650.00
112.Commander-I Class breast star-with swords	700.00
113.Commander-II Class-neck badge	300.00
114.Commander-II Class-neck badge-with swords	350.00
115.Knight-I Class	200.00
116.Knight-I Class-with swords	250.00
117.Knight-II Class	150.00

118.Knight-II Class-with swords	200.00
119.Merit Medal-I Class-silver-with gold cross obverse	125.00
120.Merit Medal-II Class-silver	75.00
121.Merit Medal-III Class-bronze	50.00

Order of the Lion of Finland-1919
122.Grand Cross badge	650.00
123.Grand Cross badge-with swords	700.00
124.Grand Cross badge-with diamonds	rare
125.Grand Cross breast star	650.00
126.Grand Cross breast star-with swords	750.00
127.Grand Cross breast star-with diamonds	rare
128.Commander-I Class-neck badge	400.00
129.Commander-I Class-with swords	450.00
130.Commander-I Class-breast star	500.00
131.Commander-I Class-breast star-with swords	550.00
132.Commander-II Class-neck badge	400.00
133.Commander-II Class-with swords	450.00
134.Knight-I Class	175.00
135.Knight-I Class-with swords	200.00
136.Knight-II Class	100.00
137.Knight-II Class-with swords	150.00
138."Pro Finlandia" Medal	150.00

The Olympic Merit Order-1952
139.I Class-neck badge	1000.00
140.II Class-breast badge	500.00
141.Merit Medal	300.00

(Note: This was not a participant's medal, but awarded to those who aided in the functioning of the Games.)

Sports Merit Order-1945
142.Grand Merit Cross-neck badge	500.00
143.Gold Merit Cross-breast badge	300.00
144.Silver Merit Cross	150.00
145.Merit Medal	100.00

Order of the Holy Lamb-1935
146.Grand Cross badge	1200.00
147.Grand Cross breast star-gold angels	900.00
148.Commander I Class-neck badge	750.00
149.Commander I Class-breast star-silver angels	750.00
150.Commander II Class-neck badge	750.00
151.Knight-I Class	500.00
152.Knight-II Class	400.00
153.Merit Medal-I Class-gilt	150.00
154.Merit Medal-II Class-silvered	100.00

FINLAND

Other Awards including campaign medals

155.Police Merit Cross-1942	75.00
156.Fire Service Merit Cross 1942	50.00
157.Vilpulla War Cross-1918	85.00
158.Rautu War Cross-1918	85.00
159.Civil Guard Merit Cross	50.00
160.War Medal-1918	25.00
(Campaign bars worn on ribbon-add $50.00 each.)	
161.Commemorative Cross 1918-22	35.00
162.Aunus Commemorative Medal-1919	35.00
163.Karelian Commemorative Medal-1919	35.00
164.Ingermanland Commemorative Cross	150.00
165.Swedish Brigade Cross-given to Swedish volunteers who participated in Finland's War for Independence	500.00
166.20th Anniversary of Liberation of Helsinki-1918-38	65.00
167.Campaign Medal 1939-40	20.00
(Campaign bars worn on ribbon-add $25.00 each.)	
168.Campaign Medal for Foreign Volunteers-1939-40	35.00
169.Kainuu Cross-1939-40	50.00
170.Keski-Kannas Cross-1939-40	50.00
171.Kolvisto Cross-1939-40	50.00
172.Kollaa Cross-1939-40	50.00
173.Lappland Cross-1939-40	75.00
174.Ladoga Medal-1939-40	75.00
175.Lansi-Kannas Cross-1939-40	50.00
176.Mohia Cross-1939-40	50.00
177.Pitkaranta Cross-1939-40	50.00
178.Summa Cross-1939-40	50.00
179.Taipale Cross-1939-40	50.00
180.Tolvajarvi Cross 1939-40	50.00
181.War Wounded Badge-1918	75.00
182.War Wounded Badge-1939-40	75.00
183.War Wounded Badge-1939-40 & 1941-44	125.00
184.War with the USSR-1941-1945	20.00

62   128 & 132

75   134

109 & 113

50   115   52

139

140

141

119-121   167

50   184

FRANCE

Kingdom till 1792
Republic 1792-1804
First Empire-1804-1814-Napoleon I
"The Hundred Days"-1815-Napoleon I
Kingdom-1814-1848
Republic-1848-1851
Second Empire-1851-1871-Napoleon III
Republic since 1871

Although France before the Revolution of 1789 had its Orders, they were reserved primarily for the upper classes, the clergy, and officers of the Army and Navy. It was Napoleon Bonaparte (Napoleon I) who was responsible for laying the foundation for the extensive system of honors and awards that France came to develop, and which has spread worldwide. Through the establishment of the Legion of Honor which was intended to honor people regardless of social class, for merit, service and bravery, he expressed the belief that incentive such as this was very useful in promoting loyalty to the state and gratitude for its rewards. Since this initial effort there has been an explosion of awards, not only for the military, but also for the large civil service, granted by the various ministries of the French government.

The ordinary veteran of the campaigns of 1792-1815 was finally rewarded by the issuance of the St Helena medal in 1857. Following this there appeared a number of medals to commemorate France's involvement in Europe, and its colonial empire, as well as the great conflicts of 1914-18 and 1939-45. For many smaller campaigns there was issued the Colonial Medal, with a large variety of campaign bars which show very clearly the country's role as an imperial power.

The Legion of Honor, as France's premier award, is a very complicated Order far beyond the five classes which ultimately developed. Due to the many changes in government which occurred in the 19th century, and the expressed desire to continue the award, the collector will find additional varieties to those listed below, as the changeover in regime caused a change in the insignia, but many holders preferred to wear their original style, but with modifications which would be acceptable to the new government. Thus, one can see a badge of the Legion of Honor which has the body of one period, but with different centres. Since these badges were worn by their recipients they should be regarded as quite legitimate, but no attempt has been made to value these pieces.

The Legion of Honor in its 1870 variety also exhibits many variations in style, and quality, depending on period of manufacturer between 1871 and 1951, and as to whether items were made by the Paris Mint, or by private manufacturers such as Bertrand. The best quality seems to date before World War I. One often sees Officer badges in gold, and Knight's badges which have gold centres. However, the Legion of Honor seems to suffer in all time periods from the poor quality of the white enamel.

In recent years there have appeared on the marked cast copies of some of the more common French medals. They can be characterized by a shiny gilt finish, with the designer's name missing or indistinct, and a line around the centre of the edge. The 1954 Indo-China medal has a copy which looks quite good at first glance, but the suspender is incorrect. To make things more complicated it should also be stated that the Mint has reissued some items, of poorer quality than the originals, and many of these may be shiny gilt in appearance.

Order of the Holy Ghost-1578-1792

1.Collar	rare
2.Cross of the Order	15,000.00
3.Breast Star of the Order	4500.00
Restoration reissue-1814-15;1815-30	
4.Collar	rare
5.Cross of the Order	10,000.00
6.Breast Star of the Order	3000.00

Order of St Michael-1469-1792

7.Collar	rare
8.Badge of the Order	rare
Restoration reissue-1814-15;1815-30	
9.Collar	rare
10.Badge of the Order	rare
11.Breast Star of the Order	rare

Military Order of St Louis-1693-1792-for Catholics

12.Grand Cross badge	12,500.00
13.Grand Cross breast star	4500.00
14.Commander-neck badge	6000.00
15.Knight	2500.00
Restoration reissue-1815-30	
16.Grand Cross badge	9500.00
17.Grand Cross breast star	3500.00
18.Commander-neck badge	5500.00
19.Knight	1500.00

(Several variations and sizes of 19 exist. A knowledge of French hallmarks is necessary to determine age of some items.)

Military Merit Order-1759-91-for Protestants

20.Grand Cross badge	rare
21.Grand Cross breast star	rare
22.Commander-neck badge	rare
23.Knight	5000.00

Order of the Legion of Honor-1802
Type I Consulate 1802-1804 & First Empire-1804-1806

24.Grand Cross badge	rare
25.Grand Cross breast star	5000.00
26.Commander-neck badge	rare
27.Officer	5000.00
28.Knight	2000.00

Type II-1806-1808
29.Grand Cross badge	rare
30.Grand Cross breast star	5000.00
31.Commander	rare
32.Officer	4000.00
33.Knight	2000.00

Type III-1808-1812
34.Grand Cross badge	rare
35.Grand Cross breast star	5000.00
36.Commander	rare
37.Officer	3500.00
38.Knight	2000.00

Type IV-1812-1814;1815
39.Grand Cross badge	rare
40.Grand Cross breast star	5000.00
41.Commander	rare
42.Officer	4000.00
43.Knight	1500.00

Type V-First Restoration 1814-1815-
Obverse Henri IV-reverse 3 lilies without crown-all types	rare

Type VI-Second Restoration-1815-1830-reverse 3 lilies.
44.Grand Cross badge	rare
45.Grand Cross breast star	5500.00
46.Commander	5000.00
47.Officer	4000.00
48.Knight	1500.00

Type VII-Louis Philippe-1830-1848-obverse Henri IV-reverse crossed tricolor flags-knight is larger than previous issues.
49.Grand Cross badge	5500.00
50.Grand Cross breast star	4000.00
51.Commander	3500.00
52.Officer	1500.00
53.Knight	500.00

Type VIII-Second Republic-Louis
Napoleon-President-1848-1852-obverse Napoleon I-reverse crossed tricolor flags.
54.Grand Cross badge	7500.00
55.Grand Cross breast star	6500.00
56.Commander	5000.00
57.Officer	4000.00
58.Knight	2000.00

Type IX-Second Empire-Napoleon III-1852-1870-care must be taken not to confuse this type with that of Napoelon I which it resembles greatly.
59.Grand Cross badge	3000.00
60.Grand Cross breast star	2000.00
61.Commander	2000.00
62.Officer	600.00
63.Knight	500.00

Type X-III Republic-1870-1951-wreath suspension-Marianne on obverse-date 1870-reverse crossed tricolor flags.

64. Grand Cross badge-gold	2000.00
65. Grand Cross badge-silver/gilt	1000.00
66. Grand Cross & Grand Officer breast star	750.00
67. Commander-gold	1200.00
68. Commander-silver/gilt	450.00
69. Officer-gold	350.00
70. Officer-silver/gilt	150.00
71. Knight	100.00

(Note: Since type X was awarded over the longest period of time one will see a great variation in the quality of the badges, with the better quality pieces made before World War I. Thus, there could be a variation in values in relation to the quality of the badges.)

Type XI-IV Republic-1951-1962-as before but date 1870 has been removed from insignia.

72. Grand Cross badge-silver/gilt	700.00
73. Grand Cross & Grand Officer breast star	650.00
74. Commander	300.00
75. Officer	100.00
76. Knight	75.00

TypeXII-V Republic-1962-reverse legend added-29 FLOREAL AN X

77. Grand Cross badges	600.00
78. Grand Cross breast star-silver/gilt	600.00
79. Grand Officer breast star-silver	500.00
80. Commander	250.00
81. Officer	75.00
82. Knight	50.00

(Note: For types X, XI, & XII the Grand Crand Officer Class (II Class) consists of the appropriate breast star worn on the right side of the chest, with the Officer badge being worn on the left side of the chest. Although twelve types of the Legion of Honor have been listed it must be emphasized that there are many more variations. Some may stem from conversion of an earlier type by replaced centres, as in the case of Napoleonic issues during the Bourbon Restoration, or as a result of different manufacturers' production.)

Order of the Reunion-1811-1813

83. Collar	rare
84. Grand Cross badge	rare
85. Grand Cross breast star-types I & II	rare
86. Commander	7500.00
87. Knight	5000.00

88. Order of the Three Golden Fleece-1809-1809	rare

(Although established in 1809, and produced, it appears not to have been awarded. See also Golden Fleece of Austria and Spain.)

Order of the Academic Palmes-1808
89.Type I-Napoleon I-large embroidered badge	600.00
90.Type II-1814-1830-smaller embroidered badge	350.00
91.Type III-1830-1848-small embroidered badge	300.00
92.Type IV-1848-1852-silver decoration	250.00
Type V-II Empire 1852-1870	
93.I Class-gold	250.00
94.II Class-silver	175.00
Type VI-Republic since 1870	
95.Commander(1945)	185.00
96.Officer-gold	200.00
97.Officer-silver/gilt	150.00
98.Knight-silver	75.00

99.Order of Liberation-1940-45   100.00
(Note: There are several variations, including one without the black enameling, which may be a copy. Liberally awarded.)

Order of Agricultural Merit-1883-1963
100.Commander	200.00
101.Officer	85.00
102.Knight	50.00

Order of Maritime Merit-1930-1963
103.Commander	200.00
104.Officer	65.00
105.Knight	50.00

Order of Social Merit-1936-1963
106.Commander	150.00
107.Officer	65.00
108.Knight	50.00

Order of Public Health-1938-1963
109.Commander	125.00
110.Officer	65.00
111.Knight	45.00

Order of Commercial Merit-1939-1963
112.Commander	125.00
113.Officer	65.00
114.Knight	45.00

Order of Artisan Merit-1948-1963
115.Commander	125.00
116.Officer	65.00
117.Knight	50.00

FRANCE

Order of Tourist Merit-1948-1963
118.Commander	125.00
119.Officer	50.00
120.Knight	25.00

Order of Combattent Merit-1953-1963
121.Commander	175.00
122.Officer	65.00
123.Knight	50.00

Order of Postal Merit-1953-1963
124.Commander	125.00
125.Officer	60.00
126.Knight	45.00

Order of the National Economy-1954-1963
127.Commander	125.00
128.Officer	65.00
129.Knight	50.00

Order of Sporting Merit-1956-1963
130.Commander	125.00
131.Officer	50.00
132.Knight	25.00

Order of Labor Merit-1957-1963
133.Commander	125.00
134.Officer	45.00
135.Knight	25.00

Order of Military Merit
136.Commander	200.00
137.Officer	75.00
138.Knight	50.00

Order of Civil Merit-1957-1963
139.Commander	125.00
140.Officer	50.00
141.Knight	35.00

Order of Arts & Letters-1957-1963
142.Commander	125.00
143.Officer	50.00
144.Knight	40.00

Order of Saharan Merit-1958-1963
145.Commander	125.00
146.Officer	50.00
147.Knight	25.00

National Order of Merit-1963
148.Grand Cross badge	375.00
149.Grand Cross breast star-gilt	375.00
150.Grand Officer badge	200.00
151.Grand Officer breast star-silvered	250.00
152.Commander	200.00
153.Officer	75.00
154.Knight	50.00

(Note: This Order was introduced in 1963 to replace items 100-154 as it was felt that the awards system had become too complicated.)

FRENCH COLONIAL ORDERS

French Colonial Orders were those which were awarded in the French colonies by native rulers to both French and native recipients. Some of these were made in France, and others locally made. Values listed are for better made insignia, usually of French origin.

Order of the Black Star of Benin-1889-1963
155.Grand Cross badge	700.00
156.Grand Cross & Commander Star	650.00
157.Commander	350.00
158.Officer	150.00
159.Knight	100.00

Order of the Star of Anjouan-1874-1963
160.Grand Cross badge	500.00
161.Grand Cross & Grand Officer breast star	450.00
162.Commander	200.00
163.Officer	100.00
164.Knight	75.00

Order of Nichan-el-Anouar-1887-1963
165.Grand Cross badge	500.00
166.Grand Cross & Grand Officer breast star	300.00
167.Commander	150.00
168.Officer	75.00
169.Knight	50.00

Order of the Dragon of Annam-1886-1946
170.Grand Cross badge	1000.00
171.Grand Cross & Grand Officer breast star	750.00
172.Commander	500.00
173.Officer	250.00
174.Knight	200.00

Royal Order of Cambodia-1864-1946
175.Grand Cross badge	600.00
176.Grand Cross & Grand Officer breast star	550.00

FRANCE

177.Commander	300.00
178.Officer	200.00
179.Knight	100.00

Order of a Million Elephants & White Parasol-Laos-according to Werlich founded 24 November 1844; according to Delande 1 May 1909.

180.Grand Officer breast star	800.00
181.Commander	400.00
182.Officer	275.00
183.Knight	200.00

Order of the Star of Comoro

184.Grand Cross badge	450.00
185.Grand Cross breast star	350.00
186.Commander	250.00
187.Knight	150.00

DECORATIONS

Medaille Militaire-(Military Medal)-1851

188.Type I-Louis Napoleon-eagle's wings touch the planchet of the award	1500.00
189.Type II-Napoleon III-eagle's wings raised	250.00
190.Type III-dated 1870-double faced suspension	250.00
191.Type IV-dated 1870-uniface suspension	35.00

(There are several variations of this type which do not affect value.)

192.Type V-date replaced by star 1951	25.00
193.Type VI-one star replaced by three stars-1962	25.00

(Note: Values for 192 & 193 are for good quality items with enamel. Some have been seen with plastic. I have also had in my possession an original prototype of the first issue. All bronze, it bears a circular disc with Napoleon III on the obverse, with crossed cannons, and a wreath. On the reverse it bears the legend "Valeur et Discipline"-estimated value 2000.00

Croix de Guerre-(War Cross)-1915

194.dated 1914-15	25.00
195.dated 1914-16	25.00
196.dated 1914-17	25.00
197.dated 1914-18	25.00
198.undated for overseas operations-Foreign Legion	25.00
199.dated 1939	30.00
200.dated 1939-45	30.00
201.undated-Free French issue-World War II	30.00

(Palms and stars, depending on the nature of the award are worn on the ribbon, add $2.50 per.)

202.Combat Cross-both world wars	15.00
203.Escaped Prisoners Medal-both World Wars	15.00
204.Combat Volunteers Cross-1914-18	20.00

205. Combat Volunteers Cross-1939-45	20.00
206. Invasion Victims-1914-18	20.00
207. Medal of Fidelity-1922-for Alsace-Lorraine	35.00
208. Resistance Medal-I Class-rosette-WWII	20.00
209. Resistance Medal-II Class	17.50
210. Wounded Medal-combat-red star	15.00
211. Wounded Medal-non-combat-white star	15.00
212. Deportees Medal-World War II	15.00
213. Medal for Internees-World War II	15.00

Reconnaissance Francaise
Type I-1914-18

214. I Class-silver/gilt	65.00
215. II Class-silver	50.00
216. III Class-bronze	35.00

Type II-1939-45

217. I Class-bronze/gilt	50.00
218. II Class-silvered	35.00
219. III Class-bronze	25.00

220. Volunteers Medal-1940-45	15.00
221. Aeronautical Medal-rectangular-enameled	45.00

Cross of Voluntary Military Service

222. Army/Navy	15.00
223. Air Force	20.00

224. Medal for the National Gendarmerie	25.00

Medals of Honor for Various Government Departments

225. Foreign Affairs-Military award	20.00
226. Foreign Affairs-Civilian award	20.00
227. Agriculture	20.00
228. Water & Forests	20.00
229. Aeronautical	35.00
230. War Department-Military Health	25.00
231. War Department-Epidemics	25.00
232. Mines	20.00
233. Customs Service	20.00
234. Physical Education & Sport	20.00
235. Railroads	20.00
236. Firemen-40 Year Long Service-silver/gilt-rosette	45.00
237. Firemen-30 Year Long Service-silver/gilt	30.00
238. Firemen-20 Year Long Service-silver	20.00
239. Firemen-Exceptional Services-silver	35.00
240. National Police	20.00
241. Prison Administration	20.00
242. Colonial Prisons	25.00
243. Education Inspectorate	20.00

FRANCE

Lifesaving Medals-usually named & dated on the reverse
244.Napoleon III-gold	750.00
245.Napoleon III-silver	200.00

Ministry of the Interior (Land)
246.Gold-with wreath & rosette	350.00
247.Silver/gilt-silver/gilt wreath	250.00
248.Silver	125.00
249.Bronze	50.00

Ministries of the Navy & Merchant Marine
250.Gold-I Class-gold wreath	350.00
251.Gold-II Class-no wreath	250.00
252.Silver Medal-I Class-with wreath	150.00
253.Silver Medal-II Class-no wreath	125.00
254.Bronze Medal	50.00

(Note: Items 246-254 are valued for recent issues; older awards, especially to British recipients will be more valuable.)

255.Merchant Marine Long Service	25.00
256.Patriots Proscrit-WWII	20.00

Medal of the French Family-1920
257.I Class-gold (silver/gilt) 10 children	50.00
258.II Class-silver-8 children	35.00
259.III Class-bronze-5 children	20.00

Campaign & War Medals
260.St Helena-1857-veterans of Napoleonic Wars	75.00
261.Austro-Sardinian War 1859-silver-several variations	75.00
262.China 1860-embroidered ribbon-by Barre	400.00
263.same-designer Falot	450.00
264.same-designer E.F.	500.00

(See also Great Britain for China 1857-60 Campaign Medal)
265.Mexico 1862-63-embroidered ribbon-by Barre	300.00
266.same-designer Falot	400.00
267.same-designer E.F.	500.00
268.same-designer Navalon	500.00

(Note:Values for 262-268 deduct 50% without ribbon.)
269.Pontifical Cross-1867-for the Defense of Rome	350.00
270.Franco-Prussian War 1870-71-large silver	75.00
271.same-large bronze	35.00
272.same-small bronze	15.00
273.Geneva Cross 1870-71-Aid to the wounded	25.00
274.Tonkin-1883-85-Army type-six campaigns on reverse	100.00
275.Tonkin-1883-85-Navy type-seven campaigns	150.00
276.Madagascar 1885	95.00
277.Dahomey 1892	95.00
278.Madagascar 1895-with bar 1895	95.00
279.Soudan	rare

280.China-1900 bar 1900-Chine-1901   200.00
281.same-without bar   150.00
282.Colonial Medal-1893-large type-clipover bar   65.00
283.Colonial Medal-large type-slipover bar   35.00
284.Colonial Medal-small type-slipover bar-WWII & later   20.00
(Note: 5 gold and over 30 silver bars have been given with this medal; some being rare. Values listed are for common bars.)
285.Morocco-bar Maroc   35.00
286.same-bar Oudjda   40.00
287.bar Casablanca   40.00
(Note: Multiple bar medals are found; add $10.00 per bar.)
288.World War I Commemorative Medal   15.00
289.World War I Victory Medal-by Morlon   20.00
290.same-but a rejected design by Charles-obverse later
    used for the Cuban Victory Medal   175.00
291.same-but another rejected design by Pautot   300.00
292.Orient Medal-Middle East Service World War I   20.00
293.Dardanelles Campaign-World War I   20.00
294.Levant Medal-large size-bar Levant-1922   35.00
295.same-but smaller dark bronze-bar Levant   25.00
296.Lebanon Campaigns-1926   25.00
297.Free French Cross-World War II   15.00
298.Volunteers Medal-World War II   15.00
299.Prisoners of War Medal   15.00
300.World War II Commemorative Medal   15.00
(Many campaign bars awarded with this medal-add $5.00 per bar.)
301.Medal of Liberated France (To the Allies)-1944   50.00
302.Italian Campaigns 1943-44-silvered   35.00
303.Indo-China 1954 (copies exist)   25.00
304.Korean War-1952 (copies exist)   50.00
305.United Nations Korea-in French   50.00
306.Medal for North Africa-bar Tunisie   25.00
307.Medal for Maintaining Security & Order-bar Algerie   25.00
308.Overseas Service Medal-with bar   20.00
(Replaced Colonial Medal-several gilt bars awarded-mostly for campaigns involving former African colonies.)
309.Military Chaplain's Cross   225.00
310.National Defense Medal-gilt   25.00
311.National Defense Medal-silvered   15.00
312.National Defense Medal-bronze   10.00

Vichy France-1940-1944
313.Croix de Guerre 1939-40   75.00
314.Croix de Guerre for Volunteers in Russia (copies exist)   rare
315.Combat Cross-1939-40   200.00
316.Black Africa Merit Medal   200.00
317.Levant Medal-bar Levant 1941   65.00
318.Colonial Medal-bar Cote Des Somalis 1941   65.00
319.National Order of Labor-Chevalier   rare

53 63 71

73, 78, 79

Tunis Nishan Iftikhar

174 183 178

164

277   260   261

262-264   265-268

279   283   276

280   274-275

GERMANY

Association of States till 1871
Empire-1871-1918
Weimar Republic-1918-1933
III Reich-1933-1945

Because of the late fusion of Germany into a unified nation, the German Empire in 1871, this country in its component parts issued a far greater number of awards than any other. Before the French Revolution there were over 300 states in Germany, which existed only as a geographical expression. Due to the violent upheaval of the French Revolution and the Napoleonic Wars a great deal of consolidation took place which left only 34 states in 1814. The chief beneficiary of this was Prussia, which became the nucleus of the united Germany, with her King Wilhelm I becoming the first German Emperor.

While some material dates before 1800, most stems from the War of Liberation of 1813, including the famous Iron Cross. Thus, eventually each State came to issue its own Orders, medals, and decorations; some few in number, while others awarded a profusion. At least 60 awarding authorities existed, but some presented for only a short time, and issued a few items.

Thus, a collector could concentrate on the awards of the German States as a collecting theme, and find a very satisfying field of interest. Even if you were to narrow your focus to the First World War there would be an excellent area to cover. Germany offers several possibilities in collecting. One can collect around a time period; Napoleonic Wars, Franco-Prussian War 1870-71, World War I or World War II. Or your collection could concentrate on a particular state, or the Orders of States etc. In a sense Germany is a microcosm for collecting with so many approaches, and presents an intriguing situation for the collector.

In the period before 1918, most awards were issued by the various states, with only a few of national origin, such as the Wilhelm I Centenary Medal 1897, the S.W.Africa Medals, Colonial Service and Boxer Rebellion Medals,to name some. The Prussian Iron Cross which is thought of as an all German award was not so in reality. Its establishment was not a permanent one, being created for the War of Liberation in 1813. It was not renewed in 1849, 1864, 1866, 1900 or for colonial campaigns. It was re-established in 1870 and 1914. Of course it was recreated in 1939 by the III Reich in a more complicated form.

At this time it would be useful to clarify some of the terms used with regard to German awards. As for most countries the Grand Cross is the highest class of an Order. However, in some cases there may also be a First Class of an Order, just below the Grand Cross, such as in the Prussian Red Eagle Order; while the Prussian Crown Order has as its highest class the First Class. Adding to the confusion is that some German Orders have as their highest class a First Class neck badge. To complete the confusion several of the states use the term First Class to apply to a pin back cross, such as the Iron Cross I Class, or the Friedrich August Cross I Class of Oldenberg. The designation Knight's Cross usually refers to the lowest class of a German Order, but in the III Reich the Knight's Cross of the Iron Cross was one of the highest classes.

In examining the rarity of awards of the German states the collector must proceed with great caution. It is true that in some cases only a very small number of a particular item were actually presented. However, this is not the same as saying how many were <u>actually made</u>! In Germany the national or state mints did not strike Orders, decorations and medals. Instead well-known jewelers were appointed by the rulers of the various states to manufacture these items. Reference to Jeffrey Jacob's **COURT JEWELERS OF THE WORLD** will be of great assistance in helping you find out what to expect in the way of hallmarks etc. Thus, it was possible for the recipient of an award to go to the jeweler who made his original item and buy another, or even several more.

Copies of awards of the German states before 1918 can present a problem for both the advanced and novice collector. In recent years many of the early issues of the German States' Orders, and to a lesser extent other items, have been copied or faked. Without a great deal of experience, or a reliable source or reference to draw upon this can be very frustrating and painful. The existence of a maker's mark on a piece is not a guarantee that said item is genuine. Nor should the item being in a genuine case sway the buyer towards acceptance. Sometimes, a very good tip is to examine the enameling as to quality. Older pieces have better enamel, as modern craftsmen do not have the expertise for the work. Certainly, a powerful magnifying glass will be of help, and the acquaintance of another, more advanced collector or dealer can be of considerable assistance.

As far as the decorations and medals of Germany are concerned there is an outstanding work on the subject, in German, but can be understood with a dictionary; von Hessenthal & Schreiber-**DIE EHRENZEICHEN DES DEUTSCHEN REICHES**, which covers the awards of Germany, and Austria, up until 1940, but does not include Orders. While this book is expensive, $400.00 to $500.00, it is invaluable for the collector of German awards, and will pay for itself many times over. There is a very clear lesson to be learned from this situation. The collector who flinches at paying a high price for a book will end up by spending far more in mistakes buying for his collection!

The tremendous interest in World War II, and the awards of the III Reich has resulted in a considerable amount of reference material being published in English. However, a major problem that all writers have avoided is the vast amount of fraudulent material that purports to be genuine, and "brought back by a veteran." It would be no exaggeration to say that a considerable amount of the III Reich material on the market today is fake, restruck, or dubious in some regard.

In the early days of the Occupation after World War II original dies were used to restrike awards as souvenirs. These dies wore out in time and new ones were created. Some of the early copies are 40 years old! Others have come to be regarded as "genuine". While some of the copies are of high quality, there are many others which are very poor and would fool only the novice.

However, there are some general guidelines which may be of assistance. No Nazi awards used safety catches. Pieces marked L/58 are to be regarded as copies. Iron Crosses should be magnetic, although one that is should not be considered genuine for that reason alone, and the swastika should just about reach up to the beading around the frame. Although I have heard of and read of reference to non-magnetic Iron Crosses, and non-magnetic Knight's Crosses of the Iron Cross as being "late issues" and still genuine I would avoid such as there are many unquestionably genuine magnetic items, without getting into this problem area. Many III Reich items were hallmarked on the suspension or ribbon ring with a number indicating the manufacturer. The presence of such a mark is not necessarily proof of its being genuine, nor is the absence of such a mark an indication of its being a fake or copy. If a piece is marked 800 or 900 this is an statement of silver content. If the piece is not silver then the number is meaningless. If epoxy glue has been used on an item then either it has been repaired or it is a fake, since epoxy glue did not exist in the time period we are referring to. Where items have rivets you must make sure there aren't hooklike projections holding the piece together instead of the rivet heads showing through. Of course the existence of proper rivets is only one factor.

None of this is meant to imply that it is impossible to amass a collection of German items from any period. However, the collector must be cautious, after all it is your money!

Finally, a brief comment should be made with regard to German Federal Republic reissues of III Reich material since 1957. At that time it was decided to allow recipients of III Reich awards to wear them as long as they did not bear a swastika on them. Thus, many III Reich awards appeared redesigned in an acceptable fashion. However, no award of the Nazi Party or of any of its branches could be worn in any form or under any conditions. Thus, Iron Crosses and other awards can be seen in modified form without swastika. These are not fakes or copies, but genuine reissues for current wear. The interest of the collector in these items is difficult to determine.

ANHALT
House Order of Albert the Bear

1.Collar	rare
2.Grand Cross with crown	1650.00
3.Grand Cross with crown & swords	rare
4.Grand Cross with swords	1250.00
5.Grand Cross badge	1200.00
6.Grand Cross breast star	2000.00
7.Commander-with crown & swords	1750.00
8.Commander-with crown	1100.00
9.Commander-with swords	650.00
10.Commander-neck badge	400.00
11.Commander-breast star	1750.00
12.Knight-I Class-with crown & swords	1000.00
13.Knight-I Class-with crown	350.00
14.Knight-I Class-with swords	300.00
15.Knight-I Class-breast badge	200.00
16.Knight-II Class-with crown & swords	650.00

17.Knight-II Class-with crown	275.00
18.Knight-II Class-with swords	250.00
19.Knight-II Class	175.00
20.Golden Medal-with crown & swords-gilt	350.00
21.Golden Medal-with crown	250.00
22.Golden Medal-with swords	125.00
23.Golden Medal	95.00
24.Silver Medal-with crown & swords	300.00
25.Silver Medal-with crown	140.00
26.Silver Medal-with swords	110.00
27.Silver Medal	95.00

Merit Order for Arts & Science

28.First Model-1873-1905	250.00
29.Second Model-1905-1912	275.00
30.Third Model-1912-1918-I Class-gilt	rare
31.II Class-gilt	300.00
32.III Class-silver	rare

Civilian Awards

33.Jubilee Medal-1867-silver	125.00
34.Jubilee Medal-1867-gilt	95.00
35.Jubilee Medal-1896-silver/gilt	250.00
36.Jubilee Medal-1896-silver	65.00
37.50 Years Service	125.00
38.Commemorative Decoration for Duchess Wite Frederick	500.00
39.Fire Service Decoration	95.00
40.Golden 40 Year Long Service Cross-I model-initial "A"	rare
41.Silver 25 Year Long Service Cross-1901	350.00
42.Golden 40 Year Long Service Cross-II model-no initial	rare
43.Silver 25 Year Long Service Cross-1904	350.00
44.Golden 30 Year Midwife Honor Decoration	rare
45.Faithful Work Service	85.00

Military Awards

46.Friedrich Cross-1914-pinback-unofficial	300.00
47.Friedrich Cross-on combat & non-combat ribbon	65.00
48.Marie Cross 1918	450.00

Long Service Awards
Type I-service bars on ribbon-pinback

49.I Class-21 years-bronze/gilt	250.00
50.II Class-15 years-silver	225.00
51.III Class-9 years-iron	150.00

Type II-on ribbon

52.I Class-15 years-cross-copper	75.00
53.II Class-12 years-medal-tombac	60.00
54.III Class-9 years-pot metal	40.00

ANHALT-BERNBURG
Civil Decorations
55.Golden Merit Medal for Arts & Science   rare
56.Silver Merit Medal for Arts & Science   rare
57.Golden Medal for 50 Years Faithful Service   rare
58.Silver Medal for 50 Years Faithful Service   325.00

Military Decorations
59.Iron Campaign Medal 1814-15   250.00
60.Alexander Carl Medal 1848-49   125.00
61.Officers' 50 Year Long Service Cross   rare
62.Officers' 25 Year Long Service Cross   rare
63.Long Service Decoration-I Class-21 years   250.00
64.Long Service Decoration-II Class-15 years   160.00
65.Long Service Decoration-III Class-9 years   140.00

ANHALT-DESSAU & ANHALT-BERNBURG
66.Civil Lifesaving Medal-1850-1918   350.00

ANHALT-DESSAU
67.Field Service Cross 1813-15   250.00

ANHALT-KOTHEN
Merit Order
68.First Class-gold   rare
69.Second Class-silver   rare

Civil Decorations
70.Golden Medal for Merit,Devotion & Loyalty   rare
71.Silver Medal   350.00

Military Decorations
72.Iron Campaign Medal-1813   350.00
73.Iron Campaign Medal-1814   350.00
74.Iron Campaign Medal-1813-14   400.00
75.Iron Campaign Medal-1815   275.00
76.Iron Campaign Medal-1813-15   350.00
77.Iron Campaign Medal-1813-14-15   300.00
78.Iron Campaign Medal-1814-15   400.00
79.Officers' 25 Year Long Service Cross   1350.00
Military Long Service Decoration-I Type-initial "H"
80.I Class-21 years   250.00
81.II Class-15 years   200.00
82.III Class-9 years   170.00
Military Long Service Decoration-II Type-initial "L"
83.I Class-21 years   200.00
84.II Class-15 years   170.00
85.III Class-9 years   125.00

ANHALT-DESSAU-KOTHEN
<u>Civil Decorations</u>
86.Golden Merit Medal for Arts & Science	rare
87.Silver Medal	rare
88.Lifesaving Decoration	rare

<u>Military Decorations</u>
89.Officers' Long Service Cross-25 years	850.00
90.Military Service Award-I Class-20-25 years	200.00
91.II Class-12-15 years	150.00
92.III Class-9 years	85.00

AUGSBERG
93.Militia Service Medal-1796	350.00

BADEN
<u>House Order of Fidelity</u>
94.Golden Collar	rare
95.Order Cross-till 1803	12,000.00
96.Order Cross-post 1803-gold	5000.00
97.Order Cross-with diamonds	rare
98.Breast Star	1500.00

<u>Military Karl-Friedrich Merit Order</u>
99.Golden Collar	rare
100.Grand Cross badge	rare
101.Grand Cross breast star	4500.00
102.Commander-neck badge	5500.00
103.Knight-breast badge-gold	2000.002
104.Knight-silver/gilt	1000.00

105.Golden Medal-I type-1807-10-stamped H.B.	rare
106.Silver Medal	rare
107.Golden Medal-II type-1810-14-stamped DOELL	rare
108.Silver Medal	1600.00
109.Golden Medal-III type-1814-15	rare
110.Silver Medal	1600.00
111.Silver Medal-IV type-1848-stamped "D"	rare
112.Golden Medal-V type-1849-stamped "D.F."	rare
113.Silver Medal	1350.00
114.Golden Medal-VI type-1849-1871-stamped "D"	rare
115.Silver Medal	1000.00
116.Golden Medal-VII type-1870-71-legend Für BADENS...	rare
117.Silver	700.00
118.Silver-VIII type-1915-18-	700.00

<u>Order of the Zahringen Lion</u>
119.Golden Collar	rare
120.Grand Cross badge-with oakleaves-cipher "L"-till 1866	rare
121.Grand Cross badge-with oakleaves	3000.00
122.Grand Cross badge-with oakleaves & swords	rare
123.Grand Cross badge	2000.00

124.Grand Cross badge-w/diamonds	rare
125.Grand Cross badge-with swords	2600.00
126.Grand Cross badge-with swords & diamonds	rare
127.Grand Cross breast star-silver & silver/gilt	1400.00
128.Grand Cross breast star-with diamonds	rare
129.Grand Cross breast star-with swords	2000.00
130.Grand Cross breast star-with swords & diamonds	rare
131.Commander-with oakleaves & cipher "L"	rare
132.Commander-with oakleaves	2250.00
133.Commander-with oakleaves & diamonds	rare
134.Commander-with oakleaves & swords	2750.00
135.Commander	1200.00
136.Commander-with diamonds	rare
137.Commander-with swords	1500.00
138.Commander-with swords on ring	rare
139.Commander breast star	1200.00
140.Commander breast star-with swords	1500.00
141.Knight-I Class-with oakleaves	600.00
142.Knight-I Class-with oakleaves-cipher "L"	rare
143.Knight-I Class-with oakleaves & swords	900.00
144.Knight-I Class	400.00
145.Knight-I Class-with swords	550.00
146.Knight-I Class-with swords on ring	rare
147.Knight-II Class-with oakleaves	350.00
148.Knight-II Class-with oakleaves & swords	550.00
149.Knight-II Class	350.00
150.Knight-II Class-with swords	300.00
151.Knight-II Class-with swords on ring	rare
151.Merit Cross-silver/gilt	275.00
152.Merit Cross-bronze/gilt-World War I	275.00

Order of Berthold I

153.Golden Collar-silver/gilt	rare
154.Grand Cross badge-gold	4000.00
155.Grand Cross badge-with swords	5500.00
156.Grand Cross breast star	2000.00
157.Grand Cross breast star-with diamonds	rare
158.Grand Cross breast star-with swords	4000.00
159.Commander-gold	3000.00
160.Commander-with swords	6000.00
161.Commander breast star	2500.00
162.Commander breast star-with swords	rare
163.Knight	1200.00
164.Knight-with swords-gold	3000.00
165.Knight-with swords-silver/gilt	1500.00

Civil Decorations

166.Large Golden Merit Medal-Grand Duke Leopold	rare
167.Medium Golden Merit Medal	rare
168.Silver Merit Medal-stamped KACHEL	950.00
169.Silver Merit Medal-stamped DOELL	400.00
170.Large Silver Merit Medal-Prince Regent Friedrich	950.00
171.Small Silver Merit Medal	550.00
172.Large Golden Merit Medal-Grand Duke Friedrich I-young	rare
173.Medium Golden Medal	rare
174.Small Golden Merit Medal	rare
175.Silver Merit Medal	600.00
176.Large Golden Merit Medal-Grand Duke Friedrich I-mature head-stamped-SCHNITZPAHN	1500.00
177.Small Golden Merit Medal	750.00
178.Silver Merit Medal	175.00
179.Large Golden Merit Medal-not stamped with designer	1500.00
180.Small Golden Merit Medal	750.00
181.Silver Merit Medal	175.00
182.Large Golden Merit Medal-Friedrich II-gold	1500.00
183.Large Golden Merit Medal-silver/gilt	75.00
184.Large Golden Merit Medal-gilt war metal	85.00
185.Small Golden Merit Medal-gold	500.00
186.Small Golden Merit Medal-silver/gilt	90.00
187.Small Golden Merit Medal-gilt war metal	85.00
188.Silver Merit Medal	45.00
189.Silver Merit Medal-silvered war metal-World War I	25.00
190.Jubilee Medal 1902-gold	1500.00
191.Jubilee Medal 1902-bronze	25.00
192.Friedrich Luisen Medal	60.00
193.Commemorative Medal for 1906	250.00
194.Commemorative Medal for 1906-with diamonds	rare
195.Commemorative Medal for 1906-with pin & enameled "F" for princely awards	1300.00
196.Commemorative Medal for 1906-with ring & enameled "F" for princely awards	1500.00
197.Commemorative Medal for 1906-with pin-gilt	600.00
198.Commemorative Medal for 1906-with ring-gilt	275.00
199.Commemorative Medal for 1906-with ring-silvered	250.00

Lifesaving Medals

200.Silver Medal-Friedrich I-stamped SCHNITZPAHN	600.00
201.Small Gold Medal	rare
202.Silver Medal-without designer's name	500.00
203.Small Gold Medal-without designer's name	rare
204.Silver Medal-Friedrich II	600.00
205.Small Gold Medal	rare

Medals for Arts & Science

206.Golden Medal-Friedrich I-stamped SCHNITZPAHN	rare
207.Silver Medal	1000.00
208.Golden Medal-without SCHNITZPAHN	rare

209.Silver Medal	1000.00
210.Golden Medal-Friedrich II	rare
211.Silver Medal	1000.00

Fire Service Medals
212.40 year Volunteer Service Decoration	100.00
213.25 year Volunteer Service Decoration	75.00

Long Service Decorations
214.Devoted Labor Service-type I	50.00
215.Devoted Labor Service-bronze	65.00
216.Devoted Labor Service-coppered iron	165.00
217.Devoted Labor Service-type II	30.00

Service Decorations for Nurses
218.40 years	400.00
219.35 years	300.00
220.30 years	275.00
221.25 years	200.00
222.20 years	175.00
223.15 years	160.00
224.10 years	125.00

Crosses for Female Domestic Servants
225.Over 60 years	rare
226.Over 50 years	400.00
227.Over 40 years	300.00
228.Over 25 years	250.00

Various Awards for Female Personnel
229.Midwives Service Medal-40 years	325.00
230.Midwives Service Medal-35 years	300.00
231.Midwives Service Medal-25 years	250.00
232.same-Treuen Dienst	200.00
233.same-40 years-Für Treuen Dienst	200.00
234.same-with bow for more than 50 years service	rare
235.Workers Cross for 50 years-silver/gilt	250.00
236.Workers Cross for 30 years-silver	200.00
237.General Cross for Females-velvet ribbon	rare
238.General Cross for Females-silver/gilt	250.00
239.General Cross for Females-silver	195.00
240.Decoration for Teachers and Women Supervisors-40 years 250.00	
241.same-for 25 years service	200.00
242.same-but no year designation	rare
243.Merit Brooch for Baden Women's Guild-silver/gilt	rare
244.same-silver	300.00

Military Decorations
245.Field Service Decoration	25.00
(With campaign bar add $30-150.00; 18 awarded)	
246.Field Service Decoration-1848-reverse engraved	rare
247.1849 Campaign Medal	30.00

248.Commemorative Cross 1870-71	150.00
249.Volunteer War Aid Cross 1914-16	80.00
250.same-but in gilt war metal	40.00
251.same-but with oak wreath	125.00
252.same-but in gilt war metal	100.00
253.War Merit Cross 1914	50.00
254.same-but in gilt war metal	30.00
255.Officers' 40 year service cross-Maltese Cross-w/crown	600.00
256.same-25 years-no crown	300.00
257.Officers' Service Cross-I Class-with crown-curved arms 250.00	
258.same-but II Class	175.00
259.25 year service bar for enlisted men	300.00
260.18 year service bar for enlisted men	200.00
261.12 year service bar for enlisted men	150.00
262.Service Bar I Class-21 years	250.00
263.Service Bar II Class-15 years	185.00
264.Service Bar III Class-9 years	65.00
265.Service Decoration(Cross)-I Class-15 years	60.00
266.Service Decoration(Medal)-II Class-12 years	60.00
267.Service Decoration(Medal)-III Class-9 years	40.00
268.Reserve Decoration-I type-bar	50.00
269.Reserve Decoration-II type-bar	35.00
270.Veterans' Golden Medal-with crown-bronze/gilt	450.00
271.Veterans' Silver Medal-silvered	250.00

BAVARIA
House & Knightly Order of St. Hubert

272.Collar	rare
273.Collar badge	9500.00
274.Badge of the Order	9500.00
275.Breast Star	2800.00
276.Decoration for Officials of the Order	rare

Military & House Order of St. George

277.Collar	rare
278.Grand Cross badge	13,500.00
279.Grand Cross breast star	2500.00
280.Commander Cross(neck badge)	4000.00
281.Commander Cross breast star	2000.00
282.Knight	4000.00
283.Knight's breast star	2250.00
284.Decoration of Officials of the Order	rare
285.Jubilee Medal in gold	3000.00
286.Jubilee Medal in silver	1500.00

House & Knightly Order of St. Michael

287.Collar	rare
288.Badge	rare
289.Breast Star	rare
290.Knight	5000.00

Order of the Lion (Palatine)
291. Collar — rare
292. Badge-gold — rare
293. Breast Star-tinsel type — 5500.00

Military Max-Joseph Order
294. Grand Cross badge-sash decoration — 15,000.00
295. Grand Cross badge-neck decoration — 12,000.00
296. Grand Cross breast star — 3250.00
297. Commander — 12,000.00
298. Knight-gold — 6500.00
299. Registrar's Badge — rare

Civil Merit Order of the Bavarian Crown
300. Grand Cross badge-gold — 8500.00
301. Grand Cross breast star — 3500.00
302. Commander-gold — 3250.00
303. Commander breast star — 2500.00
304. Knight — 2000.00
305. Golden Medal — 2000.00
306. Silver Medal — 450.00

Royal Merit Order of St Michael
307. Grand Cross badge-gold — 5000.00
308. Grand Cross breast star — 3000.00
309. First Class badge (Commander I Class till 1887)-gold — 4000.00
310. First Class breast star — 2000.00
311. Second Class badge-gold — 2250.00
312. Second Class breast star — 1750.00
313. Knight I Class(till 1887) — 2000.00
314. Honor Cross (pinback)-gold — 1250.00
315. Third Class Cross-gold — 1250.00
316. Knight II Class(till 1887) — 1650.00
317. Fourth Class-with crown — 500.00
318. Fourth Class — 400.00
319. Merit Cross-with crown — 700.00
320. Merit Cross-without crown — 225.00
321. Silver Merit Medal — 150.00
322. Bronze Merit Medal — 110.00

Military Merit Order
323. Grand Cross badge-with crown — 4500.00
324. Grand Cross badge-with crown & swords — rare
325. Grand Cross badge-gold — 3500.00
326. Grand Cross badge-with swords — 5000.00
327. Grand Cross breast star — 2500.00
328. Grand Cross breast star-with swords — 2800.00

329. First Class badge-with crown — 3000.00
330. First Class badge-with crown & swords — rare
331. First Class badge-gold — 2500.00

332.First Class badge-with swords	3000.00
333.First Class breast star	2400.00
334.First Class breast star-with swords	3000.00
335.Second Class badge-with crown	2500.00
336.Second Class badge-with crown & swords	rare
337.Second Class badge	2000.00
338.Second Class badge-with swords	2200.00
339.Second Class breast star	1750.00
340.Second Class breast star-with swords	2000.00
341.Officer-without flames-with crown-pinback	2500.00
342.Officer-without flames-with crown & swords	2750.00
343.Officer-with flames & crown-gold	2500.00
344.Officer-with flames, swords & crown-gold	2000.00
345.Third Class-with crown	1500.00
346.Third Class-with crown & swords	1000.00
347.Third Class	1000.00
348.Third Class-with swords	1100.00
349.Fourth Class-with crown	500.00
350.Fourth Class-with crown & swords	450.00
351.Fourth Class (Knight I Class till 1905)	350.00
352.Fourth Class-with swords (Knight I Class till 1905)	225.00
353.Knight II Class-with swords-without flames-gold	675.00
354.Knight II Class-gold	675.00
355.Military Merit Cross-I type-silver-to enlisted men	275.00
356.Military Merit Cross-I type-with swords	300.00
357.Military Merit Cross II type-I Class-enamel centre	450.00
358.Military Merit Cross II type-I Class-with swords	350.00
359.Military Merit Cross II type-II Class-no enamel	350.00
360.Military Merit Cross II type-II Class-with swords	275.00

(Note: In some of the grades in this Order the award without swords is more valuable. Thus, the suspension where the swords would be placed should be examined very carefully with a powerful magnifier to make sure that they have not been removed to make the piece more valuable.)

Military Merit Cross (Type III/IV-1913-1918; 1918-1919)

361.I Class-with crown-silver/gilt-obverse centre enamel	300.00
362.I Class-with crown & swords	175.00
363.I Class	150.00
364.I Class-with swords	150.00
365.II Class-with crown-silver-obverse centre enamel	125.00
366.II Class-with crown & swords	110.00
367.II Class	125.00
368.II Class-with swords	85.00
369.III Class-with crown-bronze-no enamel	150.00
370.III Class-with crown & swords	35.00
371.III Class	85.00

372.III Class-with swords	20.00
373.III Class-war metal (gray)-World War I	150.00
374.III Class-with swords-war metal(grey)-World War I	45.00

(Note: As with the Military Merit Order care must be taken to examine awards without swords to be sure that they haven't been removed to make the item more valuable. Copies exist of the I & II Classes; enameling is of poorer quality, and the crosses are gilt, and silvered.)

Maximilian Order for Arts & Science
375.Cross for Arts-gold	5500.00
376.Cross for Science-gold	5500.00

Ludwig Order
377.Honor Cross-gold	3500.00
378.Honor Medal-gold	2200.00
379.Honor Medal-silver/gilt	1400.00

Military Sanitary Order
380.I Class-gold	10,000.00
381.II Class	3500.00

Elizabeth Order
382.Cross of the Grand Mistress in diamonds	rare
383.Badge-large type	rare
384.Cross for Ladies of the Order	3300.00
385.Cross for the Officials of the Order	rare

Theresia Order
386.Cross of the Order-gold	1850.00
387.Cross of the Order-silver gilt	1200.00

Honor Cross of the Order of St Anne
388.Wurzburg Honor Cross-gold	3500.00
389.Munich Honor Cross-gold	1500.00

Civilian Decorations
390.Silver Merit Medal-1792 type-Carl Theodor	rare
391.Golden Merit Medal-1805 type-Max Joseph	rare
392.Silver Merit Medal	1000.00
393.Prince Regent Luitpold Medal-1905-gold	2000.00
394.Prince Regent Luitpold Medal-1905-silver	150.00
395.Prince Regent Luitpold Medal-1905-bronze	20.00
396.Prince Regent Luitpold Medal-in gold-with crown & dated 1821-1911	2500.00
397.Prince Regent Luitpold Medal-in silver	300.00
398.Prince Regent Luitpold Medal-in bronze	250.00
399.Ludwig Cross-1916-Iron	50.00
400.Golden Wedding of the King & Queen-1918	350.00
401.same-but in war metal	65.00
402.same-but in iron	45.00
403.100th Anniversary of the signing of the Constitution-Commemorative Cross for Parliament members	400.00

404.Merit Cross for Volunteer Nurses	65.00
405.Lifesaving Medal	450.00
406.Agricultural Jubilee Medal-gold-1910	2000.00
407.Agricultural Jubilee Medal-silver	200.00
408.Agricultural Jubilee Medal-bronze	150.00
409.Fire Service Merit Cross	375.00
410.Ludwig Medal for Arts & Science-gold	2000.00
411.Ludwig Medal for Arts & Science-silver	1500.00
412.Ludwig Medal for Industry-gold	2100.00
413.Ludwig Medal for Industry-silver	1500.00
414.Luitpold Cross-40 year state service	50.00
415.40 year service medal in the Army Workshops-silver	350.00
416.25 year bronze medal	150.00
417.35 year Security Service Award-Gendarmerie-I Class	350.00
418.20 year Security Service Award-II Class	125.00
419.Fire Service Decoration-25 years	65.00
420.Volunteer Nurses Decoration-20 years	65.00

Military Decorations

421.Golden Valor Medal-1794-Carl Theodor	rare
422.Silver Valor Medal	rare
423.Golden Valor Medal-1799-Max Joseph IV	rare
424.Silver Valor Medal	4000.00
425.Golden Valor Medal-1806-KING Max Joseph I	rare
426.Silver Valor Medal	1000.00
(Above designer "Losch".)	
427.Golden Valor Medal-1848	3000.00
428.Silver Valor Medal	550.00
(Above two no designer's name.)	
429.Golden Valor Medal-1870-gold	2250.00
430.Golden Valor Medal-1870-silver/gilt	950.00
431.Silver Valor Medal	550.00
(Above designer "Ries".)	
432.Golden Military Medical Medal	rare
433.Silver Military Medical Medal	1875.00
434.Veterans' Campaign Cross-1790-1812	60.00
435.Campaign Cross 1813-1814	50.00
436.Military Officials' Service Medal-1813-1815	400.00
437.Suppression of the Rebellion of 1849	185.00
438.Danish War Cross 1849	150.00
439.Austrian War Cross 1866	35.00
440.Austrian War Cross for Civil Doctors-1866	550.00
441.Medical Merit Cross-1870-71	250.00
442.Medical Volunteers Merit Cross-bar 1870-71	250.00
443.Jubilee Medal for the Austro-Hungarian Artillery Corps Regiment No. 10-silver-1904	375.00
444.same-in bronze	275.00
445.Army Jubilee Medal-1905	25.00
446.Golden Jubilee Medal-with crown-gold-1839-1909	rare
447.Golden Jubilee Medal-gilt	175.00
448.Golden Jubilee Medal-1821-1911-gilt	450.00
449.Bronze Jubilee Medal	450.00

450. Medical Volunteers Cross-silver crown-bar "1914"   1000.00
451. same-without crown   75.00
452. Jubilee Cross-Austro-Hungarian Infantry Regt. No. 62   500.00
453. Veterans' Badge-Army 40 year service   425.00
454. Veterans' Badge-Army 24 year service   350.00
455. Military Long Service Cross-I Class-40 years   220.00
456. Military Long Service Cross-II Class-24 years   45.00

Military Long Service Badges-Enlisted men-metal bars on ribbons
457. I Class-21 years   100.00
458. II Class-15 years   65.00
459. III Class-9 years   25.00

Military Long Service Decorations-Enlisted men
460. I Class-15 years-cross   40.00
461. II Class-12 years-medal   15.00
462. III Class-9 years-medal   15.00
463. Reserve Long Service-I Class   100.00
464. Reserve Long Service-II Class-bar   25.00
465. Reserve Long Service-II Class-medal   20.00
466. Luitpold 50 year Veterans' Medal   85.00

Flying Badges-World War I-silver-see also Empire
467. Pilot's Badge-silver   750.00
468. Observer's Badge   750.00
469. Air Gunner's Badge   1250.00
470. Flyers' Commemorative Badge   750.00
(Note: Copies or late strikings of these badges exist. Air Gunner's badge rarer than value would indicate.)

BREMEN
471. Hansa Cross 1914(see also Hamburg & Lubeck)   75.00
472. Officers' Long Service Cross-25 years   rare
473. Long Service Cross for 25 years   rare
474. 20 year service bar   rare
475. 15 year service bar   300.00
476. 10 year service bar   200.00
477. Lifesaving Medal-bronze   160.00

BRUNSWICK
House Order of Henry the Lion
478. Collar   12,000.00
479. Grand Cross badge-gold   3250.00
480. Grand Cross badge with swords under cross   rare
481. Grand Cross badge with swords-silver/gilt   4250.00
482. Grand Cross badge with swords on ring   rare
483. Grand Cross breast star   1300.00
484. Grand Cross breast star with swords   3250.00

485.I Class badge (on sash)	1000.00
486.I Class badge-with swords	2200.00
487.I Class badge-with swords on ring-silver gilt	rare
488.I Class breast star	1250.00
489.I Class breast star-with swords	1800.00
490.Commander-neck badge	1200.00
491.Commander-with swords under cross	3000.00
492.Commander-with swords	2500.00
493.Commander-with swords on ring	rare
494.Commander-breast star	1250.00
495.Commander-breast star-with swords	1600.00
496.Officer-pin back badge	800.00
497.Officer-with swords	rare
498.Knight I Class-gold	1000.00
499.Knight I Class-with swords under cross	1200.00
500.Knight I Class-with swords	1000.00
501.Knight I Class-with swords on ring	rare
502.Knight II Class	400.00
503.Knight II Class-with swords under cross	900.00
504.Knight II Class-with swords	1000.00
505.Knight II Class-with swords on ring	rare
506.Cross IV Class	350.00
507.Cross IV Class-with swords	850.00
508.Merit Cross I Class-gold	400.00
509.Merit Cross I Class-silver/gilt	275.00
510.Merit Cross I Class-with swords-gold	450.00
511.Merit Cross II Class	125.00
512.Merit Cross II Class-with swords	275.00
513.Honor Medal-I Class-silver/gilt	150.00
514.Honor Medal-I Class-silver	140.00
515.Honor Medal-II Class	100.00

Decoration for Arts & Science

516.Merit Decoration I Class	1000.00
517.Merit Decoration II Class-with crown	575.00
518.Merit Decoration II Class	500.00

Civil Awards

519.Civil Merit Medal-1815	2500.00
520.Lifesaving Medal	325.00
521.Ladies' Merit Cross I Class	1300.00
522.Ladies' Merit Cross II Class	875.00
523.Fire Service Merit Medal	200.00
524.Fire Service 25 Year Service Bar	110.00

Military Decorations

525.Field Service Cross 1809-Duke Carl-Officers	rare
526.Field Service Cross 1809-enlisted men	300.00

527.Field Service Cross 1809-Duke Wilhelm-Officers	rare
528.Field Service Cross 1809-enlisted men	400.00
529.Peninsula Medal-1810-1814-initial "C"-for Officers	500.00
530.Peninsula Medal-1810-1814-for Enlisted Men	250.00
531.Peninsula Medal-1810-1814-initial "W"-for Officers	500.00
532.Peninsula Medal-1810-1814-for Enlisted Men	375.00
533.Military Merit Medal-1815	2250.00
534.Waterloo Medal-1815-named to recipient-with rank, etc.	300.00
535.Schleswig-Holstein Campaign 1848-1849	400.00
536.Military War Merit Cross-gold-1879	rare
537.Military Merit Cross-1914-18-silver/gilt	800.00
538.War Merit Cross I Class 1914(Ernst August Cross)	125.00
539.War Merit Cross II Class-combat ribbon	35.00
540.Frontline Service Badge for 539	75.00
541.War Merit Cross II Class-non-combat ribbon	40.00
542.War Merit Cross for Ladies & Girls 1917-18	125.00

Officers' Long Service Decorations

543.Long Service Cross-25 years-1828-1833-gold	rare
544.Long Service Cross-25 years-1833-1866	500.00

Military Long Service Awards

545.Silver Cross-25 years	200.00
546.Silver Cross-21 years	200.00
547.Silver Cross-20 years	125.00
548.Bar-15 years	200.00
549.Bar-10 years	150.00
550.Bar-9 years	140.00
551.Landwehr (Reserve) Decoration-I Class	400.00
552.Landwehr Decoration-II Class	125.00

FRANKFURT

Concordia Order

553.Grand Cross badge	rare
554.Grand Cross breast star (tinsel)	rare
555.Commander	rare
556.Knight	rare

Military Decorations

557.Golden Honor Medal of the Prince Primate Carl von Dalberg	rare
558.Silver Honor Medal	rare
559.Golden Honor Medal of the Grand Duke Carl	rare
560.Silver Honor Medal	rare
561.Golden Campaign Medal for Volunteers-1814	rare
562.Silver Campaign Medal	275.00
563.Honor Cross for Officers of Reserve Battalion Volunteers at Fulda-1814	rare
(awarded in both silver/gilt & copper/gilt)	
564.Honor Cross for Enlisted Men	825.00
565.War Commemorative Medal-1814 (issued in 1846 to surviving veterans)	800.00

566.Campaign Medal-gold-1815   rare
567.Campaign Medal-silver-1815   400.00
568.Field Service Cross-1848-1849   400.00

Military Long Service Awards
569.Officers'Long Service Cross-50 years   rare
570.Officers'Long Service Cross-25 years   325.00
571.N.C.O.'s Long Service Cross-50 years   rare
572.N.C.O.'s Long Service Cross-25 years   350.00
573.N.C.O.'s Long Service Cross-15 years   300.00
574.N.C.O.'s Long Service Cross-10 years   200.00

HAMBURG
Civil Decorations
575.Medal for Assistance in the Fire of 1843   200.00

Military Decorations
576.City Militia Badge-1848   20.00
577.Hansa Cross-1914 (see also Bremen & Lubeck)   50.00
578.Officers' Long Service Cross-25 years-type I-1839-
         1858-obverse coat of arms-reverse XXV   750.00
579.same-type II-coat of arms both sides-1858-1867   450.00
580.Long Service Cross-20 years   450.00
581.Long Service Bar-20 years   450.00
582.Long Service Bar-15 years   375.00
583.Long Service Bar-10 years   300.00
584.City Militia Long Service-gold-50 years   rare
585.City Militia Long Service-silver-25 years   300.00

HANNOVER
Order of St George
586.Collar   rare
587.Badge   rare
588.Breast Star   2500.00

Royal Guelphic Order-1815-1837;1837-1867 (see also Great Britain for the period 1815-1837)
589.Collar (bronze/gilt; copper/gilt; or silver/gilt)   10,000.00
590.Grand Cross badge   rare
591.Grand Cross badge-with swords   6000.00
592.Grand Cross breast star   2000.00
593.Grand Cross breast star-with swords-silver/gold   2500.00

594.Commander-neck badge   1600.00
595.Commander-with swords   2000.00
596.Commander breast star   1500.00
597.Commander breast star-with swords-silver/gold   1950.00

598.Knight I Class-gold/enamels   850.00
599.Knight I Class-with swords   1100.00

600.Knight II Class-silver/enamels-1839-1867	600.00
601.Knight II Class-with swords	850.00
(Note: Values are for GERMAN made insignia.)	

Order of Ernst-August-1837-1867

602.Grand Cross badge - silver gilt	4500.00
603.Grand Cross breast star	1600.00
604.Commander-gold	4500.00
605.Commander breast star	5000.00
606.Knight I Class	1500.00
607.Knight II Class	650.00
608.Merit Cross I Class-gold	450.00
609.Merit Cross II Class-silver	300.00

Civil Decorations

610.Golden Merit Medal-Prince Regent George	2500.00
611.Silver Merit Medal	300.00
612.Golden Merit Medal-King William IV	rare
613.Silver Merit Medal	300.00
614.Golden Merit Medal-King Ernst August-small head	2150.00
615.Silver Merit Medal	225.00
616.Golden Merit Medal-Ernst August-small head RS	2150.00
617.Silver Merit Medal	125.00
618.General Honor Decoration for Civil Merit	85.00
619.Golden Medal for Exceptional Merit	1150.00
620.Silver Medal	185.00
621.Golden Medal for Arts & Science	rare
622.Silver Medal for 81st Birthday-Queen Marie-1898	200.00
623.Bronze Medal	100.00

Military Decorations

624.Guelphic Medal for Military Merit in War-silver	300.00
625.General Decoration for Military Merit	125.00
626.Defense of Gibraltar-1782-non-wearable	650.00
627.Volunteers' Campaign Medal-1813	85.00
628.Volunteers of the King's German Legion	75.00
(Note: See Great Britain-Military General Service Medal also awarded to King's German Legion.)	
629.Waterloo Medal-1815-named	450.00
630.50th Military Jubilee of Ernst August-1840	rare
631.Langensalza-Austrian War Medal-1866-named	50.00
632.William Cross-Officers' 25 year Long Service-gold	750.00
633.William Cross-gilt	150.00
634.Ernst August Cross-Officers' 50 years-gold	1250.00
635.Ernst August Cross-gilt	600.00
636.William IV-Golden Medal-25 years service	600.00
637.William IV-Silver Medal-16 years service	225.00
638.Ernst August-young head-Golden Medal-25 years	600.00
639.Ernst August-Silver Medal-16 years	150.00
640.Ernst August-old head-Golden Medal-25 years	600.00
641.Ernst August-Silver Medal	150.00

HANSEATIC STATES (See also Bremen, Hamburg & Lubeck)
Common Awards

642.Hanseatic Legion Medal-gold-1813-1814	2250.00
643.Hanseatic Legion Medal-silver	175.00

HESSE-DARMSTADT

Order of the Golden Lion

644.Collar	10,000.00
645.Badge-gold	3000.00
646.Breast Star	1800.00

Ludwig Order

647.Collar (monograms "L I", "L II", "L III"	rare
648.Grand Cross badge-gold	3750.00
649.Grand Cross badge-with swords	rare
650.Grand Cross breast star	1800.00
651.Grand Cross breast star-with swords	5000.00
652.Commander	3000.00
653.Commander-breast star	4500.00
654.Honor Cross	rare
655.Knight I Class	1500.00
656.Knight II Class - gold	1300.00
657.Knight II Class - silver gilt	800.00

Medals of the Ludwig Order
Ludwig III-1850-1889

658.Golden Medal "FÜR TAPFERKEIT" (Bravery)-gold	3000.00
659.Silver Medal	600.00
660.Golden Medal "FÜR FUNFZIGJAHRIGE DIENSTE" (Fifty Years Service)-gold	2200.00
661.Silver Medal	450.00
662.Golden Medal "FÜR VIELJAHRIGE TREUE DIENSTE" (Many Years Loyal Service)-gold	2200.00
663.Silver Medal	450.00
664.Golden Medal "FÜR LANGJAHRIGE TREUE DIENSTE (For longstanding loyal service)-gold	2000.00
665.Silver Medal	450.00
666.Silver Medal-with Lifesaving Bar	rare
667.Golden Medal "FÜR TREUE DIENST" (Loyal Service)-gold	1750.00
668.Silver Medal	325.00
669.Golden Medal "FÜR VERDIENSTE" (Merit)-gold	1750.00
670.Silver Medal	375.00

Ludwig IV-1889-1894

671.Golden Medal (50 years loyal service)-gold	2200.00
672.Golden Medal-silver/gilt	375.00
673.Silver Medal	275.00
674.Golden Medal (Loyal Service)-gold	2200.00
675.Golden Medal-silver/gilt	350.00
676.Silver Medal	275.00
677.Golden Medal (For Merit)-gold	2200.00

678.Golden Merit-silver/gilt	350.00
679.Silver Medal	225.00

Ernst Ludwig-1894-1918

680.Golden Medal (50 Years Loyal Service)-silver/gilt	275.00
681.Silver Medal	150.00
682.Golden Medal (Longstanding Loyal Service)-silver/gilt	200.00
683.Silver Medal	110.00
684.Golden Medal (Loyal Service)-silver/gilt	160.00
685.Silver Medal	85.00
686.Golden Medal (For Merit)	165.00
687.Silver Medal	95.00

Order of Philip the Brave
Type I-1840-1849

688.Grand Cross badge	5000.00
689.Grand Cross breast star	4000.00
690.Commander	4000.00
691.Commander breast star	4000.00
692.Knight	2650.00

Type II-1849-1918

693.Grand Cross badge-with crown-gold	5000.00
694.Grand Cross badge-with crown & swords	6000.00
695.Grand Cross badge-gold	2000.00
696.Grand Cross badge-with swords-gold	30000.00
697.Grand Cross breast star-with crown	2250.00
698.Grand Cross breast star-with crown & swords	2600.00
699.Grand Cross breast star	950.00
700.Grand Cross breast star-with swords	1750.00
701.Commander-with crown	1750.00
702.Commander-with crown & swords	2500.00
703.Commander	600.00
704.Commander-with swords-gold	1750.00
705.Commander-breast star-with crown	3000.00
706.Commander-breast star-with crown & swords	3500.00
707.Commander-breast star(with & without enamel)	1600.00
708.Commander-breast star-type II with golden rays	1750.00
709.Commander-breast star-type II-with swords	2500.00
710.Honor Cross-with crown-pinback	1200.00
711.Honor Cross-with crown & swords	1600.00
712.Honor Cross-gold	800.00
713.Honor Cross-with swords-silver/gilt	1000.00
714.Knight I Class-with crown-gold	500.00
715.Knight I Class-with crown & swords	575.00
716.Knight I Class-gold	350.00
717.Knight I Class-with swords-gold	800.00
718.Knight II Class-with crown	350.00
719.Knight II Class-with crown & swords	800.00

GERMANY-Hesse-Darmstadt

720.Knight II Class	225.00
721.Knight II Class-with swords	300.00
722.Silver Merit Cross-with crown	280.00
723.Silver Merit Cross-with crown & swords	300.00
724.Silver Merit Cross	185.00
725.Silver Merit Cross-with swords	275.00

Order of the Star of Brabant

726.Grand Cross badge	rare
727.Grand Cross breast star	rare
728.Grand Commander badge-with turquoise	rare
729.Grand Commander breast star-with turquoise	rare
730.Grand Commander badge-I Class	rare
731.Grand Commander-breast star-I Class	rare
732.Grand Commander badge-II Class with crown	rare
733.Grand Commander badge-II Class	rare
734.Grand Commander-II Class breast star	rare
735.Commander I Class-with crown	2800.00
736.Commander I Class	2000.00
737.Commander II Class-with crown	2000.00
738.Commander II Class	1700.00
739.Honor Cross I Class-with crown	1500.00
740.Honor Cross I Class	1200.00
741.Honor Cross II Class	900.00
742.Knight I Class-with crown	1200.00
743.Knight I Class	900.00
744.Knight II Class-with crown	1100.00
745.Knight II Class	700.00
746.Ladies' Cross I Class	1000.00
747.Ladies' Cross II Class	700.00
748.Silver Merit Cross I Class-with crown	1000.00
749.Silver Merit Cross I Class	1000.00
750.Silver Merit Cross II Class-with crown	1000.00
751.Silver Merit Cross II Class	1000.00
752.Silver Merit Medal	250.00
753.Ladies' Honor Cross	2500.00
754.Ladies' Silver Merit Cross	600.00
755.Ladies' Silver Merit Medal	200.00

Long Service & Lifesaving Awards
Type I-Head of Ludwig III-1849-1889

756.For Bravery	550.00
757.For Merit	350.00
758.For Loyal Service	350.00
759.Many Years Long Service	350.00
760.Long & Faithful Service	350.00
761.For 50 Years Loyal Service	400.00

762. Lifesaving — 600.00
763. For Lifesaving with Risk to One's Own Life — 700.00
764. Merit in the Fire Service — rare

Type II-Head of Ludwig IV-1889-1894
765. For Merit — 200.00
766. For Loyal Service — 200.00
767. For longstanding loyal service — 250.00
768. For fifty years loyal service — 275.00
769. For Lifeaving — 550.00

Type III-Head of Ernst Ludwig-1894-1918
770. For Bravery-silver — 50.00
771. For Bravery-silvered-World War I — 35.00
772. For War Merit-silver — 75.00
773. For War Merit-silvered-World War I — 50.00
774. For Merit — 85.00
775. For loyal service — 75.00
776. For longstanding loyal service — 100.00
777. For fifty years loyal service — 125.00
778. For Lifesaving — 250.00
779. same-at risk of one's own life — rare
780. Für treue Arbeit — 125.00

Civil Decorations
781. Silver Merit Medal — 1000.00
782. Bronze Merit Medal — 600.00
783. Honor Decoration for the Flood of 1882-1883 — 500.00
784. Alice Medal-silver — 600.00
785. Alice Medal-bronze — 350.00
786. Ernst Ludwig-Eleanor Cross — 600.00
787. Wedding Medal-1894 — 225.00
788. Wedding Medal-1905 — 250.00
789. Alice League-Jubilee Decoration for Ladies-1917 — rare
790. Lifesaving Medal — 250.00
791. Lifesaving Medal-with second award bar — rare

Merit Medals for Arts, Science, Industry & Agriculture
Obverse Head of Ruler; reverse "Dem Verdienste"
Type I-Ludwig III-1853-1889
792. Golden Medal-gold — 3000.00
793. Silver Medal — 600.00

Type II-Ludwig IV-1898-1894
794. Golden Medal-gold — 2000.00
795. Golden Medal-silver/gilt — 650.00
796. Silver Medal — 550.00

Type III-Ernst Ludwig-1894-1904
797. Golden Medal-silver/gilt — 600.00
798. Silver Medal — 575.00

Variations of Previous Group-Medals have figural & ornate designs with complete inscriptions.

799.Golden Medal-1853-1889-silver/gilt	750.00
800.Silver Medal	600.00
801.Golden Medal-1889-1894-silver/gilt	600.00
802.Silver Medal	550.00
803.Arts & Science Merit Medal-1894-1904-silver/gilt	600.00
804.Silver Medal	475.00
805.Arts & Science Merit Medal-1904-1918-silver/gilt	600.00
806.Silver Medal	575.00
807.Agriculture & Industry Merit Medal-1904-18-silver/gilt 600.00	
808.Silver Medal	475.00

Decorations for Court Officials

809.Cross for Higher Officials-50 years-gold	1500.00
810.Cross for 25 years-gold	1000.00
811.Cross for Lower Court Officials-50 years-silver	750.00
812.Cross for 25 years-silver	250.00

Fire Service Decorations

813.Decoration for 40 years	375.00
814.Decoration for 25 years	125.00
815.Decoration for 20 years	65.00
816.Decoration for 15 years	45.00

Other Civil Long Service Awards

817.Hessian State Railways-40 years	225.00
818.Hessian State Railways-25 years	150.00
819.Nursing Service Cross-25 years	225.00
820.Nursing Service Cross-20 years	150.00
821.Nursing Service Cross-15 years	125.00
822.Nursing Service Cross-10 years	75.00
823.Nursing Service Cross-no years stated	120.00

Golden Cross for Female Messenger Service

824.Cross with initials V.M. for 50 years	rare
825.Cross for 25 years	rare
826.Cross with initial E for 50 years	rare
827.Cross for 25 years	rare

Military Decorations

828.War Veterans' Decoration-1792-1815	400.00
829.Field Honor Decoration-1840-1866	25.00
830.Military Merit Cross-1870-71	300.00
831.Military Sanitary Cross-1870-71	325.00
832.same-with bar 1914 on ribbon	rare
833.War Honor Decoration-1917-iron-pinback	110.00
834.Military Sanitary Cross-1914	65.00
835.Decoration for War Suffering(World War I)	50.00
836.War Honor Decoration-bronze-World War I	50.00
837.same-but coppered	25.00
838.Jubilee Decorations for Aides-de-camp-1917	1000.00

Long Service Awards
839.Officers' Long Service Cross-50 years-gold	1600.00
840.Officers' Long Service Cross-XXV years-gold	1150.00
841.same-but 25 instead of XXV	1000.00
842.Long Service Cross-50 years-silver	750.00
843.Long Service Cross-XXV years-silver	375.00
844.same-but 25 instead of XXV	275.00

Long Service Decoration-type I-1849-1871-Bar
845.I Class-20 years	175.00
846.II Class-15 years-iron/silver	150.00
847.III Class-10 years	100.00

Type II-1871-1913-Bar
848.I Class-21 years	125.00
849.II Class-15 years	100.00
850.III Class-9 years	90.00

Type III-1913-1918
851.I Class-15 years-cross	50.00
852.II Class-12 years-medal	30.00
853.III Class-9 years-medal	20.00

Landwehr (Reserve)
854.Reserve Long Service-bar	65.00
855.Reserve Long Service-medal	20.00

HESSE-HOMBURG
Military Decorations
856.Sword Cross 1814-15-I Class neck badge-silver/gilt	rare
857.Sword Cross-silver	4000.00
858.Field Service Decoration 1850	475.00
859.Officers' Long Service Cross-50 years	rare
860.Officers' Long Service Cross-25 years	rare
861.Long Service Cross-N.C.O.'s 1850-1866-25 years	600.00
862.Long Service Decoration-I Class-20 years-bar	200.00
862.same-II Class-15 years-bar	165.00
864.same-III Class-10 years-bar	140.00

HESSE-KASSEL
Order of the Golden Lion
865.Collar	rare
866.Order Badge (Fridericus II-1770)-gold	3250.00
867.Order Badge (Wilhelmus 1803)	3250.00
868.Breast Star	3000.00

Wilhelm Order
869.Grand Cross badge	3250.00
870.Grand Cross breast star	3000.00
871.Commander	3250.00
872.Commander-with swords	rare

GERMANY-Hesse-Kassel

873.Commander-with swords on ring	rare
874.Commander breast star	2200.00
875.Knight I Class	1200.00
876.Knight I Class-with swords	rare
877.Knight II Class	700.00

Order of Military Virtue
878.Type I "FL"	rare
879.Type II "WK"	rare
880.Type III "WL"	rare

Order of the Iron Helmet
881.Brabant Cross	6000.00
882.German Cross	6500.00

Civil Decorations
883.Golden Merit Cross-type I-1832-1847-with ciphers "WKII" & "FW"-silver/gilt	rare
884.Silver Merit Cross	1250.00

885.Golden Merit Cross-type II-1847-1852-with cipher "FW" & lion-silver/gilt	rare
886.Silver Merit Cross (on war & peace ribbons)	1500.00
887.Silver Merit Cross-flat design-cipher "FW"	1275.00
888.Silver Merit Medal	550.00
889.Bronze Merit Medal	475.00

Military Decorations
890.Golden Merit Medal-silver/gilt	550.00
891.Silver Merit Medal	400.00
892.Campaign Medal-1814-15-combat	100.00
893.Campaign Medal-1814-15-non-combat	225.00
894.Officers' Long Service Cross-gilt	250.00
895.Military Long Service Cross-20 years	225.00
896.Military Long Service Cross-15 years	195.00
897.Military Long Service Cross-10 years	150.00
898.Long Service Decoration-I Class-21 years-bar	275.00
899.Long Service Decoration-II Class-15 years-bar	220.00
900.Long Service Decoration-III Class-10 years-bar	160.00

HOHENLOHE
Golden Flame Order
901.Grand Cross badge-bronze/gilt	rare
902.Grand Cross breast star	3500.00

Phoenix Order
903.Commander-gold	2500.00
904.Commander breast star	8500.00
905.Knight	3500.00

156

HOHENZOLLERN-Principality
House Order of Hohenzollern-(See also Prussia & Rumania)

906.Grand Honor Cross on collar	rare
907.Grand Honor Cross with swords on collar	rare
908.Grand Honor Cross breast star	2500.00
909.Grand Honor Cross breast star-with swords	2750.00
910.Honor Cross I Class	1200.00
911.Honor Cross I Class-with swords	1400.00
912.Honor Commander Cross-with crown	rare
913.Honor Commander Cross-with crown & swords	2000.00
914.Honor Commander Cross	1500.00
915.Honor Commander Cross-with swords	2000.00
916.Honor Commander Cross breast star	1250.00
917.Honor Commander Cross breast star-with swords	1500.00
918.Honor Cross II Class-with crown	750.00
919.Honor Cross II Class-with crown & swords	950.00
920.Honor Cross II Class-gold	800.00
921.Honor Cross II Class-with swords	1250.00
922.Honor Cross III Class-with crown	600.00
923.Honor Cross III Class-with crown & swords	550.00
924.Honor Cross III Class-with oakleaves	rare
925.Honor Cross III Class-with oakleaves & swords	800.00
926.Honor Cross III Class	250.00
927.Honor Cross III Class-with swords	300.00
928.Golden Merit Cross	550.00
929.Silver Merit Cross	350.00
930.Silver Merit Cross-with swords	550.00
931.Golden Honor Medal-type I-no date-gold	700.00
932.Silver Honor Medal-type I	250.00
933.Golden Honor Medal-type II- dated "Den 5t Dezember 1841"-gold	1100.00
934.Silver Merit Medal-type II	110.00
935.Silver Merit Medal-with swords	150.00
936.Golden Honor Medal-type III-dated "1t Januar 1842"	180.00
937.Golden Honor Medal-type III-with swords	195.00
938.Silver Merit Medal-type III	65.00
939.Silver Merit Medal-type III-with swords	100.00

Long Service Awards

940.Officers' Long Service Cross-25 years	rare
941.Enlisted I Class bar-20 years	rare
942.Enlisted II Class bar-15 years	rare
943.Enlisted III Class bar-10 years	rare

ISENBURG-BIRSTEIN
House Order

944.Cross of the Order	rare

Military Decoration

945.Silver Campaign Medal-1814-1815-several variations	850.00

KOLN (COLOGNE)
946.Golden Bravery Medal	rare
947.Silver Bravery Medal	1500.00
948.Bronze Bravery Medal	600.00

LIPPE-DETMOLD
Order of the Honor Cross-type I-monogram "LA"
949.Grand Cross badge	rare
950.Grand Cross badge with swords	rare
951.Grand Cross breast star	rare
952.Grand Cross breast star with swords	rare
953.I Class with oakleaves	3000.00
954.I Class with oakleaves & swords	3500.00
955.I Class with oakleaves & swords on ring	rare
956.I Class badge	2250.00
957.I Class with swords	rare
958.I Class with swords on ring	rare
959.II Class with oakleaves	1500.00
960.II Class with oakleaves & swords	2250.00
961.II Class with oakleaves & swords on ring	rare
962.II Class	1250.00
963.II Class with swords	1600.00
964.II Class with swords on ring	rare
965.Officers' Honor Cross	rare
966.Officers' Honor Cross with swords	rare
967.III Class with oakleaves	1000.00
968.III Class with oakleaves & swords	1200.00
969.III Class with oakleaves & swords on ring	rare
970.III Class	800.00
971.III Class with swords	1000.00
972.III Class with swords on ring	rare
973.IV Class	300.00
974.IV Class with swords	500.00
975.Golden Merit Cross-silver/gilt	200.00
976.Silver Merit Cross	125.00

Type II-monogram "L"
977.Grand Cross badge	3000.00
978.Grand Cross badge with swords	3250.00
979.Grand Cross breast star	2450.00
980.Grand Cross breast star with swords	2750.00
981.I Class with oakleaves	2750.00
982.I Class with oakleaves & swords	2950.00
983.I Class with oakleaves & swords on ring	rare

984.I Class	2500.00
985.I Class with swords-gold	3250.00
986.I Class with swords on ring	rare
987.II Class with oakleaves-gold	2200.00
988.II Class with oakleaves & swords	3000.00
989.II Class with oakleaves & swords on ring	rare
990.II Class-gold	1800.00
991.II Class with swords-gold	1800.00
992.II Class with swords on ring	rare
993.Officers' Honor Cross	900.00
994.Officers' Honor Cross with swords	800.00
995.III Class with oakleaves-gold	1000.00
996.III Class with oakleaves & swords	1100.00
997.III Class with oakleaves & swords on ring	rare
998.III Class-gold	600.00
999.III Class with swords	600.00
1000.III Class with swords on ring	rare
1001.IV Class-I Grade (with rays between arms)	200.00
1002.IV Class-I Grade with swords	320.00
1003.IV Class-II Grade (without rays between arms)	175.00
1004.IV Class-II Grade with swords	300.00

Leopold Order
Type I-1906-1908-silver cross with rose

1005.Cross with crown	1450.00
1006.Cross without crown	1275.00

Type II-1908-1910-silver cross with centre "L"

1007.Pinback cross with crown	3250.00
1008.Cross with crown (on ribbon)	2250.00
1009.Cross without crown (on ribbon)	1800.00
1010.Silver Merit Cross 1908-1918	600.00
1011.Silver Medal 1908-1918	165.00
1012.Bronze Medal 1908-1918	140.00

Type III-1910-1916-enameled-in middle a rose

1013.Collar	rare
1014.Grand Honor Cross (worn on chest)	3750.00
1015.II Class with crown	2950.00
1016.III Class without crown	1650.00
1017.Silver Merit Cross with crown-1910-1918	550.00
1018.Golden Medal 1910-1918	320.00

Type IV-1916-1918-enameled-in the middle a swallow

1019.Collar	rare
1020.Grand Honor Cross	2750.00
1021.II Class	1250.00
1022.III Class	1750.00

1023.Golden Medal with swords	500.00
1024.Silver Medal with swords	220.00
1025.Bronze Medal with swords	200.00
1026.Bertha Order-badge	rare

Order of Arts & Science-also known as the Lippe Rose

1027.I Class	800.00
1028.II Class	500.00
1029.III Class	250.00

Civil Decorations

1030.Golden Merit Medal-type I-1869-1877-gold	1000.00
1031.Silver Merit Medal	275.00
1032.Golden Merit Medal-type II-1888-1918-silver/gilt	200.00
1033.Silver Merit Medal	175.00
1034.Civil Merit Medal	165.00
1035.Merit Cross for Ladies	60.00
1036.Merit Medal for Ladies	40.00
1037.Commemorative Medal for the Regent Ernst-1897	100.00
1038.Commemorative Medal-Speech from the Throne-1905	200.00
1039.Lifesaving Medal-1888-1905-initials "E.W."	225.00
1040.Lifesaving Medal-1905-1918-without initials	185.00

Military Decorations

1041.Military Merit Medal-type I-1832-1914	110.00
1042.Military Merit Medal-type II-1914-1918	110.00
1043.Campaign Commemorative Medal 1866	225.00
1044.War Honor Cross for Bravery 1914-1918-pinback	250.00
1045.War Merit Cross 1914-1918	50.00
1046.War Honor Medal	65.00
1047.Officers' 25 Year Long Service Cross	225.00
1048.Long Service Bar-20 years	175.00
1049.Long Service Bar-10 years	120.00
1050.Veterans' Merit Cross	175.00

LUBECK

Civil Decorations

1051.Lifesaving Medal (not wearable-table medal)	400.00
1052.Lifesaving Medal-on ribbon for wearing	300.00

Military Decorations

1053.Hanseatic Cross 1914	65.00
1054.Golden Long Service Cross for 25 years	rare
1055.Silver Long Service Cross-Officers' 20 years & for N.C.O.'s for 25 years	500.00
1056.Golden Long Service bar-20 years	350.00
1057.Silver Long Service bar-15 years	250.00

MAINZ
Civil Decorations
1058.Golden Merit Medal-silver/gilt   rare
1059.Silver Merit Medal   rare

Military Decorations
1060.Golden Bravery Medal   rare
1061.Silver Bravery Medal   rare
1062.Bronze Bravery Medal   rare
1063.Mainz Militia-Silver Loyalty/Bravery Medal-1799-1800   1250.00

MECKLENBERG-SCHWERIN
Order of the Wendish Crown
1064.Collar   12,000.00
1065.Grand Cross with brass crown   5000.00
1066.Grand Cross with brass crown & swords   rare
1067.Grand Cross badge with gold crown-gold   3200.00
1068.Grand Cross badge with gold crown-silver/gilt   2500.00
1069.Grand Cross badge with gold crown-gold-with swords   6500.00
1070.Grand Cross breast star-brass crown-silver/gilt   2000.00
1071.Grand Cross breast star-brass crown-with swords   3500.00
1072.Grand Cross breast star-gold crown   2000.00
1073.Grand Cross breast star-gold crown-with swords   3250.00
1074.Commander-gold   2000.00
1075.Commander breast star   2000.00
1076.Knight-gold   650.00
1077.Knight-silver/gilt   550.00
1078.Knight-with swords-gold   1200.00
1079.Golden Merit Cross-gold   1200.00
1080.Golden Merit Cross-silver/gilt   220.00
1081.Silver Merit Cross   200.00

Order of the Griffin
1082.Grand Cross badge   650.00
1083.Grand Cross breast star   900.00
1084.Commander   400.00
1085.Commander breast star   750.00
1086.Officer-pinback badge   375.00
1087.Knight-with crown-silver/gilt   300.00
1088.Knight   200.00

Civil Decorations
1089.Golden Merit Medal-Duke Friedrich Franz 1798-1815   rare
1090.Silver Medal   750.00
1091.Golden Merit Medal-Grand Duke Friedrich Franz 1815-72   rare
1092.Silver Medal   500.00
1093.Golden Merit Medal-Friedrich Franz II-1859-1872-
       with sideburns & mustache   1450.00
1094.Silver Medal   225.00
1095.Bronze Medal-gilt   200.00
1096.Golden Merit Medal-Friedrich Franz II-1872-1883-
       old head with beard-gold   1750.00

1097.Silver Medal	175.00
1098.Bronze Medal	150.00
1099.Golden Merit Medal-1872-1918-beard-gold	1250.00
1100.Silver Medal	160.00
1101.Bronze Medal	125.00
1102.Bronze Medal-Friedrich Franz IV-1897-1918	110.00
1103.Silver Merit Medal-small civil type	125.00
1104.Flood Aid Medal-1888	200.00
1105.Commemorative Medal-Friedrich Franz III-1897	60.00
1106.Commemorative Medal-African Expedition-1907-1908	800.00
1107.Golden Medal for Arts & Science-head of Friedrich Franz I-1815-1918	2200.00
1108.Silver Medal	300.00
1109.Golden Medal-head of Friedrich Franz II-after 1872	2200.00
1110.Silver Medal	300.00

Military Decorations

1111.Golden Military Merit Medal-oval-1813-1815	2200.00
1112.Silver Medal	575.00
1113.Small Silver Merit Medal	60.00
1114.Campaign Medal-1808-1815 (awarded 1841)	125.00
1115.same-with jubilee bar 1813-1863	285.00
1116.Campaign Medal 1848-1849	125.00

Military Merit Cross-I Class pinback; II Class on ribbon; dated

1117.I Class-1848	rare
1118.II Class	300.00
1119.I Class-1849	rare
1120.II Class	300.00
1121.I Class-1859	rare
1122.II Class	rare
1123.I Class-1864	600.00
1124.II Class	300.00
1125.II Class-ladies-bow ribbon	500.00
1126.I Class-1866	450.00
1127.II Class	175.00
1128.II Class-ladies-bow ribbon	400.00
1129.I Class-1870	300.00
1130.II Class	125.00
1131.II Class-ladies-bow ribbon	300.00
1132.I Class-1877	rare
1133.II Class	rare
1134.II Class-1900	500.00
1135.II Class-without date	300.00
1136.I Class-1914	100.00
1137.II Class	35.00
1138.II Class-ladies-bow ribbon	200.00

(Note: Values for the I Class are based on the normal flat type issue. The vaulted or arched type will command a small premium.)

1139.Friedrich Franz Cross-1917-1918	125.00
1140.Friedrich Franz-Alexandra Cross-1912-1918-silver	200.00

Long Service Awards

1141.Officers' Long Service Cross-gold-65 years; 60 years; 55 years; 50 years; 45 years; 40 years	all rare
1142.same-35 years-gold	1600.00
1143.same-30 years-gold	750.00
1144.same-25 years-gold	300.00
1145.same-25 years-gilt	210.00
1146.Long Service Cross-XXV years-1841-1868	200.00
1147.same-XX years	125.00
1148.same-XV years	85.00
1149.same-X years	70.00
1150.Long Service Cross-XXI years-1868-1913	125.00
1151.same-XV years	85.00
1152.same-IX years	50.00
1153.Long Service Cross-15 years-1913-1918	50.00
1154.same-12 years	55.00
1155.Landwehr (reserve) Decoration-bar	100.00
1156.Landwehr Decoration-medal	45.00
1157.War Veterans' Medal	75.00

MECKLENBURG-STRELITZ

Order of the Wendish Crown

1158.Collar	rare
1159.Grand Cross badge with brass crown-gold	8000.00
1160.Grand Cross badge with brass crown & with swords	rare
1161.Grand Cross badge with gold crown-gold	5000.00
1162.Grand Cross badge with gold crown & with swords	rare
1163.Grand Cross breast star-brass crown	4000.00
1164.Grand Cross breast star-brass crown & with swords	8000.00
1165.Grand Cross breast star-gold crown	3750.00
1166.Grand Cross breast star-gold crown & with swords	4250.00
1167.Commander-gold	3500.00
1168.Commander breast star	2750.00
1169.Knight-gold	1000.00
1170.Golden Merit Cross-silver/gilt	300.00
1171.Silver Merit Cross	250.00

Civil Decorations

1172.Golden Merit Medal-cipher "AF"-1904-1914-silver/gilt	200.00
1173.Silver Medal	110.00
1174.Bronze Medal	95.00
1175.Golden Medal-Adolf Friedrich-silver/gilt 1914-18	195.00
1176.Silver Medal	110.00
1177.Bronze Medal	65.00
1178.Golden medal for the Golden Jubilee of the marriage of the Grand Duke & Duchess-gold	900.00
1179.same-but in silver/gilt	300.00
1180.same-but for Diamond Jubilee-silver/gilt	300.00
1181.same-silver	150.00
1182.same-bronze	110.00
1183.Adolf Friedrich Commemorative Medal 1914	110.00
1184.Silver Lifesaving Medal	200.00

1185.Order for Arts & Science-silver/gilt	800.00
1186.Order for Arts & Science-silver	550.00
1187.Golden Cross for Female Staff for 40 years	450.00
1188.Golden Cross for Female Satff for 25 years	300.00
1189.Silver Cross for Female Staff for 40 years	250.00
1190.Silver Cross for female Staff for 25 years	200.00

Military Decorations

1191.War Service Cross "FW" 1871-1914-"Für Tapferkeit"	255.00
1192.same-legend "Tapfer und Treu"-gallantry & loyalty	100.00
1193.War Service Cross I Class 1914-1916-silver	400.00
1194.same-1917-1918-but silvered	240.00
1195.same-II Class-"AF"-1914-16-silver	280.00
1196.same-1916-1918-but silvered	210.00
1197.same-II Class-"Tapfer und treu"-1914-1916-silver	110.00
1198.same-1916-1924-but silvered	70.00
1199.same-for ladies-1915-1917-silver	300.00
1200.same-but silvered	210.00
1201.Adolf Friedrich Cross	125.00

Military Long Service Awards

1202.Officers' 25 year Long Service Cross-1846-1872-gold	500.00
1203.same-but gilt	185.00
1204.Long Service Cross-I Class 25 years	165.00
1205.II Class-18 years	165.00
1206.III Class-12 years	140.00
1207.I Class-21 years-1869-1924-silver	175.00
1208.II Class-15 years-bronze	140.00
1209.III Class-9 years-bronze	70.00
1210.I Class-15 years 1913-1924-silvered	85.00
1211.II Class-12 years-bronze	65.00
1212.III Class-9 years-bronze	40.00
1213.Landwehr Decoration (reserve)-bar	125.00
1214.same-but medal	50.00
1215.War Veterans' Association Medal	150.00

NASSAU (See also Luxembourg)
House Order of the Golden Lion

1216.Badge	rare
1217.Breast star	rare

Merit Order of Adolph of Nassau

1218.Grand Cross badge	2000.00
1219.Grand Cross badge with swords	2700.00
1220.Grand Cross breast star	1350.00
1221.Grand Cross breast star with swords	2200.00
1222.Commander-gold	1375.00
1223.Commander with swords	1500.00
1224.Commander breast star	1350.00
1225.Commander breast star with swords	1750.00
1226.Knight	450.00
1227.Knight with swords	500.00

1228.IV Class	400.00
1229.IV Class with swords	225.00
1230.Silver Merit Cross	110.00
1231.Silver Merit Cross with swords	140.00

Civil Decorations

1232.Golden Merit Medal-Duke Friedrich August	rare
1233.Silver Medal (not wearable)	1000.00
1234.Silver Medal-Duke Wilhelm	1000.00
1235.Golden Merit Medal-Duke Adolph-young head	1800.00
1236.Silver Medal	400.00
1237.Silver Medal-Duke Adolph-old head	600.00
1238.Lifesaving Medal-Duke Adolph-young head	1000.00
1239.Lifesaving Medal-Duke Adolph-old head	950.00
1240.Golden Medal for Arts & Science	1500.00
1241.Silver Medal	600.00

Military Decorations

1242.Golden Bravery Medal-Duke Friedrich I. August	rare
1243.Silver Bravery Medal	600.00
1244.Golden Bravery Medal-Duke Wilhelm	rare
1245.Silver Bravery Medal	650.00
1246.Golden Bravery Medal-Duke Adolph	rare
1247.Silver Bravery	600.00
1248.Waterloo Medal-gold	rare
1249.Waterloo Medal-silver	250.00
1250.Medal for Eckernforde 1849	650.00
1251.Austrian War Medal 1866-silver	225.00

Military Long Service Decorations

1252.Officers' Cross-50 years	2800.00
1253.Officers' Cross-25 years	300.00
1254.Enlisted Men's Cross-22 years	300.00
1255.Enlisted Men's Cross-16 years	240.00
1256.Enlisted Men's Cross-10 years	185.00

OLDENBURG

House & Merit Order of Peter Frederick Louis

1257.Collar	rare
1258.Golden Grand Cross badge-gold	2750.00
1259.Golden Grand Cross badge with swords-gold	4000.00
1260.Golden Grand Cross badge with swords on ring	3000.00
1261.Golden Grand Cross badge with swords & wreath	rare
1262.Golden Grand Cross breast star	600.00
1263.Golden Grand Cross breast star with swords	1150.00
1264.Golden Grand Cross breast star with swords above	1250.00
1265.Golden Grand Cross breast star with swords & wreath	rare
1266.Grand Cross badge	1250.00
1267.Grand Cross badge with swords	1450.00
1268.Grand Cross badge with swords on ring	2350.00
1269.Grand Cross badge with swords & wreath	rare

1270.Grand Cross breast star	650.00
1271.Grand Cross breast star with swords	1750.00
1272.Grand Cross breast star with swords above	1550.00
1273.Grand Cross breast star with swords & wreath	rare
1274.Grand Commander Cross-silver/gilt	1150.00
1275.Grand Commander Cross with swords-silver/gilt	1550.00
1276.Grand Commander Cross-swords on ring-silver/gilt	2000.00
1277.Grand Commander Cross breast star	650.00
1278.Grand Commander Cross breast star with swords	1350.00
1279.Grand Commander Cross breast star with swords above	1650.00
1280.Commander-gold	1200.00
1281.Commander with swords-gold	2200.00
1282.Commander with swords on ring-gold	1950.00
1283.Commander with swords & wreath	rare
1284.Officer-gold	1100.00
1285.Officer with swords	1200.00
1286.Officer with swords above	1200.00
1287.Officer with swords & swords above	2500.00
1288.Knight I Class-gold	650.00
1289.Knight I Class with swords-gold	1000.00
1290.Knight I Class with swords on ring	1500.00
1291.Knight I Class with swords & wreath	rare
1292.Knight II Class with crown	450.00
1293.Knight II Class with crown & swords	750.00
1294.Knight II Class with crown & swords on ring	rare
1295.Knight II Class	300.00
1296.Knight II Class with swords	550.00
1297.Honor Cross I Class with crown	300.00
1298.Honor Cross I Class with crown & swords	rare
1299.Honor Cross I Class with crown & swords on ring	rare

(Note: According to research only three of item 1299 were prepared, and none presented.)

1300.Honor Cross I Class	175.00
1301.Honor Cross I Class with swords	550.00
1302.Honor Cross I Class with swords on ring	1250.00
1303.Honor Cross II Class	200.00
1304.Honor Cross II Class with swords	300.00
1305.Honor Cross II Class with swords on ring	600.00
1306.Honor Cross III Class	185.00
1307.Honor Cross III with swords	300.00
1308.Golden Medal	275.00
1309.Silver Medal	220.00
1310.Bronze Medal	140.00
1311.Insignia of Order Official	rare

Civil Decorations
1312. Golden Merit Medal-1813	2000.00
1313. Silver Medal	500.00
1314. Commemorative Medal-Grand Duke Friedrich August	165.00
1315. Lifesaving Medal	400.00
1316. same-but with an additional award bar on ribbon	rare
1317. Golden Merit Medal for Art-Nicholas Frederick Peter	1850.00
1318. same-but silver/gilt	850.00
1319. Silver Medal for Art	rare
1320. Gold Medal-I Class-Friedrich August	rare
1321. Golden Medal-II Class	400.00
1322. Fire Service Merit Medal	150.00
1323. Red Cross Medal	400.00
1324. Loyal Service in Work (factory)	115.00

Military Decorations
1325. Campaign Medal-1815	450.00
1326. Commemorative Medal-1848-1849	300.00
1327. Commemorative Medal-Campaigns of 1866	70.00
1328. Silver Commemorative Medal-1870-71	315.00
1329. Bronze-1870-71	200.00
1330. Merit Cross-Sacrifice & Devotion to Duty-1871-74	250.00
1331. Friedrich August Cross I Class-1914	75.00
1332. Friedrich August Cross II Class-1914	35.00
1333. same-combat/frontline service bar "Vor dem Feinde"	75.00
1334. War Merit Medal-1916-18-iron	95.00

Military Long Service Awards
1335. Officers' Cross for 25 years-bronze/gilt	300.00
1336. Silver Cross-25 years	200.00
1337. I Class bar-18 years	210.00
1338. II Class bar-12 years	140.00
1339. III Class bar-9 years	110.00
1340. Gendarmerie Cross-18 years	350.00
1341. Gendarmerie Medal-12 years	325.00
1342. Gendarmerie Medal-9 years	300.00
1343. War Veterans Merit Cross-silver	150.00

PRUSSIA
Order of the Black Eagle
1344. Collar	rare
1345. Cross of the Order-gold	10,000.00
1346. Breast Star of the Order	3500.00

(Note: Copies of this Order exist in varying degrees of quality.)

Merit Order of the Prussian Crown-all insignia extremely rare.

Pour Le Mérite-military
1347. Grand Cross badge	rare
1348. Grand Cross breast star	rare
1349. Neck badge-gold	6000.00
1350. Neck badge-silver/gilt	3200.00

1351.Neck badge-with crown-gold   6500.00
1352.Neck badge-with oakleaves-gold   6200.00
1353.Neck badge-with crown & oakleaves-gold   rare
(Note: The above values are for World War I era items. Earlier pieces will command much more. However, since this is one of the most heavily copied pieces, great caution should be exercised. Some copies are very obvious from the last 10-20 years in a dark blue enamel, with a very garish gilt look to them. Other copies, including gold ones are much more dangerous. Even the existance of hallmarks is no guarantee of genuineness. This award is frequently referred to as the "Blue Max", and is labeled as Germany's highest award to flyers in World War I. However, it was a Prussian, as opposed to an all-German award, and was awarded to Officers as such, not just flyers.)

Pour Le Mérite for Arts & Sciences
1354.Badge in gold   6000.00
1355.Badge in silver/gilt   3000.00
(Note: This award was revived by the German Federal Republic after World War II in the same design.)

Order of the Red Eagle
Type I-1792-1810
1356.Badge   rare
1357.Breast star   rare

Type II-1810-1846-lilac eagle
1358.I Class badge   5500.00
1359.I Class badge with oakleaves   6600.00
1360.I Class breast star   rare
1361.I Class breast star with oakleaves   rare
1362.II Class badge   4000.00
1362.II Class badge with oakleaves   4400.00
1364.II Class breast star   rare
1365.II Class breast star with oakleaves   rare
1366.III Class   500.00
1367.III Class with bow   600.00
1368.IV Class-silver   350.00

Type III-1846-1918-brick red eagle
1369.Collar   rare
1370.Grand Cross badge with crown-gold   9500.00
1371.Grand Cross badge with crown & oakleaves-gold   14,500.00
1372.Grand Cross badge with crown, oakleaves & swords   10,000.00
1373.same-but with swords on ring   9500.00
1374.Grand Cross badge with crown & swords-gold   10,000.00
1375.same-but also with swords on ring   rare
1376.Grand Cross badge with oakleaves-gold   6000.00
1377.Grand Cross badge with oakleaves & swords-gold   9000.00
1378.same-but also with swords on ring-gold   rare
1379.Grand Cross badge with oakleaves & swords on ring   8000.00
1380.Grand Cross badge with swords-gold   6000.00
1381.Grand Cross badge with swords on ring (copies exist)   6500.00
1382.Grand Cross badge-gold (copies exist)   4000.00

1383.Grand Cross breast star with oakleaves	2500.00
1384.Grand Cross breast star with oakleaves & swords	2600.00
1385.same-but also with swords above	rare
1386.Grand Cross breast star with oakleaves & swords above	3000.00
1387.Grand Cross breast star with swords	2400.00
1388.Grand Cross breast star with swords & swords above	3250.00
1389.Grand Cross breast star with swords above	3500.00
1390.Grand Cross breast star	2000.00
1391.I Class badge with crown-gold	3250.00
1392.I Class badge with crown & oakleaves-gold	3750.00
1393.I Class badge with crown, oakleaves & swords-gold	4000.00
1394.same-but also with swords on ring	rare
1395.I Class badge with crown,oakleaves & swords on ring	4000.00
1396.I Class badge with crown & swords	3200.00
1397.same-but also with swords on ring	rare
1398.I Class badge with crown & swords on ring-gold	3300.00
1399.I Class badge with oakleaves-gold	1650.00
1400.I Class badge with oakleaves & swords-gold	2500.00
1401.same-but also with swords on ring-gold	6000.00
1402.I Class badge with oakleaves & swords on ring-gold	2200.00
1403.I Class badge with swords-gold	2000.00
1404.I Class badge with swords & swords on ring-gold	2500.00
1405.I Class badge with swords on ring-gold	2200.00
1406.I Class badge-gold	1650.00
1407.I Class badge for non-Christians	rare
1408.I Class breast star with oakleaves	1600.00
1409.I Class breast star with oakleaves & swords	2000.00
1410.same-but also with swords above-gold	rare
1411.I Class breast star with oakleaves & swords above	2000.00
1412.I Class breast star with swords	1750.00
1413.I Class breast star with swords & swords above	1500.00
1414.I Class breast star with swords above	1500.00
1415.I Class breast star	1700.00
1416.II Class badge with crown-gold	1600.00
1417.II Class badge with crown & oakleaves-gold	2000.00
1418.II Class badge with crown, oakleaves & swords-gold	2800.00
1419.same-but also with swords on ring-gold	3200.00
1420.II Class badge with crown, oakleaves & swords on ring	3500.00
1421.II Class badge with crown & swords-gold	3000.00
1422.II Class badge with crown, swords & swords on ring	3000.00
1423.II Class badge with crown & swords on ring-gold	3750.00
1424.II Class badge with oakleaves-gold	1500.00
1425.II Class badge with oakleaves & swords	2000.00
1426.II Class badge with oakleaves, swords,swords on ring	2200.00
1427.II Class badge with oakleaves & swords on ring-gold	2000.00
1428.II Class badge with swords-gold	1500.00
1429.II Class badge with swords & swords on ring-gold	2200.00
1430.II Class badge with swords on ring-gold	1500.00
1431.II Class badge-gold	1200.00
1432.II Class badge for non-Christians	rare

1433.II Cl breast star with oakleaves	1750.00
1434.II Class breast star with oakleaves & swords	1600.00
1435.same-but also with swords above	1800.00
1436.II Class breast star with oakleaves & swords above	2500.00
1437.II Class breast star with swords	1600.00
1438.II Class breast star with swords & swords above	2700.00
1439.II Class breast star with swords above	1600.00
1440.II Class breast star	1500.00
1441.III Class breast badge with crown-gold	1600.00
1442.III Class breast badge with crown & bow-gold	1400.00
1443.III Class breast badge with crown & swords	1600.00
1444.same-but also with swords on ring	rare
1445.III Class badge with crown & swords on ring	rare
1446.III Class badge with bow-gold	600.00
1447.III Class badge with bow & swords-gold	1100.00
1448.III Class badge with bow,swords & swords on ring	rare
1449.III Class badge with bow & swords on ring-gold	rare
1450.III Class badge with swords-gold	900.00
1451.III Class badge with swords & swords on ring-gold	rare
1452.III Class badge with swords on ring-gold	rare
1453.III Class badge-gold	600.00
1454.III Class badge for non-Christians	rare
1455.IV Class badge-smooth,flat arms-no enamel	250.00
1456.IV Class badge-smooth,flat arms-centre enamel	350.00
1457.same-but also with swords	450.00
1458.IV Class badge with crown-raised, stippled arms	350.00
1459.same-but also with swords	600.00
1460.IV Class badge with swords	400.00
1461.IV Class-stippled arms	175.00
1462.IV Class for non-Christians	rare
1463.Medal-type I-1842-1871-FWIV-silver	1350.00
1464.Medal-type II-1871-1908-W-silver	60.00
1465.Medal-type II-silver/gilt	110.00
1466.Medal-type III-1908-1916-gilt/copper	110.00
1467.Medal-type III-1908-1916-gilt/zinc	75.00

Order of the Crown-type I-1861-1888-small rounded crown on obverse centre. Also awarded with: 50, 60, 70 year buttons on ring; Maltese Cross; diamonds (brilliants).

1468.I Class badge	6000.00
1469.I Class badge with swords	6600.00
1470.I Class badge with swords & swords on ring	rare
1471.I Class badge with swords on ring	rare
1472.I Class breast star	4800.00
1473.I Class breast star with swords	5500.00
1474.I Class breast star with swords & swords above	rare
1475.I Class breast star with swords above	rare

1476.II Class badge	2600.00
1477.II Class badge with swords	2250.00
1478.II Class badge with swords & swords on ring	2850.00
1479.II Class badge with swords on ring	2850.00
1480.II Class breast star	2250.00
1481.II Class breast star with swords	2500.00
1482.II Class breast star with swords & swords above	rare
1483.II Class breast star with swords above	rare
1484.III Class badge	500.00
1485.III Class badge with swords	925.00
1486.III Class badge with swords & swords on ring	rare
1487.III Class badge with swords on ring	rare
1488.III Class badge with red cross	rare
1489.IV Class badge	300.00
1490.IV Class badge with swords	400.00
1491.IV Class badge with red cross	rare

Order of the Crown-type II-1888-1918-large crown obverse centre

1492.I Class badge	1800.00
1493.I Class badge with swords-gold	2200.00
1494.I Class badge with swords-silver	1250.00
1495.I Class badge with swords & swords on ring	2800.00
1496.I Class badge with swords on ring	3000.00
1497.I Class breast star	1150.00
1498.I Class breast star with swords	1750.00
1499.I Class breast star with swords & swords above	rare
1500.I Class breast star with swords above	3200.00
1501.II Class badge-gold	725.00
1502.II Class badge with swords-gold	950.00
1503.II Class badge with swords-silver/gilt	600.00
1504.II Class badge with swords & swords on ring	rare
1505.II Class badge with swords on ring	rare
1506.II Class breast star	1000.00
1507.II Class breast star with swords	1500.00
1508.II Class breast star with swords & swords above	rare
1509.II Class breast star with swords above	rare
1510.III Class badge-gold	275.00
1511.III Class badge-silver/gilt	175.00
1512.III Class badge with swords-gold	600.00
1513.III Class badge with swords & swords on ring	rare
1514.III Class badge with swords on ring-gold	rare
1515.III Class badge with red cross-gold	650.00
1516.IV Class badge	125.00
1517.IV Class badge with swords	250.00
1518.IV Class badge with red cross	300.00
1519.Medal-gilt	100.00

House Order of Hohenzollern (See also Hohenzollern & Rumania.)

1520.Collar	rare
1521.Cross of the Grand Commander-gold	6000.00
1522.Cross of the Grand Commander with swords-gold	6650.00
1523.same-but also with swords on ring	8500.00
1524.Eagle Badge of the Grand Commander	800.00
1525.Grand Commander breast Star	5000.00
1526.Grand Commander breast star with swords	6000.00
1527.Grand Commander breast star with swords above	rare
1528.Commander	1250.00
1529.Commander with swords	1750.00
1530.Commander with swords on ring	4000.00
1531.Commander breast star	1500.00
1532.same-but also with swords above	rare
1533.Eagle of Commander	600.00
1534.Knight-gold	650.00
1535.Knight with swords-gold	675.00
1536.Knight with swords-silver/gilt	275.00
1537.same-but also with swords on ring	rare
1538.same-but only with swords on ring	rare
1539.Knight's Eagle-gold	1000.00
1540.Inhaber Cross	550.00
1541.Inhaber Cross with swords	500.00
1542.Inhaber Eagle	200.00
1543.same-but special type without enamel	650.00

Johanniter Order (Order of St John)-[Knights of Malta] (See also Great Britain, Austria-Hungary etc.)

1544.Commander Cross with crown (Rechtsritter)-silver/gilt	600.00
1545.Commander Cross without crown (Ehrenritter)-silver/gilt	500.00

Louise Order

Types of 1813-1814; 1848-1849; 1865 all rare

1914-18 type

1546.Grand Cross badge	rare
1547.Grand Cross breast star	rare
1548.Order Cross-I Class-gold	rare
1549.Order Cross-I Class-golden crown-silver/gilt	3250.00
1550.Order Cross-I Class-silver crown-silver	3000.00
1551.Order Cross-II Class-silver-enamel centres	1200.00

General Honor Decorations

1552.Golden Medal-1st striking-1810-1817	rare
1553.Silver Medal	rare
1554.Silver Cross I Class-1814-1830	rare
1555.Silver Medal II Class-1814-1918 (FWIII)	45.00
(This medal is found on several ribbons.)	
1556.Silver Medal-50 year button	rare
(This medal is also found with 60, 65 and 70 year buttons.)	
1557.Silver Medal with red cross	225.00
1558.General Honor Decoration in gold	1000.00
1559.same-but with 50 year button (see also 1556)	1000.00

1560.Cross with crown	400.00
1561.Cross without crown	65.00
1562.Cross with 50 year button (see also 1556)	225.00
1563.General Honor Decoration-bronze	65.00
1564.same-but in war metal	45.00
1565.same-but in zinc	45.00

Civilian Decorations

1566.Gold Merit Cross with crown-gilt	300.00
1567.Gold Merit Cross without crown-gilt	100.00
1568.Silver Merit Cross with crown	250.00
1569.Silver Merit Cross without crown	100.00
1570.Ladies' Gold Merit Cross-royal crown-silver/gilt	1400.00
1571.same-with Imperial crown	1400.00
1572.same-silver-royal crown	1000.00
1573.same-silver-Imperial crown	1000.00
1574.Olberg Cross-silver/gilt	800.00
1575.Coronation Medal 1861	120.00
1576.Ladies' Cross 1870-1871(resembles Iron Cross)	400.00
1577.Golden Wedding Medal-I Class-1879	600.00
1578.Golden Wedding Medal-II Class	400.00
1579.Golden Wedding Medal-III Class	300.00
1580.Royal Household Decoration for Ladies	275.00
1581.Jerusalem Cross 1898	500.00
1582.Silver Wedding Decoration 1906	250.00
1583.Lifesaving Medal-large, non-wearable type	550.00
1584.Lifesaving Medal "Koenig"	75.00
1585.Lifesaving Medal "König"-three strikings	75.00
1586.Red Cross Decoration-I Class	300.00
1587.Red Cross Decoration-II Class-silver/enamel	55.00
1588.Red Cross Decoration-III Class-bronze	20.00
1589.same-but in war metal or zinc	15.00
1590.same-in steel	20.00
1591.Red Cross Decorations with colonial campaign bars	175.00
1592.Fire Service Merit Decoration-bronze	50.00
1593.same-but in war metal	60.00
1594.Railroad 40 year Long Service Badge	60.00
1595.Railroad 25 year Long Service Badge	30.00

Military Decorations

Iron Cross-1813

1596.Breast Star	one
1597.Grand Cross badge (neck badge)	rare
1598.I Class-pin back	3000.00
1599.II Class	1500.00
1600.Kulm Cross	2000.00
(Note: Copies exist, many made in the last 20 years.)	

Iron Cross-1870

1601.Grand Cross badge	rare
1602.I Class	2000.00

1603.II Class   300.00
1604.II Class with 25 year oakleaves   450.00
(Note: Copies exist, many recently made. There are several varieties of the 25 year oakleaves, with different means of attachment.)

Iron Cross-1914
1605.Breast Star   one
1606.Grand Cross badge   rare
1607.I Class   from 125.00
1608.II Class   35.00
1609.Commemorative Clasp for 1870 Iron Cross   500.00
(Note: There are many variations of the 1914 I Class Iron Cross. Some are arched or vaulted; some are screwback with a plate. Add 50% for these varieties. Others were struck in the 1920's and 1930's, for wearing-but not in silver. These were allowed to be worn during the Nazi period so they had some official standing.)

Military Merit & Campaign Awards
1610.Golden Medal-I type-1793-1797-dated 1793   rare
1611.Silver Medal   rare
1612.Golden Medal-II type-1797-1814-no date   rare
1613.Silver Medal   rare
1614.Military Honor Decoration-I Class Cross-type I-
       1814-1847-35mm   rare
1615.same-type II-1848-1864-38mm   850.00
1616.same-type III-1864-1918   600.00
1617.Military Honor Decoration II Cl-medal   75.00
1618.Military Merit Cross-gold   2000.00
1619.Military Merit Cross-silver/gilt   750.00
(The Military Merit Cross was the highest award for bravery in the Prussian army to enlisted men, as they were not eligible for the Pour Le Mérite, which was an officers' decoration.)
1620.War Merit Medal-type I-FWIIIR   100.00
1621.War Merit Medal-type II-WR   75.00
Campaign Medals-1813-1815-combat
Type I-cross on obverse has squared off arms
1622.1813   65.00
1623.1814   75.00
1624.1813-14   75.00
1625.1815   100.00
Type II-cross on obverse has rounded off arms
1626.1813   85.00
1627.1814   75.00
1628.1813-14   110.00
Campaign Medals 1813-1815-non-combat-iron
1629.1813   200.00
1630.1814   175.00
1631.1813-14   225.00
1632.1815   125.00
1633.Commemorative Medal 1813-1815-1863-combat   75.00
1634.same-for non-combattents   250.00
1635.same-for Ladies of the Louise Order   300.00
1636.Neufchatel Commemorative Medal 1832   175.00

1637.Commemorative Medal for the 25th Anniversary of Frederick William IV as honorary head of the Imperial Russian Kaluga Infantry Regiment-gold	1900.00
1638.Hohenzollern Campaign Medal 1848-1849-combat	45.00
1639.same-for non-combattents	250.00
1640.Duppel Storm Cross 1864-Danish War	75.00
1641.same-for reserve troops	65.00
1642.same-for doctors & clergy	250.00
1643.Alsen Cross 1864	75.00
1644.same-for reserve troops	95.00
1645.same-for doctors & clergy	225.00
1646.Campaign Medal 1864-combat (see also Austria)	50.00
1647.same-non-combattents	175.00
1648.Koniggratz Cross 1866	40.00
1649.Der Main Armee Cross 1866	50.00
1650.Treuen Kriegern Cross 1866	65.00
1651.Non-combat Cross 1866	125.00

Hanoverian Regimental Commemorative Medals

1652.19 Dezember 1803/19 Dezember 1903	200.00
1653.21 April 1804/21 April 1904	350.00
1654.25 November 1805/25 November 1905	300.00
1655.10 Dezember 1805/10 Dezember 1905	285.00
1656.24 Marz 1813/18 Juni 1913	225.00
1657.26 Marz 1813/26 Marz 1913	200.00
1658.27 November 1813/3 August 1913	300.00
1659.27 November 1813/27 November 1913	220.00
1660.30 November 1813/16 August 1913	300.00

Commemorative Medals of the Electoral Hesse Regiments

1661.1813/22 November/1913	350.00
1662.1813/23 November/1913	350.00
1663.1813/30 November/1913	285.00
1664.1813/5 Dezember/1913	350.00

1665.War Aid Service Cross-1915-war metal	25.00

Royal Household & Aide-de-Camp Badges-with royal cipher. As these appear to be much rarer than previous believed their separate listing is being deleted, with all being considered   rare

Long Service Decorations-Officers-XXV Year Long Service Cross

1666.type I-flat arms-smooth-1825	275.00
1667.type II-flat arms-stippled appearance-1870	150.00
1668.type III-raised arms-stippled appearance	25.00

Long Service Awards-Enlisted Men
Type I-1825-1913

1669.I Class bar-21 years	60.00
1670.II Class bar-15 years	50.00
1671.III Class bar-9 years	25.00

GERMANY-Reuss

Type II-1913-1918
1672.I Class cross-15 years	20.00
1673.II Class medal-12 years	20.00
1674.III Class medal-9 years	15.00

Reserve Decorations (Landwehr)
1675.I Class cross-XX years	50.00
1676.II Class-type I-bar	20.00
1677.II Class-type II-medal	15.00

REUSS-Old & Young Lines Combined
Honor Cross
1678.I Class badge with crown	1300.00
1679.I Class badge with crown & swords	1800.00
1680.I Class badge-gold	1100.00
1681.I Class badge with swords-gold	1800.00
1682.Officer Cross	1000.00
1683.Officer Cross with swords-gold	1400.00
1684.Officer Cross with date "1894"	rare
1685.II Class badge with crown	800.00
1686.II Class badge with crown & swords-gold	900.00
1687.II Class badge	600.00
1688.II Class badge with swords	700.00
1689.III Class badge with crown	250.00
1690.III Class badge with crown & swords	450.00
1691.III Class badge	225.00
1692.III Class badge with swords	300.00
1693.IV Class badge with crown	325.00
1694.IV Class badge with crown & swords	500.00
1695.IV Class badge	275.00
1696.IV Class badge with swords	300.00
1697.Golden Merit Medal with crown	100.00
1698.Golden Merit Medal with crown & swords	115.00
1699.Golden Merit Medal	85.00
1700.Golden Merit Medal with swords	95.00
1701.Silver Merit Medal	60.00
1702.Silver Merit Medal with swords	65.00

Civil Decorations
1703.Merit Cross for Arts & Science-I Class-silver/gilt	600.00
1704.Merit Cross II Class-silver	500.00
1705.Golden Medal for Arts & Science-silver/gilt	225.00
1706.Silver Medal	185.00

Military Decorations
1707.Honor Campaign Cross 1814-1815	650.00
1708.Commemorative Cross for Eckernförde	600.00

1709.War Merit Cross 1914	650.00
1710.Medal for Sacrificial Service in War-1915-1918	60.00

Long Service Awards

1711.Officers' Cross for 25 years	325.00
1712.Officers' Cross for 25 years with swords	400.00
1713.Enlisted Long Service Cross for 25 years	250.00
1714.Enlisted Long Service Cross for 25 years with swords	300.00
1715.Enlisted Long Service Decoration-I Class-15 years	125.00
1716.Enlisted Long Service Decoration-II Class-12 years	110.00
1717.Enlisted Long Service Decoration-III Class-9 years	100.00

REUSS-Senior Line
Civil Decorations

1718.Merit Cross I Class	500.00
1719.Merit Cross II Class	225.00
1720.Merit Cross III Class	175.00
1721.Merit Cross IV Class	125.00
1722.Silver Honor Medal for Loyalty & Merit	100.00
1723.same-but with swords on obverse	250.00
1724.same-but with swords on ring	275.00
1725.Golden Merit Medal "Merito ac Dignitati"-silver/gilt	210.00
1726.Silver Medal	160.00
1727.Fire Service Decoration	220.00
1728.Honor Decoration for non-government employees	110.00

Military Long Service Awards

1729.I Class-21 years	300.00
1730.II Class-15 years	275.00
1731.III Class-9 years	250.00

REUSS-Junior Line
Civil Decorations

1732.Golden Merit Cross-gold	550.00
1733.Golden Merit Cross-silver/gilt	300.00
1734.Silver Merit Cross	300.00
1735.Silver Merit Medal with crown	200.00
1736.Silver Merit Medal	60.00
1737.Lifesaving Medal	325.00
1738.Fire Service Decoration	200.00
1739.Decoration for Workers & Domestic Servants	80.00
1740.Commemorative Silver Jubilee Decoration for princely guests-pinback-1909	500.00
1741.same-regular issue-ribbon type	185.00
1742.same-ladies' issue-bow ribbon-enameled crown	325.00
1743.same-ladies' issue-pinback-unenameled crown	210.00
1744.same-ladies' issue-pinback-enameled crown	320.00

Military Long Service Awards

1745.I Class-21 years	300.00
1746.II Class-15 years	150.00
1747.III Class-9 years	140.00

REUSS-LOBENSTEIN-EBERSDORF
Civil Decorations
1748.Silver Merit Medal	800.00
1749.Bronze Merit Medal	525.00

SAXONY-Kingdom
House Order of the Rue Crown
1750.Collar	rare
1751.Badge-gold	2250.00
1752.Ladies' decoration	rare
1753.Breast Star	1800.00

Military Order of St Henry
1754.Type I-1736-both grades	rare
1755.Type II-1768-all grades	rare
1756.Type III-1796-all grades	rare
Type IV-1807-1918	
1757.Collar	rare
1758.Grand Cross badge	rare
1759.Grand Cross badge with laurel	rare
1760.Grand Cross breast star	3000.00
1761.Grand Cross breast star with laurel	rare
1762.Commander badge-gold	4500.00
1763.Commander breast star	2200.00
1764.Knight-gold	1200.00
1765.Knight-silver/gilt	400.00
1766.Golden Military Merit Medal-II type 1806-1848-	
Friedrich August-designer "Hoeckner"	rare
1767.Silver Medal	850.00
1768.Golden Medal-type III-1848-1918-"F.U."-gold	1700.00
1769.Golden Medal-silver/gilt & bronze/gilt	600.00
1770.Silver Medal	110.00
1771.Golden Medal-type IV-1866-designer "Rothe"-gold	rare
1772.Silver Medal	150.00

Civil Merit Order
Awarded with and without crown in all grades. Usual reverse "Für Treue und Verdienste"-when awarded to foreigners reads "Für Verdienste", these rare.-2nd Model-type 2-1910
1773.Grand Cross badge-gold	1750.00
1774.Grand Cross badge with swords	2500.00
1775.Grand Cross badge with swords on ring	rare
1776.Grand Cross badge with red cross	rare
1777.Grand Cross breast star-six points	2500.00
1778.Grand Cross breast star-eight points	3000.00
1779.Grand Cross breast star with swords-six points	3000.00
1780.Grand Cross breast star with swords-eight points	3500.00
1781.Grand Cross breast star with red cross	rare
1782.Commander badge-gold	1850.00
1783.Commander badge-silver/gilt	900.00
1784.Commander badge with swords-gold	2500.00

1785.Commander badge with swords-silver/gilt	1000.00
1786.Commander badge with swords on ring-gold	rare
1787.Commander badge with swords on ring-silver/gilt	rare
1788.Commander breast star	1500.00
1789.Commander breast star with swords	1750.00
1790.Commander breast star with swords above	rare
1791.Knight I Class-gold	600.00
1792.Knight I Class-silver/gilt	400.00
1793.Knight I Class with swords-gold	rare
1794.Knight I Class with swords-silver/gilt	rare
1795.Knight I Class with swords on ring-gold	rare
1796.Knight I Class with swords on ring-silver/gilt	rare
1797.Knight II Class	175.00
1798.Knight II Class with swords	200.00
1799.Knight II Class with swords on ring	rare
1800.Silver Merit Cross (in one piece & separate centres)	120.00
1801.Silver Merit Cross with swords	150.00

Albert Order-type I-old head obverse centre

1802.Grand Cross badge	2000.00
1803.Grand Cross badge with swords	2500.00
1804.Grand Cross badge with swords on ring	rare
1805.Grand Cross breast star	1600.00
1806.Grand Cross breast star with swords	2200.00
1807.Grand Cross breast star with swords above	rare
1808.Commander badge	1600.00
1809.Commander badge with swords	2500.00
1810.Commander badge with swords on ring	rare
1811.Commander breast star	2000.00
1812.Commander breast star with swords	2000.00
1813.Commander breast star with swords above	rare
1814.Knight	800.00
1815.Knight with swords	1000.00
1816.Knight with swords on ring	rare
1817.Honor Cross-unenameled arms	600.00
1818.Honor Cross with swords	rare
1819.Honor Cross with swords on ring	rare
1820.Golden Medal	1450.00
1821.Silver Medal	400.00

Albert Order-type II-young head obverse centre

1822.Grand Cross badge-special class	2200.00
1823.Grand Cross badge-special class-with swords	1800.00
1824.Grand Cross badge-special class-with swords on ring	rare
1825.Grand Cross-special class-breast star with crown	4200.00
1826.same-but also with swords	rare

1827.same-but without crown or swords	2800.00
1828.same-but with swords	2500.00
1829.same-but with swords above	rare
1830.Grand Cross badge-gold	1500.00
1831.Grand Cross badge-silver/gilt	1000.00
1832.Grand Cross badge with swords-gold	1600.00
1833.Grand Cross badge with swords-silver/gilt	1000.00
1834.Grand Cross badge with swords on ring-gold	rare
1835.same-but silver/gilt	rare
1836.Grand Cross breast star	1100.00
1837.Grand Cross breast star with swords	1400.00
1838.Grand Cross breast star with swords above	rare
1839.Commander Cross-gold	1250.00
1840.Commander Cross-silver/gilt	600.00
1841.Commander Cross-with swords-gold	1150.00
1842.Commander Cross-with swords-silver/gilt	1000.00
1843.Commander Cross-with swords on ring-gold	3200.00
1844.Commander Cross-with swords on ring-silver/gilt	rare
1845.Commander breast star	1000.00
1846.Commander breast star with swords	1150.00
1847.Commander breast star with swords above	3200.00
1848.Officer-pinback-gold	850.00
1849.Officer-silver/gilt	500.00
1850.Officer-silver/gilt-with swords	550.00
1851.Officer-silver/gilt-with swords above	rare
1852.Knight I Class with crown-gold	450.00
1853.Knight I Class with crown-silver/gilt	225.00
1854.Knight I Class with crown & swords-gold	550.00
1855.Knight I Class with crown & swords-silver/gilt	275.00
1856.Knight I Class with crown & swords on ring-gold	rare
1857.Knight I Class with crown & swords on ring-silver/gilt	rare
1858.Knight I Class-gold	375.00
1859.Knight I Class-silver/gilt	200.00
1860.Knight I Class with swords-gold	450.00
1861.Knight I Class with swords-silver/gilt	250.00
1862.Knight I Class with swords on ring-gold	rare
1863.Knight I Class with swords on ring-silver/gilt	rare
1864.Knight II Class	125.00
1865.Knight II Class with swords	175.00
1866.Knight II Class with swords on ring	rare
1867.Silver Merit Cross-type I-separate centres applied (Albert Cross)	150.00
1868.Silver Merit Cross with swords	550.00
1869.Silver Merit Cross-type II-made in one piece	150.00
1870.Silver Merit Cross with swords	200.00

Sidonia Order
1871. Cross-gold   3200.00
1872. Cross-silver/gilt   2950.00

Maria Anna Order
1873.I Class badge with crown-silver/gilt   3000.00
1874.II Class-gold   1000.00
1875.III Class   600.00

General Awards
1876.Honor Cross with crown   200.00
1877.Honor Cross with crown & swords   500.00
1878.Honor Cross   75.00
1879.Honor Cross with swords   100.00

Lifesaving Medals
1880.Gold-type I-King Anton/Regent Friedrich August 1831-36   rare
1881.Silver   500.00
1882.Bronze   300.00
1883.Gold-Plauen flood 1834   rare
1884.Silver   1000.00
1885.Gold-type II-Friedrich August II-1836-54   rare
1886.Silver   400.00
1887.Bronze   275.00
1888.Gold-type II-Johan-1854-73   rare
1889.Silver   300.00
1890.Bronze   200.00
1891.Silver Medal-quarry disaster near Schmilka 1862   600.00
1892.Gold-type IV-Albert 1873-1902   950.00
1893.Silver   200.00
1894.Bronze   175.00
1895.Gold-type V-George 1902-1904   rare
1896.Silver   300.00
1897.Bronze   225.00
1898.Gold-type VI-Friedrich August III-1904-1918   1100.00
1899.Silver   600.00
1900.Bronze   225.00

Medals for Arts & Science
1901.Large Golden Medal-"Virtuti et ingenio"-type I-
        Albert 1873-1902   2500.00
1902.Small Gold Medal   1500.00
1903.Large Gold Medal-type II-George 1902-04   rare
1904.Small Gold Medal   rare
1905.Large Gold Medal-type III-Friedrich August III
        -1904-18   1500.00
1906.Large Gold Medal-"Bene merentibus"-type I-Albert 1873-1902   rare
1907.Small Gold Medal-1st & 2nd striking   1500.00
1908.Large Gold Medal-type II-George-1902-04   rare
1909.Small Gold Medal   rare
1910.Large Gold Medal-type III-Friedrich August III-1904-18   rare
1911.Small Gold Medal   1250.00

Various Civil Awards

1912.Honor Cross for Medical Service in peacetime	400.00
1913.Crown Princess Carola Gold Medal-gold-1871	rare
1914.Silver Medal	rare
1915.Carola Medal-gold-1892-1915	800.00
1916.Silver Medal	120.00
1917.Bronze Medal	100.00
1918.Carola Medal-gold-1915-18-undated reverse-gold	rare
1919.same-with ribbon clasp "Weltkrieg 1914/16"	rare
1920.same-with oakleaf clasp for ladies	rare
1921.Silver Medal	500.00
1922.same-clasp "Weltkrieg 1914/16"	550.00
1923.same-oakleaf clasp	650.00
1924.Bronze Medal	75.00
1925.same-clasp "Weltkrieg 1914/16"	115.00
1926.same-oakleaf clasp	150.00
1927.Medal for 40 years Fire Service	300.00
1928.Fire Service Decoration	110.00
1929.Medal for loyalty in labor-type I-Albert-1894	85.00
1930.same-type II-George-1902-04	125.00
1931.same-type III-Friedrich August III-1904-18	60.00

Military Decorations

1932.Friedrich August Medal-silver	35.00
1933.same-silvered-World War I issue	25.00
1934.same-ribbon clasp "Weltkrieg 1914/16" (World War)	150.00
1935.same-ribbon clasp "Weltkrieg 1914/18"	200.00
1936.same-oakleaf clasp "Weltkrieg 1914/16"	125.00
1937.Friedrich August Medal-bronze	25.00
1938.same-ribbon clasp "Weltkrieg 1914/16"	125.00
1939.same-oak leaf clasp	150.00
1940.Schleswig-Holstein Cross-combat-1849	175.00
1941.War Commemorative Cross 1849	200.00
1942.same-for Holstein 1863/64	175.00
1943.same-1866	85.00
1944.Nursing Cross-1870-71	90.00
1945.War Merit Cross 1915-18-bronze	60.00
1946.Nursing Cross-1914-1915	80.00
1947.Nursing Cross-1914-1916	80.00
1948.Nursing Cross-1914-1917	80.00
1949.Nursing Cross-1914-1918	75.00

Long Service Awards

1950.Officers' Cross-25 years	50.00
1951.Silver Medal-15 years-1831-1874	500.00
1952.Bronze Medal-10 years	125.00
1953.Gold Medal-21 years-1874-1877	1150.00
1954.Silver Medal-15 years	110.00
1955.Bronze Medal-9 years	50.00
1956.Cross I Class-15 years	45.00
1957.Medal II Class-12 years	40.00

1958.Medal-III Class-9 years	25.00
1959.Reserve Cross I Class	55.00
1960.Reserve Bar-II Class	40.00
1961.Reserve Medal-II Class	35.00

SAXE-WEIMAR
Order of White Falcon
Type I-1732	rare

Type II-1815	
1962.Collar	rare
1963.Grand Cross badge	2400.00
1964.Grand Cross badge with swords	3000.00
1965.Grand Cross badge for General Merit	3000.00
1966.Grand Cross breast star	1300.00
1967.Grand Cross breast star with swords	1900.00
1968.Grand Cross breast star for General Merit	1550.00
1969.Commander	1500.00
1970.Commander with swords	1750.00
1971.Commander for General Merit	1800.00
1972.Commander breast star	1500.00
1973.Commander breast star with swords	2200.00
1974.Knight I Class-gold	800.00
1975.Knight I Class with swords-gold	1000.00
1976.Knight I Class for General Merit	1100.00
1977.Knight II Class-type I-initials "CA"-gold	650.00
1978.Knight II Class-type I-with swords	700.00
1979.Knight II Class-type II-silver initials "WE"	350.00
1980.Knight II Class-type II-with swords	400.00
1981.Knight II Class-type II-General Merit	400.00
1982.Merit Cross-type I	175.00
1983.Golden Merit Cross-type II-silver/gilt	175.00
1984.Golden Merit Cross-type II-with swords-silver/gilt	200.00
1985.Silver Cross-type II	150.00
1986.Silver Cross-type II-with swords	200.00

General Awards (For Merit, & Loyal Service.)
1987.Golden Medal-Dem Verdienste-silver/gilt	150.00
1988.same-with ribbon clasp & swords	175.00
1989.Silver Medal	110.00
1990.same-with ribbon clasp & swords	125.00
1991.Bronze Medal	85.00
1992.same-with ribon clasp & swords	110.00
1993.Golden Medal-Treue Dienste(Loyal Service)-silver/gilt	185.00
1994.Silver Medal	150.00
1995.Bronze Medal	110.00
1996.Golden Medal-Treue Arbeit(Loyal Labor)-silver/gilt	185.00
1997.Silver Medal	150.00

1998.Bronze Medal	95.00
1999.Golden Medal-"WE"-silver/gilt	150.00
2000.Silver Medal	125.00
2001.Bronze Medal	85.00

Civil Decorations

2002.Golden Merit Medal-type I-Carl Friedrich-1834-1857	rare
2003.Silver Medal	600.00
2004.Bronze Medal	285.00
2005.Golden Medal-type II-young head-Carl Alexander-1857-92	rare
2006.Silver Medal	225.00
2007.Bronze Medal	105.00
2008.Golden Medal-type III-old head-Carl Alexander-1892-1902 rare	
2009.Silver Medal	150.00
2010.Bronze Medal	115.00
2011.Golden Recognition Medal	275.00
2013.Silver Medal	150.00
2014.Bronze Medal	100.00
2015.Golden Medal for Golden Wedding Jubilee-gold	850.00
2016.Silver/gilt Medal	120.00
2017.Silver Medal	85.00
2018.Bronze	65.00
2019.Ladies' Decoration-I Grade	250.00
2020.II Grade	400.00
2021.III Grade	600.00
2022.Lifesaving Medal	300.00

Decorations for Arts & Science

2023.Golden Medal-"Protectori bonarum artium"	rare
2024.Silver Medal	800.00
2025.Golden Medal-"Mitescunt aspera saecla"	rare
2026.Silver Medal	1000.00
2027.Bronze Medal	600.00
2028.Golden Medal-"Meritis Nobilis"	rare
2029.Silver Medal	300.00
2030.Bronze Medal	200.00
2031.Golden Medal-"Doctarum frontium praemia"	rare
2032.Silver Medal	400.00
2033.Bronze Medal	250.00
2034.Golden Medal-Arts & Science-I Class-head of Carl Alexander 1892-1902-oval-gold	1500.00
2035.II Class-round-gold	800.00
2036.Silver Medal-"Dem Verdienst in der Kunst"-(Arts)	300.00
2037.I Class Medal-William Ernst-gold	1100.00
2038.II Class-silver/gilt	600.00
2039.III Class-silver	300.00
2040.Fire Service Decoration	400.00

Military Decorations

2041.War Medal-1809-1815-silver	400.00
2042.War Medal-1809-1815-silvered	150.00
2043.Golden Merit Medal-Grand Duke Carl August-1815	rare

2044.Silver Medal	600.00
2045.Bronze Medal	400.00
2046.Silver Medal-1870-young head-Carl Alexander	225.00
2047.same-with clasp & swords on ribbon	250.00
2048.same-type II-old head-Carl Alexander	rare
2049.same-with clasp & swords on ribbon	rare
2050.Honor Decoration for Exemplary Service-1870-71 War	450.00
2051.Wilhelm-Ernst War Cross-1915-1918	1200.00
2052.Golden Honor Decoration-silver/gilt-1914	100.00
2053.same-bronze/gilt	85.00
2054.same-with ribbon clasp with swords-silver/gilt	200.00
2055.same-bronze/gilt	85.00
2056.General Honor Decoration-1914-silver	100.00
2057.same-silvered	55.00
2058.same-with ribbon clasp & swords-silver	125.00
2059.same-but silvered	85.00
2060.Bronze	75.00
2061.same-bronze plated	65.00
2062.same-with ribbon clasp & swords-bronze	80.00
2063.same-but bronze plated	60.00
2064.Home Front Meritorious Service Decoration-1914-18	125.00
2065.Honor Decoration for Women's War Merit	175.00

Long Service Awards

2066.Military Service Cross-20 years-1834-1872	500.00
2067.same-10 years	250.00
2068.I Class-21 years-Carl Alexander-bar-1872-1902	150.00
2069.II Class-15 years	110.00
2070.III Class-9 years	75.00
2071.I Class-21 years-W.E.-1902-13	125.00
2072.II Class-15 years	110.00
2073.III Class-9 years	75.00
2074.I Class Cross-15 years	85.00
2075.II Class Medal-12 years	60.00
2076.III Class Medal-9 years	60.00
2078.War Veterans' Honor Cross	125.00

SAXON DUCHIES-Each, besides issuing its own decorations, also shared in the award of the Saxe-Ernestine House Order, with some of the insignia of the Order showing the Duchy awarding it.

SAXE-ALTENBURG
General Awards

2079.Duke Ernst Gold Medal-silver/gilt-1906-1909	180.00
2080.Silver Medal	125.00
2081.Duke Ernst II-pinback cross-with swords-1909-1918	1100.00
2082.Duke Ernst Medal with crown & swords	250.00
2083.same-with ribbon clasp "1914"	225.00
2084.Duke Ernst Medal with crown & clasp "1914"	250.00
2085.same-without crown	225.00

2086.Duke Ernst Medal with oakleaves "1914/15"	350.00
2087.same-but also with swords	400.00
2088.Duke Ernst Medal	85.00
2089.Duke Ernst Medal with swords	75.00

General Civil Awards

2090.Exemplary Behavior Medal-Palace Fire 1864	175.00
2091.50th Anniversary Medal of the Duchy-1826-1876	400.00
2092.Saal District flood medal-1890	400.00
2093.Jubilee Medal 1903-gold	rare
2094.Silver Medal	600.00
2095.Bronze Medal	115.00
2096.Lifesaving Medal-type I-Ernst I-1882-1908	600.00
2097.same-type II-Ernst II-1908-1918	300.00

Decorations for Arts & Science

2098.Golden Medal with crown-type I-Ernst I-1874-91- silver/gilt	600.00
2099.same-without crown	350.00
2100.Silver Medal with crown	500.00
2101.same-without crown	325.00
2102.Golden Medal with crown-type II-Ernst I-1891-1908 -silver/gilt	600.00
2103.same-without crown	300.00
2104.Silver Medal-with crown	475.00
2105.same-without crown	250.00
2106.Golden Medal with crown-type III-Ernst II- 1908-1918-silver/gilt	400.00
2107.same-without crown	300.00
2108.Silver Medal with crown	250.00
2109.same-without crown	225.00

Civilian Long Service Awards

2110.Fire Service Decoration	300.00
2111.Court & State Officials;Clergy & Teachers Decoration	275.00
2112.Female Domestic Servants-Silver Cross	250.00
2113.Domestic Service-type I-Für treue Dienste-silver	225.00
2114.same-type II-50 years-Für treue und Arbeit	300.00
2115.same-30 years	225.00

Military Decorations

2116.Campaign Medal-1849(awarded 1874)	250.00
2117.Veterans' Commemorative Medal for 1813-14;(1863)	220.00
2118.same-for 1813-15	220.00
2119.same-for 1814-15	220.00
2120.War Commemorative Medal-1870-71	600.00
2121.Bravery Medal-1914-18-bronze	65.00
2122.same-bronze plated	60.00
2123.same-copper plated	60.00
2124.same-war metal	60.00

Military Long Service Awards

2125.Officers' Cross-type I-initials "JFE"-1836-48	400.00
2126.same-type II-initials "GFK"-1848-53	600.00
2127.same-type III-initial "E"-1853-67	700.00
2128.Military Decoration-I Class-12 years-"JFE"-1836-48	220.00
2129.same-II Class-9 years	200.00
2130.same-III Class-6 years	125.00
2131.same-I Class-12 years-initials "GFK"-1848-53	250.00
2132.same-II Class-9 years	200.00
2133.same-III Class-6 years	180.00
2134.same-I Class-12 years-initial "E"-1853-1913	100.00
2135.same-II Class-9 years	85.00
2136.same-III Class-6 years	75.00

SAXE-COBURG-GOTHA
Grand Ducal Medals

2137.Duke Ernst Golden Medal-silver/gilt	rare
2138.Silver Medal (neck ribbon)	400.00
2139.Silver Medal (breast ribbon)	125.00
2140.Duke Alfred Medal (neck ribbon)	400.00
2141.Duke Alfred Medal (breast ribbon)	110.00
2142.Duke Carl-Eduard Medal-I Class-silver	375.00
2143.same-II Class-silver	115.00
2144.Duke Carl-Eduard Medal-oval with crown-silver	110.00

Civil Decorations

2145.Silver Wedding Medal-Duke Alfred-1899	100.00
2146.Wedding Medal-Duke Carl-Eduard-1905	100.00
2147.Lifesaving Medal-type I-Ernst II-1883-95	350.00
2148.Lifesaving Medal-type II-Alfred-1895-1907	400.00
2149.Lifesaving Medal-type III-Carl-Eduard-1907-18	300.00
2150.Golden Medal for Civic Merit-39mm-1835-37	1150.00
2151.Silver Medal	350.00
2152.Bronze Medal	250.00
2153.Golden Medal-24mm-1837-58	1150.00
2154.Silver Medal	300.00
2155.Golden Medal-1858-93	900.00
2156.Silver Medal	200.00

Decorations for Arts & Science

2157.Merit Cross-type I-Ernst II-1860-75-silver/gilt	400.00
2158.same-type II-1875-1892-silver/gilt	400.00
2159.same-type III-1892-95-green wreath	300.00
2160.same-type IV-Alfred-1895-"Dem Verdienste"-silver/gilt	350.00
2161.same-type V-1895-1905-"Für Kunst und Wissenschaft"	320.00
2162.same-type VI-Carl-Eduard-1906-18-pinback-silver/gilt	600.00
2163.same-but ribbon style-with crown	385.00
2164.same-without crown	300.00

Civil Honor Awards

2165.Silver Medal-Alfred-type I-"Dem Verdienste"	150.00
2166.same-type II-"Für Kunst und Wissenschaft"	325.00

2167.Golden Medal with crown-type I-Carl-Eduard-	
without wreath-silver/gilt	400.00
2168.same-without crown	250.00
2169.Silver Medal	250.00
2170.Golden Medal-type II-with crown & wreath-silver/gilt	325.00
2171.same-without crown	225.00
2172.Silver Medal	220.00

Ladies' Merit Awards

2173.Golden Medal for Female Merit-type I-Duchess	
Alexandrine-1869-1907-silver/gilt	300.00
2174.same-type II-with crown-Duchess Adelheid-1907-17	300.00
2175.Silver Medal	250.00
2176.Fire Service Decoration	200.00

("Dem Verdienste"-For Merit. "Für Kunst und Wissenschaft"-For Arts & Science.)

Military Decorations

2177.Officers' Cross for Eckernfoerde-1849	800.00
2178.same-NCO's & Enlisted Men	600.00
2179.Carl-Eduard oval medal-clasp/swords-dated 1914	225.00
2180.same-dated 1914/5,1914/6,1914/7,1914/8	200.00
2181.same-with swords on ring-1935	650.00
2182.same-but without swords for home service	100.00
2183.Carl-Eduard War Cross-1916-18	1100.00
2184.Carl-Eduard Cross with diamonds	rare
2185.Honor Cross for Home Service	100.00
2186.War Commemorative Cross 1914-18-ribbon type	100.00
2187.same-but pinback variation	300.00

Military Long Service Awards

2188.Officers' Cross-25 years	600.00
2189.I Class-initial "E"-type I-21 years-1846-1888	300.00
2190.II Class-15 years	250.00
2191.III Class-9 years	190.00
2192.I Class-"E" with oakleaves-type II-1888-1894	300.00
2193.II Class-15 years	280.00
2194.III Class-9 years	190.00
2195.I Class-initial "A"-type III-1894-1901	300.00
2196.II Class	220.00
2197.III Class	175.00
2198.I Class-initials "CE"-type IV-1901-13	225.00
2199.II Class	175.00
2200.III Class	150.00

SAXE-COBURG-SAALFELD
Order of St Joachim

2201.Cross with helmet	rare
2202.Cross with Death's Head	rare
2203.Cross without helmet or death's head	rare
2204.Breast Star	1250.00

Other Awards
2205.	Volunteers Medal-1814-officers	750.00
2206.	same-for enlisted men	220.00

SAXE-GOTHA-ALTENBURG
2207.	Campaign Medal 1814-15-officers-42mm	525.00
2208.	Campaign Medal 1814-15-N.C.O.'s	300.00
2209.	Campaign Medal 1814-15-enlisted men	220.00

SAXE-MEININGEN
Civil Decorations
2210.	Lifesaving Medal	300.00
2211.	Merit Order for Arts & Science-I Class Cross-type I-"Herzog zu Sachsen"	450.00
2212.	II Class Medal-silver/gilt	225.00
2213.	same-I Class Cross-type II-"Herzog von Sachsen"	400.00
2214.	II Class Medal	250.00

Military Decorations
2215.	Campaign Medal 1814-15	400.00
2216.	War Merit Cross 1915-18-bronze	80.00
2217.	War Merit Cross 1915-18-war metal	75.00
2218.	War Merit Medal 1915-18-bronze	60.00
2219.	War Merit Medal 1915-18-war metal	75.00
2220.	War Merit Cross for women-bronze	225.00
2221.	War Merit Cross for women-zinc	200.00

Long Service Awards
2222.	Officers' Cross-25 years	175.00
2223.	I Class-24 years-type I-"B.H.z.S.M."-1852-67	225.00
2224.	II Class-16 years	210.00
2225.	III Class-8 years	175.00
2226.	I Class-21 years-type II-"G.H.z.S.M."	250.00
2227.	II Class-15 years	150.00
2228.	III Class-9 years	125.00
2229.	I Class-21 years-type III-initial "G"-1888-1913	225.00
2230.	II Class-15 years	200.00
2231.	III Class-9 years	110.00

SAXON DUCHIES-Shared Military Decorations Till 1825
2232.	Golden Military Merit Medal-1814	1850.00
2233.	Silver Medal	1000.00

Saxe-Ernestine House Order-Shared by the Saxon Duchies from 1826.
Type I-with letter on upper arm of cross to denote the Duchy.
 a.F-Saxe-Altenburg
 b.E-Saxe-Coburg-Gotha
 c.B-Saxe-Meiningen

2234.Grand Cross badge-oak wreath	3600.00
2235.Grand Cross badge-with swords-laurel wreath	3800.00
2236.Grand Cross breast star	2750.00
2237.Grand Cross breast star-with swords	2800.00
2238.Commander Cross	1800.00
2239.Commander Cross with swords	1900.00
2240.Commander breast star-I Class-without letter	2000.00
2241.same-with swords	2500.00
2242.Knight	1000.00
2243.same-with swords	1500.00

(Awards to foreigners are without the wreath and command 20% to 30% more.)

Saxe-Ernestine House Order-type II-no letters

2244.Collar	rare
2245.Collar with swords	rare
2246.Grand Cross badge-gold	2650.00
2247.Grand Cross badge with swords-gold	2250.00
2248.Grand Cross badge with date-gold	rare
2249.Grand Cross badge with swords on ring	rare
2250.Grand Cross badge with swords & swords on ring	rare
2251.Grand Cross badge with diamonds	rare
2252.Grand Cross breast star	1650.00
2253.Grand Cross breast star with swords	1200.00
2254.Grand Cross breast star with date	rare
2255.Grand Cross breast star with swords above	rare
2256.Grand Cross breast star with swords & swords above	rare
2257.Grand Cross breast star with diamonds	rare
2258.Commander-gold	1500.00
2259.Commander with swords-gold	2000.00
2260.Commander with date-gold	3000.00
2261.Commander with swords on ring-gold	1500.00
2262.Commander with swords & swords on ring	rare
2263.Commander breast star	1200.00
2264.Commander breast star with swords	1600.00
2265.Commander breast star with date	rare
2266.Commander breast star with swords above	2000.00
2267.Commander breast star with swords & swords above	rare
2268.Knight I Class-gold	500.00
2269.Knight I Class-silver/gilt	400.00
2270.Knight I Class with swords-gold	600.00
2271.Knight I Class with swords-silver/gilt	500.00
2272.Knight I Class with date	2000.00
2273.Knight I Class with swords on ring-gold	600.00
2274.Knight I Class with swords on ring-silver/gilt	550.00
2275.Knight II Class	225.00
2276.Knight II Class with swords	375.00
2277.Knight II Class with date	1350.00
2278.Knight II Class with swords on ring	1000.00

2279.Cross for Princesses	5500.00
2280.Silver Merit Cross-type I-founding date	150.00
2281.Silver Merit Cross-type II-flat arms-no date	125.00
2282.same-with swords-1866,1870-71-flat centre	200.00
2283.same-raised centre	300.00
2284.same-type III 1890-raised arms-struck in one piece	120.00
2285.same-but reverse centre separately applied	140.00
2286.same-with swords	180.00
2287.Silver Merit Cross-dated 1914 upper arm-home merit	450.00
2288.same-dated 1914 lower arm-war merit	400.00
2289.same-dated 1915	350.00
2290.same-dated 1916	300.00
2291.same-dated 1917	250.00
2292.same-dated 1918	200.00

Saxe-Ernestine House Order
Merit Medal for SAXE-ALTENBURG

2293.Silver Medal-Duke Friedrich 1834-1871	200.00
2294.Golden Medal-1864-1871-silver/gilt	400.00
2295.Golden Medal-Ernst I-1871-1890-silver/gilt	200.00
2296.Silver Medal	150.00
2297.Silver Medal with ribbon clasp 1870/1	250.00
2298.Silver Medal with ribbon clasp & swords	275.00
2299.Golden Medal-Ernst I-1891-1908-silver/gilt	200.00
2300.Silver Medal	150.00
2301.Golden Medal-Ernst II-1908-1918-type I	200.00
2302.same-type II-but without designer's name	200.00
2303.same-with swords	225.00
2304.same-with ribbon clasp 1914	300.00
2305.Silver Medal	110.00
2306.Silver Medal with swords	175.00
2307.Silver Medal with ribbon clasp 1914	250.00

Merit Medal for SAXE-COBURG-GOTHA

2308.Silver Medal-Ernst I-1834-1892	180.00
2309.Golden Medal-1864-1869-gold	1000.00
2310.Golden Medal-1870-1895-silver/gilt	240.00
2311.Silver Medal-ribbon clasp 1870/1	220.00
2312.Silver Medal-swords & ribbon clasp 1870/1	250.00
2313.Golden Medal-1892-1895-no designer's name-silver/gilt	300.00
2314.Silver Medal	250.00
2315.Golden Medal-Alfred-1895-1905-silver/gilt	120.00
2316.Silver Medal	100.00
2317.Golden Medal-1905-1914-Carl Eduard-marked M.v.K.	100.00
2318.Silver Medal	75.00
2319.Silver Medal with swords on ribbon	300.00
2320.Golden Medal-1914-1935-not marked-silver/gilt	100.00
2321.same-but in bronze/gilt	85.00
2322.same-ribbon clasp 1914 for home service-silver/gilt	200.00

2323.same-ribbon clasp 1914/5	185.00
2324.same-ribbon clasp 1914/6	185.00
2325.same-ribbon clasp 1914/7	165.00
2326.same-ribbon clasp 1914/8	150.00
2327.same-with swords & ribbon clasp 1914-for War Merit	260.00
2328.same-with swords & ribbon clasp 1914/5	250.00
2329.same-with swords & ribbon clasp 1914/6	240.00
2330.same-with swords & ribbon clasp 1914/7	240.00
2331.same-with swords & ribbon clasp 1914/8	220.00
2332.Golden Medal with swords on ring-Carl Eduard-1935	500.00
2333.Silver Medal-1914-1935-Carl Eduard-no designer's name	80.00
2334.same-Silvered bronze	60.00
2335.same-Silvered War Metal	50.00
2336.same-ribbon clasp 1914-for Home Service	160.00
2337.same-ribbon clasp 1914/5	150.00
2338.same-ribbon clasp 1914/6	150.00
2339.same-ribbon clasp 1914/7	140.00
2340.same-ribbon clasp 1914/8	140.00
2341.same-with swords & ribbon clasp 1914-War Merit	240.00
2342.same-with swords & ribbon clasp 1914/5	225.00
2343.same-with swords & ribbon clasp 1914/6	225.00
2344.same-with swords & ribbon clasp 1914/7	125.00
2345.same-with swords & ribbon clasp 1914/8	150.00
2346.Silver Medal with swords on ring-1935-Carl Eduard	375.00

Merit Medal for SAXE-MEININGEN

2347.Silver Medal-Bernhard Erich Freund-1836-53-young head	250.00
2348.Golden Medal-1864-1867-old head-silver/gilt	525.00
2349.Silver Medal-1853-1867	250.00
2350.Golden Medal-1867-1871-George-young head-silver/gilt	525.00
2351.Silver Medal	250.00
2352.Golden Medal-1871-1890-old head-legend HERZOG ZU	
SACHSEN MEININGEN-silver/gilt	175.00
2353.Silver Medal	140.00
2354.same-with ribbon clasp 1870/1	215.00
2355.same-with swords & ribbon clasp 1870/1	300.00
2356.Golden Medal-1890-1914-old head-legend HERZOG VON	
SACHSEN MEININGEN-silver/gilt	140.00
2357.Silver Medal	90.00
2358.Golden Medal-Bernhard-1914-18-silver/gilt	120.00
2359.Golden Medal with ribbon clasp-home merit	185.00
2360.Golden Medal with ribbon clasp & swords-war merit	210.00
2361.Silver Medal	75.00
2362.Silver Medal with ribbon clasp 1914	120.00
2363.Silver Medal with ribbon clasp & swords 1914	150.00

Military Decorations in Common to the Saxon Duchies

2364.Long Service Cross-1913-1918-15 years-I Class	100.00
2365.Long Service Medal-1913-1918-12 years-II Class	75.00
2366.Long Service Medal-1913-1918-9 years-III Class	60.00

SCHAUMBURG-LIPPE
House Order

2367.	I Class badge-gold	2200.00
2368.	I Class badge with swords-gold	3750.00
2369.	I Class badge with swords on ring-gold	4000.00
2370.	II Class badge with oakleaves-gold	2000.00
2371.	II Class badge with oakleaves & swords-silver/gilt	2250.00
2372.	II Class badge with oakleaves & swords on ring	rare
2373.	II Class badge	1500.00
2374.	II Class badge with swords	2000.00
2375.	II Class badge with swords on ring	rare
2376.	Officers' Honor Cross-gold	1500.00
2377.	Officers' Honor Cross with swords-gold	1750.00
2378.	III Class badge with crown	rare
2379.	III Class badge with crown & swords	rare
2380.	III Class badge with crown & swords on ring	rare
2381.	III Class badge	600.00
2382.	III Class badge with swords	950.00
2383.	III Class badge with swords on ring	1000.00
2384.	IV Class badge with crown	rare
2385.	IV Class badge with crown & swords	500.00
2386.	IV Class badge	275.00
2387.	IV Class badge with swords	400.00
2388.	Golden Merit Cross-gold-1869-1918	475.00
2389.	Golden Merit Cross-silver/gilt-1917-1918	275.00
2390.	Silver Merit Cross	175.00

Order for Arts & Science

2391.	I Class-type I-1899-1914-silver	650.00
2392.	I Class-type II-1914-18-silver/gilt	650.00
2393.	II Class-type I-1899-1902-Medal	400.00
2394.	II Class-type II-1902-1918-Silver Cross	375.00

Civil Decorations

2395.	Civil Merit Medal-1830-1869-bronze	250.00
2396.	Golden Merit Medal-type I-1869-1877-obverse "AG"-reverse coat of arms & shield	2000.00
2397.	Silver Medal	250.00
2398.	Golden Merit Medal-type II-1885-1890-obverse head of Adolph George-reverse coat of arms	1500.00
2399.	Silver Medal	400.00
2400.	Golden Merit Medal-type III-1890-1893-obverse "AG"-reverse star & rose-gold	1550.00
2401.	Silver Medal	200.00
2402.	Golden Medal-type IV-1893-1905-obverse coat of arms, shield & rose; reverse "Für Treue und Verdienst" in four lines-gold	1500.00

2403.Silver Medal	185.00
2404.Golden Medal-type V-1905-1915-obverse shield, coat of arms & rose; reverse "Für Treue und Verdienst" in script-gold	600.00
2405.Silver Medal	185.00
2406.Golden Medal-type VI-1914-18-obverse head of Adolph; reverse shield & coat of arms-silver/gilt	rare
2407.Silver Medal	300.00
2408.Silver Wedding Commemorative Medal-1907	100.00
2409.Lifesaving Medal	250.00
2410.Prince Adolph Medal	rare
2411.Fire Service Medal for 25 Years Merit	300.00

Military Decorations

2412.Campaign Medal 1808-1815	500.00
2413.Field Service Cross 1849-bronze	400.00
2414.Military Merit Medal 1850	500.00
2415.Military Merit Medal with crossed sabres	250.00
2416.Military Merit Medal with crossed swords	150.00
2417.Military Merit Medal with red cross	200.00
2418.Loyal Service Cross 1870	600.00
2419.Loyal Service Cross 1914-I Class-pinback	550.00
2420.Loyal Service Cross 1914-II Class-ribbon	85.00

Long Service Awards

2421.Officers' Long Service Cross-50 years-gold	rare
2422.Officers' Long Service Cross-25 years-gilt	150.00
2423.Long Service Decoration-I Class	225.00
2424.Long Service Decoration-II Class	200.00
2425.Long Service Decoration-III Class	125.00

SCHLESWIG-HOLSTEIN
Order of St Anne

2426.Cross of the Order	rare
2427.Breast Star of the Order	rare

Civil Awards

2428.Proclamation Medal of Friedrich VIII as Duke-1863	175.00
2429.50th Birthday Medal of Duke Ernst Gunther 1913-silver	225.00
2430.same-but bronze/gilt	200.00

Military Decorations

2431.War Cross 1848-1849	85.00
2432.Officers' Long Service Cross-30 years	600.00
2433.Officers' Long Service Cross-20 years	525.00
2434.Military Long Service for 16 years	450.00
2435.Military Long Service for 8 years	300.00

SCHWARZBURG-RUDOLSTADT
Honor Cross-reverse initials "FG"

2436.I Class with crown-gold	2500.00
2437.I Class with crown & swords-gold	3000.00

2438.I Class-gold	1750.00
2439.I Class with swords-gold	2500.00
2440.I Class with oakleaves	2500.00
2441.II Class	600.00
2442.II Class with swords	700.00
2443.II Class with oakleaves-gold	800.00
2444.III Class	250.00
2445.III Class with swords	275.00
2446.III Class with oakleaves	350.00
2447.IV Class	250.00
2448.IV Class with swords	275.00
2449.IV Class with oakleaves	275.00
2450.IV Class with oakleaves and swords	400.00

Gold & Silver Honor Decorations

2451.Golden Honor Medal-gold	500.00
2452.Golden Honor Medal-silver/gilt	175.00
2453.Golden Honor Medal with oakleaves-1914/15	250.00
2454.Silver Honor Medal	100.00
2455.Silver Honor Medal with oakleaves-1914/15	150.00

Civil Decorations

2456.Golden Merit Medal for Arts & Science,Business etc	175.00
2457.Silver Medal	150.00
2458.Silver Recognition Medal 1899-1918	200.00
2459.Bronze Recognition Medal 1899-1918	150.00

Military Decorations

2460.War Cross 1814/15	1200.00
2461.War Merit 1870	625.00
2462.Golden Merit Medal-bar 1917	225.00
2463.Silver Medal	200.00
2464.Silver Recognition Medal-bar 1917	200.00
2465.Bronze Recognition Medal	175.00

Long Service Awards

2466.Officers 20 Year Cross 1850-1867	300.00
2467.Enlisted 25 year cross-1850-1867	350.00
2468.same-16 year service medal	250.00
2469.same-9 year service	250.00
2470.I Class bar 1867-1914-gilt	300.00
2471.II Class bar-silver	250.00
2472.II Class bar-silvered iron	210.00

SCHWARZBURG-SONDERHAUSEN
Honor Cross-reverse cipher "GFC"

2473.I Class-gold	1325.00
2474.I Class with crown-gold	2500.00

2475.I Class with swords-gold	3000.00
2476.I Class with crown & swords-gold	5000.00
2477.I Class with oakleaves-gold	3000.00
2478.II Class-gold	600.00
2479.II Class with swords	850.00
2480.II Class with oakleaves	850.00
2481.III Class	160.00
2482.III Class with swords	325.00
2483.III Class with oakleaves	325.00
2484.IV Class	210.00
2485.IV Class with swords	250.00
2486.IV Class with oakleaves	250.00
2487.Golden Honor Medal-gold	500.00
2488.Golden Honor Medal-silver/gilt	150.00
2489.same-oakleaves 1914/15-silver/gilt	200.00
2490.Silver Honor Medal	95.00
2491.same-with oakleaves 1914/15	125.00

Civil Decorations

2492.Silver Lifesaving-type I-1868-90-initials "GFC"	250.00
2493.Golden Lifesaving-type II-1890-98-obverse bust-gold	1100.00
2494.Silver Lifesaving Medal	250.00
2495.Golden Lifesaving-type III-1898-1918-gold	950.00
2496.Silver Lifesaving Medal	210.00
2497.Jubilee Medal-1905	95.00
2498.Golden Medal-Arts & Science-type I-Gunther Friedrich Karl II-young bust-1846-1857-gold	1250.00
2499.Silver Medal	250.00
2500.Golden Medal-type II-1857-1889-old bust	1000.00
2501.Silver Medal	250.00
2502.Golden Medal-type III-1889-1918-Karl Gunther	650.00
2503.Silver Medal	125.00
2504.Golden Merit Medal for Commerce-type I-1889-1898	850.00
2505.Golden Merit Medal for Commerce-type II-1898-1918	850.00
2506.Silver Merit Medal-type I-1889-1898	195.00
2507.Silver Merit Medal-type II-1898-1918	225.00
2508.Golden Merit Medal-Agriculture-type I-1889-1898	850.00
2509.Golden Merit Medal-Agriculture-type II-1898-1918	750.00
2510.Silver Merit Medal-type I-1889-1898	195.00
2511.Silver Merit Medal-type II-1898-1918	210.00
2512.Medal for Domestic Servants & Workers	165.00
2513.same-with device "50"	300.00
2514.same-with device "60"	400.00
2515.Cross for Female Domestic Servants	300.00
2516.Brooch for 30 years in the Midwife Service	400.00

Military Decorations
2517.Campaign Medal-1814-15	300.00
2518.Honor Medal-1870-71	400.00

Military Long Service Awards
2519.Officers' Cross for 20 years service	1000.00
2520.same-but with crown	1200.00
2521.same-but the Princely version	2500.00
2522.Long Service Bar I Class	185.00
2523.Long Service Bar II Class	140.00
2524.Gendarmerie Long Service Bar I Class	215.00
2525.Gendarmerie Long Service Bar II Class	195.00

SCHWARZBURG-RUDOLSTADT & SCHWARZBURG-SONDERHAUSEN
Decorations Awarded in Common by both Principalities
Civil Awards
2526.Merit Order for Arts & Science	1250.00
2527.Fire Service I Class Decoration	500.00
2528.Fire Service II Class Decoration	275.00

Military Decorations
2529.Silver Medal for War Merit-silver-1914	60.00
2530.same-but silvered	50.00
2531.Anna-Louise Merit Decoration 1918	600.00

Military Long Service Awards
2532.Long Service Cross-15 years-N.C.O.'s I Class	110.00
2533.Long Service Medal-12 years-II Class	85.00
2534.Long Service Medal-9 years-III Class	65.00

THURN & TAXIS
House Order of Perfect Amity
2535.Cross of Prince Albert in diamonds	rare
2536.Cross for Gentlemen-gold	3000.00
2537.Cross for Ladies-gold	2600.00

TRIER
Military Decorations
2538.Golden Bravery Medal-1796-1801	rare
2539.Silver Medal	2500.00

WALDECK
Order of Merit-1871-1896
2540.I Class with oakleaves	1400.00
2541.II Class-small medal for Arts & Science	1100.00
2542.III Class Cross	500.00
2543.IV Class Cross	250.00

Cross of Merit-1896-1918
2544.I Class with crown-gold	2000.00
2545.I Class with crown-silver/gilt	1500.00

2546.II Class with oakleaves-gold	1500.00
2547.II Class with oakleaves-silver/gilt	800.00
2548.II Class with swords-gold	1500.00
2549.II Class with swords-silver/gilt	800.00
2550.Officers Cross	1250.00
2551.Officers Cross with swords	1400.00
2552.III Class-silver/gilt	400.00
2553.III Class with swords	500.00
2554.IV Class	225.00
2555.IV Class with swords	250.00
2556.Honor Cross	350.00
2557.Honor Cross with swords	500.00
2558.Golden Merit Medal 1899-1917-silver/gilt	125.00
2559.Golden Merit Medal 1899-1917-bronze/gilt	100.00
2560.Silver Merit Medal 1878-1899-small crown-silver	100.00
2561.Silver Merit Medal 1915-1918-large crown-silver	100.00
2562.Silver Merit Medal 1915-1918-silvered	85.00
2563.Silver Merit Medal 1915-1918 with swords-silver	125.00
2564.Silver Merit Medal 1915-1918 with swords-silvered	100.00

Military Merit Cross-1854-1896

2565.Officers' Cross for 25 years-1854-1867-enameled	2000.00
2566.I Class with oakleaves-gold	1500.00
2567.II Class-silver/gilt	650.00
2568.III Class-silver & gilt	300.00

Civil Awards

2569.Personal Service Medal-25 years	300.00
2570.Personal Service Decoration-25 years-brooch	400.00
2571.Personal Service Decoration-40 years-brooch	500.00
2572.Medal-Arts & Sciences-1857-1918-star on ribbon-gold	1100.00
2573.Large Medal for Arts & Science-1903-1918	rare
2574.Small Medal for Arts & Science-silver/gilt	850.00
2575.Fire Service Decoration	500.00

Military Decorations

2576.Campaign Medal 1813	600.00
2577.Campaign Medal 1813-1814	600.00
2578.Campaign Medal 1814	600.00
2579.Campaign Medal 1813-1815	600.00
2580.Campaign Medal 1814-1815	600.00
2581.Campaign Medal 1815	600.00
2582.Campaign Medal 1849	1000.00
2583.Friedrich Bathildis Medal 1915-1918	150.00
2584.same-but without designer's name	150.00

Military Long Service Awards
2585.Long Service Decoration-I Class bar	300.00
2586.Long Service Decoration-II Class bar	240.00
2587.Long Service Decoration-III Class bar	200.00
2588.Gendarmerie-I Class Decoration	300.00
2589.Gendarmerie-II Class Decoration	250.00
2590.Gendarmerie-III Class Decoration	200.00
2591.War Veterans'Association Decoration	275.00

WESTPHALIA
Order of the Westphalian Crown-1810-1813
2592.Collar	rare
2593.Grand Cross badge	rare
2594.Grand Cross breast star	rare
2595.Commander badge	rare
2596.Knight I Class	6000.00
2597.Knight II Class	3250.00

(Note: I have seen at least two copies of the Knight II Class of this Order, copies of other grades may exist!)

Various Decorations
2598.Golden Honor Medal-1809-1813-round	rare
2599.Silver Medal	2000.00
2600.Golden Medal-1809-13-oval-six cannonballs	rare
2601.Silver Medal	650.00
2602.Golden Medal-1809-13-oval-seven cannonballs	1600.00
2603.Silver Medal	500.00
2604.Decoration for Ladies of the Royal Household	rare

WUERTEMBERG
Order of St Hubert
2605.Badge of the Order	rare
2606.Breast Star of the Order	rare

2607.Order of the Golden Eagle - All insignia	rare

Order of the Crown
2608.Grand Cross badge	6500.00
2609.Grand Cross badge with swords	7000.00
2610.Grand Cross badge with diamonds	rare
2611.Grand Cross breast star	3200.00
2612.Grand Cross breast star for the sovereign	3500.00
2613.Grand Cross breast star with swords	4000.00
2614.same-for the sovereign	rare
2615.Grand Cross breast star with diamonds	rare
2616.Commander	1350.00
2617.Commander with swords-gold	4000.00
2619.Commander with diamonds	rare
2620.Commander breast star	rare
2621.Commander breast star with swords	rare

2622.Honor Cross-gold	1000.00
2623.Honor Cross-silver/gilt	600.00
2624.Honor Cross with swords-gold	1250.00
2625.Honor Cross with swords-silver/gilt	700.00
2626.Honor Cross with crown	rare
2627.Honor Cross with crown & swords	rare
2628.Knight I Class-gold	1000.00
2629.Knight I Class-silver/gilt	500.00
2630.Knight I Class with swords-gold	1400.00
2631.Knight I Class with swords-silver/gilt	850.00
2632.Knight with Lion & swords-gold	2000.00
2633.Knight with Lion & swords-silver/gilt	1200.00
2644.Merit Medal-gold	600.00
2645.Merit Medal-silver/gilt	125.00

2646.Civil Merit Order-All insignia of this order are rare

Carl Military Order
2647.Badge of the Order	rare

Military Merit Order
Type I-1799-obverse initial "W"-all insignia rare
Type II-1806-obverse initials "FR"-all insignia rare
Type III-1818-obverse laurel wreath-initial "W"-all insignia rare

Type IV-1870-initials "KR"
2648.Grand Cross badge	rare
2649.Grand Cross breast star	rare
2650.Commander-gold	rare
2651.Knight-gold	rare
2652.Knight-silver/gilt	5000.00

Type V-1892-initials "WR"
2653.Grand Cross badge	8000.00
2654.Grand Cross breast star	3000.00
2655.Commander-gold-with crown	3500.00
2656.Commander-gold-without crown	5000.00
2657.Knight-gold	2000.00

Friedrich Order
Type I-1830-rare
Type II-1856
2658.Grand Cross badge with crown	rare
2659.Grand Cross badge with crown & swords	6000.00
2660.Grand Cross badge	5000.00
2661.Grand Cross badge with swords	5000.00
2662.Grand Cross breast star with crown	rare
2663.Grand Cross breast star with crown & swords	rare
2664.Grand Cross breast star-silver & gold	2500.00
2665.Grand Cross breast star with swords-silver & gold	4250.00

2666.Commander-gold	1400.00
2667.Commander-silver/gilt	1000.00
2668.Commander with swords-gold	2000.00
2669.Commander with swords-gold & silver/gilt	1300.00
2670.Commander breast star	2200.00
2671.Commander breast star with swords	3000.00
2672.Knight I Class-gold	400.00
2673.Knight I Class-silver/gilt	300.00
2674.Knight I Class with swords-gold	600.00
2675.Knight I Class with swords-silver/gilt	300.00
2676.Knight II Class	250.00
2677.Knight II Class with swords-silver & gold	250.00
2678.Knight II Class with swords-silver & gilt	175.00
2679.Merit Medal-silver/gilt	85.00
2680.Merit Medal-gilt war metal	60.00

Olga Order
2681.Badge of the Order	250.00

Civil Decorations
2682.Silver Merit Cross-1900-1918	125.00
2683.Silver Merit Cross-war metal silvered	85.00
2684.Golden Merit Medal-type I-1806-1818 "FR"	rare
2685.Silver Medal	500.00
2686.Golden Merit Medal-type II-1818-25-Wilhelm	rare
2687.Silver Medal	750.00
2688.Golden Merit Medal-type III-1825-40-bearded head of Wilhelm-reverse "Dem Verdienste"	rare
2689.Silver Medal	750.00
2690.Golden Merit Medal-type IV-1840-64-beardless Wilhelm	2200.00
2691.Silver Medal	275.00
2692.Golden Merit Medal-type IV-1864-91-head of Karl	800.00
2693.Silver Medal	110.00
2694.Golden Merit Medal-type V-1892-1918-Wilhelm II	350.00
2695.Silver Medal	60.00
2696.Charlotte Cross-1916-1918	75.00
2697.Golden Jubilee Medal-25th Year of Reign 1889	600.00
2698.Silver Medal	50.00
2699.Bronze Medal	50.00
2700.Silver Wedding Medal 1911	85.00
2701.Golden Lifesaving Medal	rare
2702.Silver Lifesaving Medal	500.00

2703.Karl-Olga Medal-"Ora et labora"-silver	200.00
2704.same-for Red Cross Merit	70.00
2705.Karl-Olga Medal-bronze	150.00
2706.Jubilee Recognition Medal-type I-Wilhelm	65.00
2707.same-type II-head of Karl	85.00

Medals for Arts & Science

Types I & II-large & small gold medals	rare
2708.Small Golden Medal-Karl-1865-1892	2500.00
2709.Large Golden Medal-type IV-1892-1918-Wilhelm II	5000.00
2710.Small Golden Medal	2800.00

Civil Long Service Awards

2711.Jubilee Honor Decoration for 50 Years Court Service	rare
2712.Fire Service Decoration-type I-oval	60.00
2713.same-type II-bronze medal	45.00
2714.Golden Honor Decoration for Female Domestic Servants	250.00
2715.Silver Decoration	150.00

Military Decorations

2716.Golden Military Merit Medal-type I-	
1800-1806-"Ludwig Eugen"	rare
2717.Silver Medal	rare
2718.Golden Medal-type II-1806-1818-"FR"	rare
2719.Silver Medal	1200.00
2720.Golden Medal-type III-1818-1840-Wilhelm I-young head	rare
2721.Silver Medal	rare
2722.Golden Medal-type IV-1840-1864-Wilhelm I-old head	rare
2723.Silver Medal	rare
2724.Golden Medal-type V-1864-1892-Karl	rare
2725.Silver Medal	400.00
2726.Golden Medal-type VI-1892-1918-Wilhelm II-gold	600.00
2727.same-but gilt	75.00
2728.Silver Medal	25.00
2729.Wilhelm Cross with swords-pinback	650.00
2730.Wilhelm Cross with swords-II Class-on ribbon	75.00
2731.Wilhelm Cross for War Merit	75.00
2732.same-For Merit in Public Welfare-reverse blank	100.00
2733.Charlotte Cross 1916-1918	75.00

Military Commemorative Decorations

2734.Golden Medal-Victory at Brienne 1.2.1814	3000.00
2735.Silver Medal	1100.00
2736.Golden Medal-Victory at La Fere 25.3.1814	3000.00
2737.Silver Medal	1100.00
2738.Golden Medal for Battle for Paris 30.3.1814	3000.00
2739.Silver Medal	1100.00
2740.Golden Honor Cross 1815	rare
2741.Silver Honor Cross	rare
2742.Silver Honor Medal	1100.00

Campaign Medal-1793-1815-obverse gothic "W" & wreath & reverse Für treuen
Dienst (For Loyal Service) and a number of campaigns
2743."In einem Feldzuge" (one campaign)	45.00
2744."In zwei Feldzugen" (two)	90.00
2745."In drei Feldzugen" (three)	150.00
2746."In vier Feldzugen" (four)	250.00
2747."In funf Feldzugen" (five)	325.00
2748."In sechs Feldzugen" (six)	450.00
2749."In sieben Feldzugen" (seven)	500.00
2750."In acht Feldzugen" (eight)	650.00

(with reverses for nine through fourteen campaigns-all rare.)
2751.same-for 1849-one campaign	1100.00

Campaign Medal-1866-obverse Gothic letter "K"
2752.One campaign	50.00
2753.Two campaigns	800.00

Badge for Aides of Wilhelm I & II
2754.Pinback badge-silver & gold	rare
2755.Pinback badge-silver & gilt	3000.00

Military Long Service Awards
2756.I Class-1833-1850-Officers' Cross-25 years	400.00
2757.II Class-Enlisted Men-silver cross-20 years	500.00
2758.I Class-1850-1864-Enlisted Men-gilt-30 years	350.00
2759.II Class-silver cross-18 years	400.00
2760.I Class-1864-1891-Officers-silver/gilt-25 years	70.00
2761.II Class-N.C.O.'s-21 years	50.00
2762.I Class-1891-1921-all ranks-25 years-gilt	110.00
2763.II Class-silver cross-enlisted men	110.00
2764.Long Service bar-30 years-1851-1870	rare
2765.same-24 years	rare
2766.same-18 years	rare
2767.same-12 years	600.00
2768.same-6 years	300.00
2769.Long Service bar I Class-"KR"-1874-1892-15 years	110.00
2770.II Class-9 years	125.00
2771.I Class-"W"-1892-1913-15 years	90.00
2772.II Class-12 years	60.00
2773.I Class Cross-1913-1921-15 years	45.00
2774.II Class Medal-12 years	35.00
2775.III Class Medal-9 years	25.00

Landwehr (Reserve)
2776.Reserve Decoration-I Class cross-type I-"K"	800.00
2777.same-II Class-bar	400.00

GERMANY-Wuertemberg

2778.same-type II-Cross "W"	200.00
2779.same-bar "W"	35.00
2780.same-type III-medal	20.00

War Veterans
2781.Commemorative Medal-silver	250.00
2782.same-but with swords over the medal-silvered	700.00

WURZBURG
2783.Golden Bravery Medal	rare
2784.Silver Medal	1250.00

GERMAN EMPIRE

Civil Decorations
2785.90th Birthday of Kaiser Wilhelm I-1797-1887-silver	75.00
2786.100th Birthday of Wilhelm I-1797-1897	15.00
2787.Jerusalem Cross	500.00

Military Awards
2788.Campaign Medal-1870-71-combat-around rim "AUS ERO-BERTEM GESCHUTZ" (From Captured Guns)	15.00
2789.Twenty five campaign bars of several different types which fit on ribbon-ranging in value from	15.00 to 80.00
2790.Non-combattents-steel-frequently found in rusted or partly rusted condition	40.00
2791.China 1900 (Boxer Rebellion)-combat-bronze	85.00
2792.Thirteen campaign bars on ribbon-from	75.00 to 200.00
2793.Non-combattents-steel-see 2790 above	60.00
2794.S.W.Africa-combat-bronze	75.00

(Copies of the last item do not have the designer's name under the bust of Germania.)

2795.Sixteen campaign bars on ribbon-from	75.00-200.00
2796.S.W. Africa-non-combat-steel	75.00
2797.Colonial Campaign Medal-to Europeans	100.00
2798.Colonial Campaign Medal-to natives	600.00
2799.Ninety-one bars which fit on ribbon-from	100.00-300.00

2800.War Merit Medal-I Class in gold-silver/gilt-reverse-KRIEGER VERDIENST	1250.00
2801.I Class in silver for native officers	1700.00
2802.II Class in gold-silver/gilt	200.00
2803.II Class in silver-native officers & men	100.00
2804.II Class-reverse KRIEGS VERDIENST-silvered	250.00
2805.Helvetia-Benigna Medal-large-not for wearing	3000.00
2806.same-small size-for wearing on ribbon	3000.00
2807.same-small on brooch	600.00

Naval Service Badges
2808.Submarine Badge-bronze/gilt	250.00
2809.Submarine Badge-war metal/gilt	150.00

2810.Naval Pilot's Badge-sea-1913-silver/gilt	525.00
2811.same-bronze/gilt	425.00
2812.same-zinc/gilt	375.00
2813.Naval Pilot's Badge-land-1915-silver/gilt	600.00
2814.same-bronze/gilt	550.00
2815.same-tombac/gilt	500.00
2816.Naval Observer Badge-silver/gilt	650.00
2817.same-bronze/gilt	600.00
2818.same-tombac/gilt	500.00
2819.Commemorative Pilot & Observer Badge-bronze/gilt	500.00
2820.same-tombac/gilt	400.00
2821.same-war metal/gilt	350.00

Military Flying Badges (See also Bavaria)

2822.Military Pilot Badge-silver	325.00
2823.same-silvered brass	250.00
2824.same-silvered zinc	225.00
2825.Military Observer Badge-silver	325.00
2826.same-silvered	225.00
2827.Military Air Gunner Badge-silver	500.00
2828.same-silvered tombac	400.00
2829.Fliers' Commemorative Badge-silver	425.00
2830.same-silvered tombac	375.00

(Note: Hallmarked pieces command 25-50% more-copies exist.)

Victory in Air War Goblets-1916

2831.Fliers' Honor Goblet-silver	2650.00
2832.Fliers' Honor Goblet-silvered zinc	1100.00
2833.Fliers' Honor Goblet-silvered brass	1200.00
2834.Fliers' Honor Goblet-silvered iron	1200.00

Wound Badges-stamped out metal-pinback

2835.Gold-Army	75.00
2836.Silver-Army	50.00
2837.Black-Army	20.00
2838.Gold-Navy	300.00
2839.Silver-Navy	140.00
2840.Black	100.00

WEIMAR REPUBLIC-1918-1933

As a matter of policy, the Weimar Republic did not make awards, with the exception of the World War I Commemorative Crosses, awarded in 1933 & later, and the unofficial Red Cross awards. However,some of the states continued to issue decorations without royal or princely patronage. Other groups,including war veterans' associations awarded decorations as well. Some of these non-official awards were recognized and allowed to be worn during the III Reich period,

2841.Silesian Eagle-I Class-with oakleaves & swords	125.00
2842.Silesian Eagle-I Class-with oakleaves	85.00
2843.Silesian Eagle-I Class-with swords	100.00
2844.Silesian Eagle-I Class	70.00

2845.Silesian Eagle-II Class-with oakleaves & swords   75.00
2846.Silesian Eagle-II Class-with oakleaves   65.00
2847.Silesian Eagle-II Class-with swords   60.00
2848.Silesian Eagle-II Class   50.00
2849.Colonial Service Badge-Elephant Order   125.00
2850.Tank Battle Badge-silver (beware of copies)   1250.00
2851.same-silvered bronze   1250.00
2852.same-silvered brass   1100.00
2853.same-silvered copper   1200.00
2854.same-silvered zinc   1000.00
2855.Army Zeppelin Commemorative Badge-silver   1000.00
2856.same-silvered bronze   800.00
2857.same-silvered war metal   625.00
2858.Navy Zeppelin Commemorative Badge-silver   1150.00
2859.same-silvered   750.00
2860.same-silvered war metal   600.00
2861.Honor Cross 1914-18-with swords-combat   10.00
2862.Honor Cross-without swords-non-combat   15.00
2863.Honor Cross-next of kin (blackened iron)   20.00
2864.Eagle Shield of the President   rare
2865.Honor Medal of the President   rare
2866.Honor Decoration of the Red Cross-I Class neck badge   500.00
2867.same-but special class breast star   700.00
2868.same-II Class breast badge   75.00
2869.German Gymnastics & Sports Badge   50.00
2870.German National Sports Badge   25.00

VETERANS' AWARDS & DECORATIONS FOR WORLD WAR I
2871.Kyffhauserbund Service Cross   25.00
2872.same-Service Medal   20.00
(This may be found with campaign bars on ribbon-add $5.00 per.)
2873.Marine Corps Flanders Cross   75.00
(This may be found with campaign bars on ribbon-add $15.00 per.)
2874.German Honor Legion Officers' Cross-silver/enamels   200.00
2875.same-enlisted men-Iron Cross on reverse   25.00
2876.Eastern Front Cross   75.00
2877.Champagne Cross   75.00
(Similar crosses for the Western Front - 75.00.)
2878.Prussian War Commemorative Cross   125.00
2879.Saxon Cross for Officers   150.00
2880.same-enlisted men   75.00

FREIKORPS BADGES & DECORATIONS-awarded by the many private military groups which sprang up in the aftermath of the Russian & German revolutions between 1918-1920. Although not official they were allowed to be worn during the III Reich period. These listed are only a small selection of those known to exist.
2881.German Order Shield of the Eastern Border Force   125.00
2882.V Army Corps   140.00
2883.Bug Star   200.00
2884.Ehrhardt Naval Brigade Decoration   250.00
2885.Wilhelmshaven Naval Brigade Badge   75.00

2886.Loewenfeld Cross-I Class-pinback cross	200.00
2887.same-II Class-on ribbon	85.00
2888.Annaberg Cross-I Class-neck badge	300.00
2889.same-II Class-pinback cross	200.00
2890.same-III Class-on ribbon	150.00
2891.Reinhardt Freicorps badge	75.00
2892.Courland Brigade Medal	85.00
2893.Silesian Shield 1919	60.00
2894.Berlin Militia Badge	85.00
2895.Hamburg Decoration	85.00
2896.Munich Decoration	45.00
2897.Schlageter Badge-large-oval	125.00
2898.same-small-round	140.00

(This last item often found with campaign bars-add $25.00 per.)

DECORATIONS OF THE STAHLHELM-This was one of the major veterans' organizations after World War I. Its awards were allowed to be worn during the III Reich period.

Members' Badge-circular & silver- pinback-earlier issues had date of membership engraved on the back.

2899.Dated 1918	rare
2900.Dated 1919	260.00
2901.Dated 1920	275.00
2902.Dated 1921	140.00
2903.Dated 1922	140.00
2904.Dated 1923	100.00
2905.Dated 1924	100.00
2906.Dated 1925	115.00
2907.Dated 1926	85.00
2908.Dated 1927	85.00
2909.Dated 1928	120.00
2910.Dated 1929	85.00
2911.Dated 1930	65.00
2912.Dated 1931	85.00
2913.Dated 1932	65.00
2914.Stahlhelm Breast Star	rare
2915.Stahlhelm Sports Cross	800.00
2916.Stahlhelm Sports Badge	75.00

DANZIG FREE STATE-Set up by the League of Nations after World War I, and later absorbed into the III Reich. Its decorations were allowed to be worn during the III Reich Period.

2917.Danzig Cross I Class-pinback (beware of copies)	1400.00
2918.Danzig Cross II Class-on ribbon(beware of copies)	600.00
2919.Lifesaving Medal	1200.00
2920.Fire Service Commemorative Badge	350.00
2921.Fire Service Decoration I Class	550.00
2922.same-II Class	500.00
2923.Faithful Service Decoration-50 years-gilt	750.00
2924.same-40 years-gilt	600.00
2925.same-25 years-silvered	500.00

2926.Police Long Service-25 years-gilt	700.00
2927.Police Long Service-18 years-silvered	500.00
2928.Police Long Service-8 years-silver medal	400.00
2929.Red Cross Decoration-type I-no swastika	600.00
2930.same-type II-with swastika	800.00
2931.Red Cross Merit Cross I Class-pinback	900.00
2932.same-II Class on ribbon	450.00

THIRD REICH 1939-1945

Order of the German Eagle-genuine insignia of this Order should be hallmarked 900 (silver content) & 21 (for Godet the maker.) Values given for the badges are for the II type which had a fan suspension, instead of just a ring;values for type I are from 10% to 15% higher.

2933.Golden Grand Cross badge 66mm	rare
2934.Golden Grand Cross breast star-91mm-8 points	rare
2935.Grand Cross badge-60mm	6000.00
2936.Grand Cross breast star-80mm-8 pointed-silver & gilt	4750.00
2937.Grand Cross badge with swords	5500.00
2938.Grand Cross breast star with swords	3250.00
2939.I Class-(sash badge)-50mm	3000.00
2940.I Class-breast star-80mm-8 points-silver	3000.00
2941.I Class badge with swords	3500.00
2942.I Class breast star with swords	3250.00
2943.II Class badge-neck decoration-50mm	1500.00
2944.II Class breast star-6 points-75mm	2000.00
2945.II Class neck badge with swords	2000.00
2946.II Class breast star with swords	2200.00
2947.III Class neck badge-same as 2943	1500.00
2948.III Class neck badge with swords-same as 2945	1750.00
2949.IV Class-pinback cross-50mm	1250.00
2950.IV Class with swords	1500.00
2951.V Class breast badge-45mm	1000.00
2952.V Class with swords	1250.00
2953.Silver Merit Medal-Gothic letters	450.00
2954.Silver Merit Medal-Roman letters	750.00
2955.Silver Merit Medal-with swords-Gothic letters	650.00
2956.Silver Merit Medal-with swords-Roman letters	750.00
2957.Bronze Medal-Roman letters	400.00
2958.Bronze Medal-with swords	500.00

(Note: This Order was issued in two stages, with the classes changing designation. Thus, there can be two types of the same award, the only difference being the suspension. Consult a specific reference from the bibliography for this matter.)

2959.German National Prize for Arts & Science   rare

German Order of the Greater German Reich
2960.Neck badge with swords & oakleaves-I Class   rare
2961.Neck badge-II Class   rare
2962.Pinback Cross-III Class-silver/gilt   rare
2963.same-bronze/gilt   10,000.00

German Red Cross Decorations-type II-1934-1937 (See Weimar Republic for type I.)-no swastika
2964.Breast Star   2500.00
2965.I Class neck badge   800.00
2966.Merit Cross-pinback   400.00
2967.Honor Decoration-breast decoration on ribbon   200.00

Type III-1937-1939-similar design to type II-with swastika added.
2968.Grand Cross badge   4750.00
2969.Grand Cross breast star   5200.00
2970.I Class with diamonds   rare
2971.I Class neck badge-neck badge   1250.00
2972.Merit Cross-pinback   600.00
2973.II Class-on ribbon   225.00
2974.Ladies' Cross   200.00
2975.Red Cross Medal   200.00

German Social Welfare Decoration-1939-1945 (This award replaced all German Red Cross decorations.)
2976.Special Class-neck badge   rare
2977.Special Class-breast star   rare
2978.I Class-with diamonds   rare
2979.I Class neck badge   2000.00
2980.II Class-pinback   600.00
2981.III Class-on ribbon   250.00
2982.III Class with swords   300.00
2983.Medal-bronze   45.00
2984.Medal-zinc   35.00
2985.Medal with swords-bronze   150.00
2986.Medal with swords-zinc   100.00

Nurse Awards
2987.Cross for Senior Hospital Matrons   1400.00
2988.Cross for Hospital Matrons   500.00
2989.Cross for 25 years as a nurse   350.00
2990.Cross for 10 years as a nurse   250.00

Civil Decorations & Awards
2991.Lifesaving Medal-on ribbon-silver   400.00
2992.same-silver colored metal   275.00
2993.Commemorative Lifesaving & Rescue Medal-not wearable   525.00

Mothers' Cross-type I reverse "Das Kind adelt die Mutter"
2994.Gold Cross	2500.00
2995.Silver Cross	2200.00
2996.Bronze Cross	1800.00

Mothers' Cross-type II-reverse "16 Dezember 1938"
2997.Gold Cross	45.00
2998.Silver Cross	30.00
2999.Bronze Cross	20.00

Fire Service Awards
3000.Fire Service Cross I Class-pinback	1000.00
3001.Fire Service Cross I Class-on ribbon-gilt/enamels	450.00
3002.II Class-on ribbon-silvered/enamels	110.00

Mine Service Awards
3003.Mine Rescue Service Badge-I Class-pinback	1400.00
3004.Mine Rescue Service Badge-II Class-on ribbon	300.00

Air Raid Service Awards
3005.Air Raid Service Decoration (Luftschutz)-I Class	500.00
3006.Air Raid Service Decoration-II Class	40.00

Civilian Long Service Awards
3007.Faithful Service Cross-50 years	220.00
3008.Faithful Service Decoration-40 years-gilt	40.00
3009.same-with oak leaves	800.00
3010.Faithful Service Decoration-25 years-silvered	25.00

Police Long Service Awards
3011.Police Long Service-I Class-oakleaves for 40 years	rare
3012.same-I Class-25 years	150.00
3013.same-II Class-18 years	95.00
3014.same-III Class-8 years	65.00

3015.Decoration for the Customs Service	200.00

Labor Service Awards
3016.Labor Service-I Class-gilt-men	400.00
3017.II Class-silvered	200.00
3018.III Class-silvered	150.00
3019.IV Class-bronze	60.00
3020.I Class-women	475.00
3021.II Class	300.00
3022.III Class	220.00
3023.IV Class	175.00

Railroad Service Awards
3024.Railroad Service Badge-I Class-gilt	600.00
3025.II Class-silver	475.00
3026.III Class-bronze	300.00

Sports Decorations

Olympic Awards
3027. Olympic Decoration-I Class neck badge	2200.00
3028. Olympic Decoration II Class-on ribbon	700.00
3029. Olympic Medal	100.00

(The last three items, like many other III Reich items, have been copied. However, the Olympic Medal is somewhat difficult to detect. Examination of the eagle's head on the obverse will reveal that it looks more like that of an owl than an eagle. Also you may come across several which look exactly alike in virtual mint condition.)

3030. National Sports Badge-type I-no swastika-DRA-gold	85.00
3031. II Class-silver	55.00
3032. III Class-bronze	35.00
3033. same-type II-no swastika-I Class-DRL-gold	75.00
3034. II Class-silver	55.00
3035. III Class-bronze	35.00
3036. same-type III-with swastika-I Class-DRL-gold	85.00
3037. II Class-silver	65.00
3038. III Class-bronze	35.00

3039. National Youth Sports Badge-type I-I Class-no swastika	60.00
3040. same-for girls	75.00
3041. same-II type with swastika	60.00
3042. same-for girls	75.00

3043. German Riders' Badge-gold class	525.00
3044. Silver Class	180.00
3045. Bronze Class	80.00
3046. German Youth Riders' Badge	165.00
3047. German Horse Driver Badge-gold class	250.00
3048. Silver Class	150.00
3049. Bronze Class	90.00
3050. German Rider & Driver Badge	450.00
3051. German Master Rider Badge	2000.00
3052. Badge for Horse Care-gold class	275.00
3053. Silver Class	225.00
3054. Bronze Class	165.00

3055. Motor Sports Badge (NSKK)-gold class	1550.00
3056. Silver Class	1100.00
3057. Bronze Class	825.00
3058. Heavy Athletics Badge	275.00
3059. Achievement & Championship Badges-silver	185.00
3060. same-with date	210.00
3061. same-in bronze	120.00
3062. same-with date	125.00
3063. Championship badge	200.00

3064. S.A. Sports Badge-gold class	250.00
3065. Silver Class	125.00
3066. Bronze Class	35.00

3067.Naval S.A. Sports Badge	500.00
3068.S.A. Master Riding Badge	1300.00
3069.Germanic Proficiency Runes-silver	2500.00
3070.Bronze	1500.00

Police Awards

3071.Gendarmerie High Alpine Award	2500.00
3072.Gendarmerie Alpine Award	2500.00
3073.Police Expert Skier Award	2500.00
3074.Police Expert Mountain Climber Award	2500.00

Aviation Badges

3075.DLV Pilot Badge	30.00
3076.DLV Radioman's Badge	325.00
3077.DLV Balloon Flier-1932-1933-gilt	1500.00
3078.DLV Balloon Flier-silvered	1250.00
3079.DLV Balloon Flier-bronzed	1150.00
3080.same-1933-1938-silvered	1500.00
3081.NSFK Powered Flight Pilot's Badge-type I	1200.00
3082.same-type II-airplane	1500.00
3083.NSFK Radioman's Badge	125.00
3084.NSFK Free Balloon Badge-1938-1945	1100.00
3085.NSFK Large Glider Pilot's Badge	850.00
3086.NSFK Civil Gliding Proficiency Badge-A	45.00
3087.same-Class B	65.00
3088.same-Class C	85.00
3089.NSFK Aero-Modeling Proficiency Badge-A	800.00
3090.same-Class B	550.00
3091.same-Class C	375.00

Decorations of the Nazi Party & Associated Bodies

3092.Blood Order-type I-signed Fuess	2500.00
3093.same-type II-without signature	2200.00
3094.Golden Party Badge-large (many copies exist)	300.00
3095.Golden Party Badge-small (many copies exist)	250.00
3096.Party Badge	25.00
3097.Party Badge in gold for foreigners	1600.00
3098.Frontbann badge	700.00
3099.Gau Badges for 1923-various	1100.00
3100.Gau Badges for 1925-various	1000.00
3101.Coburg Decoration	2000.00
3102.Nuremburg Party Day Badge	200.00
3103.Brunswick S.A. Rally Badge-1931-type I	550.00
3104.Brunswick S.A. Rally Badge-1931-type II	1500.00
3105.Gau Badge for Baden 1933-gilt	1800.00
3106.Silvered	1200.00
3107.Gilt-on brooch for females	1800.00
3108.Silvered	800.00

3109.Thuringia-silver/gilt	2200.00
3110.Silver	1800.00
3111.Bronze	1400.00
3112.Gau Badge East Hanover 1933-gilt	2200.00
3113.Silvered	1400.00
3114.Bronze	700.00
3115.Gau Badge Wartheland 1939-1940-silver/silver/gilt	3200.00
3116.Gau Badge Sudetenland 1943	2600.00

(Note: Many of the above have been extensively copied.)

Service Decorations of the Nazi Party & Associated Organizations

3117.Nazi Party Long Service Cross-I Class-gold (gilt)	1500.00
3118.II Class-silver	250.00
3119.III Class-bronze	125.00
3120.Golden Hitler Youth Badge	250.00
3121.same-with oakleaves around the edge-gold	2200.00
3122.High Command Badge of the Hitler Youth-for distinguished foreigners	850.00
3123.Potsdam Badge of the Hitler Youth-silver	125.00
3124.Bronze	110.00
3125.S.S. Long Service-25 years-golden swastika	1250.00
3126.12 years-silver swastika	1000.00
3127.8 years-bronze medal	350.00
3128.4 years-blackened bronze medal	250.00

(Note: The last four items have been copied extensively.)

3129.Silver Badge of the National Socialist German Students Federation	360.00
3130.Decoration for Defense Economy Leaders	450.00
3131.Honor Badge-Members of the National Culture Senate	3500.00
3132.National Trade Competition Winner's Badge-national level (Reichssieger)-1938	800.00
3133.same-1939	800.00
3134.same-1944	800.00
3135.same-State Level (Gausieger)-1938	275.00
3136.same-1939	165.00
3137.same-1944	295.00
3138.same-local level (Kreissieger)-1938	140.00
3139.same-1939	150.00
3140.same-1944	120.00
3141.Honor Decoration of the Technical Emergency Service (Technischen Nothilfe)-dated 1919	475.00
3142.same-1920	450.00
3143.same-1921	400.00
3144.same-1922	400.00
3145.same-1923	450.00
3146.Pioneer of Labor Decoration	2500.00
3147.Dr Fritz Todt Prize-gold(gilt)	2500.00
3148.Silvered	1250.00
3149.Bronzed steel	750.00

(Note: The last three items have been copied extensively.)

MILITARY DECORATIONS

Spanish Civil War-1936-1939

3150.Spanish Cross in gold with diamonds	12,500.00
3151.Spanish Cross in gold with swords-silver/gilt	1200.00
3152.same-bronze/gilt	1000.00
3153.Spanish Cross in silver with swords-silver	650.00
3154.same-silvered bronze	550.00
3155.Spanish Cross in silver without swords-silver	1000.00
3156.same-silvered bronze	750.00
3157.Spanish Cross in bronze with swords	450.00
3158.Spanish Cross in bronze without swords	550.00
3159.Spanish Cross for next of kin	1500.00
3160.Condor Legion Tank Badge-gold	rare
3161.Condor Legion Tank Badge-silver	1500.00
3162.same-silvered brass	1000.00
3163.Gold Wound Badge (Struck but never awarded.)	300.00
3164.Silver Wound Badge	200.00
3165.Black Wound Badge	100.00

(Note: Most of the above have been copied extensively. Beware!)

Commemorative Medals

3166.Annexation of Austria 13 Marz 1938(Anschluss)	45.00
3167.Annexation of the Sudetenland 1 Oktober 1938	40.00
3168.same-with "Prague Castle" bar (March 1939)	75.00
3169.Memel Returned Medal	150.00
3170.Westwall Medal (several strikings)	20.00

Iron Cross-1939-all grades extensively copied

3171.Grand Cross of the Iron Cross   5000.00

(Although only one award of this decoration was made, to Goering, and that piece was lost in an air raid, it is known that at least a dozen others were struck for him. The above value is considered reasonable for one of those.)

3172.Knight's Cross with golden oakleaves, swords & diamonds	one
3173.Knight's Cross with oakleaves,swords & diamonds	rare
3174.Knight's Cross with oakleaves & swords	7000.00
3175.Knight's Cross with oakleaves	5500.00
3176.Knight's Cross	3250.00
3177.I Class-flat type-pinback	125.00
3178.same-vaulted-pinback	150.00
3179.same-screwback-plain type	175.00
3180.same-screwback-clamshell type	200.00
3181.II Class	45.00
3182.I Class bar 1939 to Iron Cross I Class 1914	250.00
3183.II Class bar 1939 to Iron Cross I Class 1914	85.00

(Note: Due to the popularity among collectors for this award, and to the rarity and price of the higher grades special care should be taken before buying. Good reference books are necessary. This award is also interesting because the highest grades could only be achieved by receiving the lower ones starting with the

II Class. Hence the term, step decoration. The appearance of the mark L12 should give the buyer pause before purchasing the Knight's Cross. While there are genuine items, many fakes with this mark have appeared.)

War Merit Cross
3184.Golden Knight's Cross with swords	10,000.00
3185.Golden Knight's Cross without swords	11,000.00
3186.Knight's Cross with swords	3000.00
3187.Knight's Cross without swords	3500.00
3188.I Class with swords-pinback	75.00
3189.same-screwback	100.00
3190.I Class without swords-pinback	125.00
3191.same-screwback	150.00
3192.II Class with swords	20.00
3193.II Class without swords	20.00
3194.War Merit Medal	15.00

(Note: Knight's Crosses may be hallmarked on the suspension and/or on the lower arms towards the points. Most commonly seen are 900 (silver content) and 21 (for the maker J.Godet of Berlin. As a matter of correcting a common mistake it should be noted that this award in German is known as "Kriegsverdienstkreuz", which translates to "War Merit Cross". Frequently, it is referred to as "War Service Cross", which in German would be "Kriegsdienstkreuz". The Knight's Crosses are frequently copied.)

War Order of the German Cross-1941-known as the "German Cross".
3195.German Cross in gold with diamonds (combat)	rare
3196.German Cross in gold (combat)	1000.00
3197.German Cross in gold-cloth & metal version	250.00
3198.German Cross in silver (non-combat)	2000.00

(Note: This decoration sometimes confuses collectors as it is a breast star. The "German Cross" referred to is the swastika. There are two types of this award. One with four rivets on the reverse and one with six rivets, and is usually hallmarked on the pin. Any unriveted piece, or other combination of rivets is a copy. This decoration has been copied extensively.)

Honor Roll Clasps
3199.Army	1200.00
3200.Navy	2000.00
3201.Air Force	1400.00

(Note: In as much as these are only stamped out pieces of thin metal on an Iron Cross ribbon original items are difficult to tell.)

Campaign Medals
3202.Campaign Medal-1939-1940	2200.00
3203.Campaign Medal-1939-1941	2200.00
(The above medals were prepared, but not awarded.)	
3204.Winter Campaign in Russia-1941-1942	25.00
3205.Commemorative Medal for Spanish Troops in Russia	75.00

Wound Badges
3206.Gold Wound Badge-gilt bronze-type II	85.00
3207.same-gilt brass	75.00
3208.same-gilt zinc	60.00
3209.Silver Wound Badge (silvered war metal, brass & zinc)	35.00
3210.Black Wound Badge-hollow	15.00
3211.Gold Wound Badge-20 Juli 1944-type III	rare
3212.Silver Wound Badge-20 Juli 1944	rare
3213.Black Wound Badge-20 Juli 1944	rare

(Note-The last three items have been copied. Beware!)

Eastern Peoples' Awards-Ostvolker
Combat-For Bravery-with swords
3214.I Class in gold-pinback	275.00
3215.I Class in silver-pinback	180.00
3216.II Class in gold-ribbon	110.00
3217.II Class in silver-ribbon	85.00
3218.II Class in bronze	75.00

Non-combat-For Merit-without swords
3219.I Class in gold	180.00
3220.I Class in silver	140.00
3221.II Class in gold	100.00
3223.II Class in silver	85.00
3224.II Class in bronze	75.00

Army & Navy Long Service Awards
3225.I Class-with oakleaves for 40 years	450.00
3226.I Class Cross for 25 years	175.00
3227.II Class Cross for 18 years	125.00
3228.III Class Medal for 12 years	65.00
3229.IV Class Medal for 4 years	45.00

(Note: The Army & Navy versions have the standard III Reich Eagle in metal on the ribbon.)

Air Force Long Service Awards
3230.I Class-with oakleaves for 40 years	550.00
3231.I Class Cross for 25 years	175.00
3232.II Class Cross for 18 years	125.00
3233.III Class Medal for 12 years	65.00
3234.IV Class Medal for 4 years	45.00

SS Long Service Awards
(See Decorations of the Nazi Party, items 3125-3128)

Sleeve Shields/Arm Bands/Sleeve Badges
3235.Narvik Shield in silver	150.00
3236.Narvik Shield in gold-Navy	180.00
3237.Cholm Shield	600.00
3238.Crimea Shield	75.00
3239.Demjansk Shield	150.00
3240.Kuban Shield	85.00

3241.Warsaw Shield (beware of copies)	rare
3242.Lappland Shield (beware of copies)	450.00
3243.Lorient Shield (beware of copies)	1200.00
3244.Afrika Corps Armband	180.00
3245.Crete Armband	180.00
3246.Kurland Armband (beware of copies)	450.00
3247.Driver badge in gold	50.00
3248.Driver badge in silver	35.00
3249.Driver badge in bronze	25.00

War Service Badges of the Army

3250.Close Combat badge in gold	1800.00
3251.Close Combat badge in silver	250.00
3252.Close Combat badge in bronze	175.00
(Note: The above three badges have been extensively copied.)	
3253.Infantry Assault Badge-silver	50.00
3254.Infantry Assault Badge-bronzed zinc	65.00
3255.same-bronzed war metal	65.00

General Assault Badges

3256. 100 Engagements	3000.00
3257. 75 Engagements	2000.00
3258. 50 Engagements	850.00
3259. 25 Engagements	600.00
3260. Standard issue-solid	50.00
3261. same-but hollow reverse	60.00

(Note: Be very cautious about buying the higher numbered versions of this badge, especially the 100 Engagements; many copies abound.)

Tank Battle Badge-silver

3262. 100 Engagements	3000.00
3263. 75 Engagements	1850.00
3264. 50 Engagements	1000.00
3265. 25 Engagements	650.00
3266. Standard issue-silvered bronze	75.00
3267. same-silvered zinc	65.00
3268. same-but hollow reverse-brass	75.00
(See note after 3261.)	

Tank Battle Badge-bronze

3269. 100 Engagements	rare
3270. 75 Engagements	3000.00
3271. 50 Engagements	1250.00
3272. 25 Engagements	850.00
3273. standard issue-oxydised bronze	65.00
3274. same-bronzed zinc	65.00
3275. same-hollow reverse-brass	75.00
(See note after 3261.)	
3276.Army Anti-aircraft badge	225.00

3277.Single Handed Tank Destruction Badge-gold	1200.00
3278.same-silver	200.00
3279.Air Plane Destruction badge-gold	rare
3280.same-black	rare
3281.Army Paratroop badge (beware of copies)-silver	3000.00
3282.same-aluminum	950.00
3283.same-silvered bronze	850.00
3284.Balloon Observer Badge-gold	rare
3285.same-silver	rare
3286.same-bronze	3000.00

(Note: Beware of copies of the last three items. It appears doubtful that they were ever awarded.)

War & Service Badges of the Navy

3287.U-Boat Combat Clasp-silver	850.00
3288.same-bronze	550.00
3289.U-Boat War Badge with diamonds (beware of copies)	rare
3290.U-Boat War Badge-gilt bronze	225.00
3291.same-gilt brass	225.00
3292.same-gilt zinc	175.00
3293.Destroyer Badge-gilt tombac	200.00
3294.same-gilt zinc	150.00
3295.Minesweeping Badge-gilt & silvered brass/bronze	125.00
3296.same-gilt & silvered zinc	75.00
3297.Auxiliary Cruiser Badge with Diamonds (beware!)	rare
3298.Auxiliary Cruiser Badge-gilt & silvered bronze	275.00
3299.same-gilt & silvered zinc	250.00
3300.High Seas Fleet Badge-gilt tombac	250.00
3301.same-gilt zinc	175.00
3302.E-Boat Badge-type I (beware of copies)	800.00
3303.E-Boat Badge-type II-gilt tombac & bronze	375.00
3304.same-gilt & silvered zinc	325.00
3305.same-with diamonds-silver & silver/gilt	rare

(Beware of copies of this last item.)

3306.Naval Artillery Badge-gilt & silvered tombac	175.00
3307.same-gilt zinc	75.00
3308.Blockade Runners Badge-gilt & silvered tombac	250.00
3309.same-silvered zinc	200.00
3310.Naval Combat Clasp	400.00

(Note: The West German reissue of this last item is almost identical to the original, as it was one of the few Nazi items which had no swastika on it, and thus needed no extensive redesign change.)

Combat Badge for Small Battle Units

3311.Cloth Patch-1st award	rare
3312.2nd award	rare
3313.3rd award	rare
3314.4th award	rare

(Note:5th - 7th awards exist; actual awards are questionable.

Operational Flying Clasps of the Air Force
Day Fighters
3315.Clasp in gold with diamonds	rare
3316.Clasp in gold with hanger & number	rare
3317.Clasp in gold with hanger	800.00
3318.Clasp in gold	550.00
3319.Clasp in silver	275.00
3320.Clasp in bronze	225.00

Nightfighters
3321.Clasp in gold with hanger & number	rare
3322.Clasp in gold with hanger	1200.00
3323.Clasp in gold	600.00
3324.Clasp in silver	500.00
3325.Clasp in bronze	350.00

Long Range Fighter & Night Intruder
3326.Clasp in gold with hanger & number	rare
3327.Clasp in gold with hanger	1100.00
3328.Clasp in gold	600.00
3329.Clasp in silver	500.00
3330.Clasp in bronze	425.00

Long Range Day Fighters
3331.Clasp in gold with hanger & number	rare
3332.Clasp in gold with hanger	rare
3333.Clasp in gold	600.00
3334.Clasp in silver	425.00
3335.Clasp in bronze	420.00

Heavy & Medium Dive Bombers
3336.Clasp in gold with hanger & number	rare
3337.Clasp in gold with hanger	550.00
3338.Clasp in gold	265.00
3339.Clasp in silver	165.00
3340.Clasp in bronze	140.00

Reconnaissance
3341.Clasp in gold with hanger & number	rare
3342.Clasp ingold with hanger	600.00
3343.Clasp in gold	380.00
3344.Clasp in silver	250.00
3345.Clasp in bronze	200.00

Transport & Glider Squadrons
3346.Clasp in gold with hanger & number	rare
3347.Clasp in gold with hanger-gilt bronze	800.00
3348.same-gilt zinc	600.00
3349.Clasp in gold	450.00
3350.Clasp in silver	350.00
3351.Clasp in bronze	190.00

Air to Ground Support Squadrons

3352.Clasp in gold with diamonds	rare
3353.Clasp in gold with hanger & number	1000.00
3354.Clasp in gold with hanger-gilt tombac	900.00
3355.same-gilt zinc	900.00
3356.Clasp in gold	900.00
3357.Clasp in silver	375.00
3358.Clasp in bronze	300.00

Air Force War Badges

3359.Anti-aircraft badge	150.00
3360.Ground Assault badge-silvered tombac	65.00
3361.same-oxydised zinc	55.00

(Note: Ground Assault badges for 25, 50, 75 & 100 Engagements must be regarded with suspicion, as none were awarded, and their very existance is one of dispute.)

3362.Combat Clasp in gold	rare
3363.same-silver	rare
3364.same-bronze	rare

(Note: The award of the Combat Clasp in any class is unknown!)

3365.Tank Battle badge-silver-100 Engagements	rare
3366.same-75 Engagements	rare
3367.same-50 Engagements	rare
3368.same-25 Engagements	rare
3369.same-standard issue	850.00

(Note: The actual award of items 3365-3368 is unknown, as is the award of 3365-3369 in black.)

3370.Sea Battle badge (award unknown)	rare

Air Qualification & Service Badges

3371.Pilot's Badge	250.00
3372.Observer's Badge	250.00
3373.Combined Pilot/Observer Badge in gold with diamonds	rare
3374.Combined Pilot Observer Badge	700.00
3375.Radio Operator Badge	350.00
3376.Air Gunner Badge	300.00
3377.Air Gunner Badge with black wreath	650.00
3378.Paratroop Badge	300.00
3379.Glider Pilot's Badge-silvered	1200.00
3380.same-oxydised zinc	1000.00
3381.Flyer's Commemorative Badge	1600.00
3382.Civil Anti-aircraft badge	300.00

Non-Portable Awards of the Air Force

3383.Honor Goblet-silver	3000.00
3384.Honor Goblet-marked Alpaka	2100.00
3385.Salver of Honor	8000.00
3386.Medallion "For Outstanding Achievements in the Technical Branch of the Air Force"	450.00
3387.Medallion-Air District West-France	500.00
3388.Medallion-Air District-Belgium	500.00
3389.Plaque-Air District-Norway	400.00
3390.Plaque-S.E. Command	550.00

3391.Plaque-Air District Staff-Finland-1942 650.00
3392.same-1943 450.00
3393.Plaque-Air District XI 600.00
3394.Plaque-Special Merit-Battle of Crete 650.00

Guerrilla War Badges of the Waffen SS & Police
3395.Badge in gold with diamonds (not awarded) rare
3396.Badge in gold-gilt bronze 1800.00
3397.same-gilt zinc 1200.00
3398.Badge in silver-silvered bronze 825.00
3399.same-silvered zinc 575.00
3400.Badge in bronze-oxydised bronze 550.00
3401.same-bronzed zinc 425.00
(Note: This badge came in both hollow back & solid back types, and has been extensively copied.)

Badges of Russian Volunteer Units Serving with the German Armed Forces during World War II.
3402.Cross of the II Siberian Cavalry Regiment 1500.00
3403.Cross of the V Don Cossack Regiment 1500.00
3404.Badge of XV Cossack Cavalry Corps 1000.00
3405.Badge of the 1st Officers' School of the ROA(POA)-
       "Russian Army of Liberation" rare
(Note: These items should be approached with caution. Since the recipients were regarded as Nazi collaborationists, with many of them being turned over to the Soviet Union after World War II, the survival rate of these pieces must be considered low. However, like many other German made pieces, one cannot know how many were originally made.)

FEDERAL REPUBLIC

By law in 1957 the swastika was proclaimed a forbidden symbol in the Federal Republic of Germany (West Germany), and awards bearing that symbol could not be worn. III Reich decorations, except for those of the Nazi Party and its various branches, were allowed to be worn if there was no swastika on them. Thus, many awards appeared in a new design reflecting the political changes. All III Reich awards listed below are therefore reissues without swastika.

Iron Cross
3406.Knight's Cross with swords & oakleaves 450.00
3407.Knight's Cross with oakleaves 400.00
3408.Knight's Cross 300.00
3409.I Class 85.00
3410.II Class 50.00
3411.I Class-without date or oakleaves-Austrian version 200.00
3412.II Class-without date or oakleaves-Austrian version 125.00

War Order of the German Cross
3413.Gold 250.00
3414.Silver 250.00

War Merit Cross

3415.Knight's Cross with swords	350.00
3416.Knight's Cross without swords	350.00
3417.I Class with swords	75.00
3418.I Class without swords	75.00
3419.II Class with swords	25.00
3420.II Class without swords	25.00
3421.Medal	20.00

Order of Merit of the Federal Republic

3422.Grand Cross-special class-badge, sash, 8 pointed star	rare
3423.Grand Cross-special design-badge, sash, 6 pointed star	1200.00
3424.Grand Cross-badge, sash, 4 pointed star	900.00
3425.Grand Merit Cross-as above-different 4 pointed star	800.00
3426.Grand Merit Cross-neck badge & star as in 3425	600.00
3427.Grand Merit Cross-neck badge	150.00
3428.Merit Cross I Class-pinback	125.00
(Note: 3428 is used as a high military decoration.)	
3429.Merit Cross II Class-ribbon	50.00
3430.same-with 50 year bar	85.00
3431.Merit Medal	45.00

3432.Order Pour Le Mérite for Arts & Science	3000.00
(Note: This is a reissue of the Prussian award of the same name.)	

149 47

317 113, 115, 117

150 370 346 & 350

318 152

498 & 502

539 538 539 & 540

1053

598 & 600   606 & 607

716 & 720   737

906

998 & 1001 930

2381 & 2386 910

1088   1169

1045   2419

1289 & 1293   1331

1332 & 1333   2270, 2271, 2276

1349 & 1350

1346

1431   1502 & 1503

1510 & 1511   1535 & 1536   1456

1599   1576   1604

1604 & 1609   1603 & 1609

1709

1690   2553

1762

1839 & 1840

1784 & 1785

1854 & 1855   1975   1793, 1794, 1798

1878   1945

1946 - 1949

1915, 1918, 1921, 1924   1877   1934 & 1938

2207 - 2209   2216 & 2217

2270, 2271, 2276   2249

2630 & 2631

2677 & 2678

2731

2733

2730

2835 & 2836   2835 & 2836   2837

2839   2838   2840

2917

2918

2929

2922

2945 & 2948

2950   2952

3027

3028   3029

3157

3158

3159

3175

3187

3177 3181 3183

1608 & 3183 1607 & 3182

3308 & 3309   3298 & 3299

3300 & 3301   3303

3281 - 3283   3371   3378

3375   3376

GREAT BRITAIN

The Orders, decorations and medals of this country have a special interest for this author, since that is what he collected. Thus, you might detect some extra enthusiasm in this presentation. Nevertheless, the collector will be made aware of all aspects of Britain's awards, negative as well as positive.

If you are English speaking, then as a collector of British items you have an enormous advantage over those who collect from non-English speaking countries. There is a vast amount of material published on British awards, of great benefit to the collector. Moreover, collectors of British items are very willing to share their knowledge of discoveries with other collectors, which is extremely helpful especially to the beginner.

British Orders have always been made to a high standard of quality, whether by private manufacturers such as Garrard, or by the Royal Mint. Furthermore, unlike the practice of some European countries, the number struck is reflected very closely by the number awarded. Only under careful scrutiny has it been possible for a replacement to be obtained. Indeed with some Orders on promotion to a higher class the lower one would have to returned for reissue to another recipient. The Royal Victorian Order is unique among British Orders in that it is the only one to be numbered on the reverse of badges and stars. This is for British subjects, with foreign recipients being considered honorary awardees only, and their insignia are not numbered. The two highest classes, Grand Cross, and Knight Commander should have insignia with matching numbers. Since the Knight Commander's neck badge (II Class) is the same size and appearance as the Commander's neck badge (III Class) the only distinction is the number on the reverse. The Knight Commander's number being preceded by the letter "K", and the Commander's badge number being preceded by the letter "C".

The Orders of the Garter, The Thistle, and St Patrick are one class only; the St Patrick being obsolete. The Order of the Bath, in three classes, has two divisions, military and civil, very distinctive in appearance for the badges, but quite similar for the breast stars. The ribbon is the same for both. There are also two other Orders of one class; the Order of Merit, and Companion of Honour, worn around the neck, with the former being unique among British Orders in that as a military award it is worn with crossed swords through the arms. The Order of St Michael and St George has three classes, and the British Empire and Royal Victorian Orders have five classes. Although the British Empire Order has both military and civil divisions the only difference is that the military award has a extra vertical stripe in the ribbon; red for the type I, and pearl gray for type II. The British Empire Order is also unique in that it is the only British Order whose insignia were changed completely, in 1935. While India was the jewel of the British Empire there were two great Orders; the Star of India (which included platinum and diamonds in its highest class), and the Indian Empire Order, whose badges were always of genuine gold. In deference to the many non-Christian recipients of these Orders the highest class was known as the Knight Grand Commander, rather than Knight Grand Cross. For the most part except for some recent copies of the Order of Merit there have not been very many cases of copies of British Orders. With perhaps the exception of British Orders made in Paris in 1814, all British Orders with a non-British hallmark or maker's name may be considered as copies.

George IV as Prince Regent in Paris 1814 did authorize some insignia of the Bath to be made in Paris so that he could make awards quickly. Since the sovereign is the fount of honor in Great Britain these items do have a legitimate air to them.

ORDERS OF KNIGHTHOOD
Order of the Garter-K.G.

1.Collar	rare
2.Collar Badge (The George)	rare
3.Star-metal-early 20th century	4000.00-8000.00
4.Star-embroidered	800.00-2000.00
5.Sash badge (Lesser George)	50,000.00-60,000.00
6.Garter-embroidered lettering-excellent	1000.00
7.same-but worn condition	500.00
8.Garter-gold lettering,buckle & tab	4000.00

(Values are for privately made items. Official insignia are returnable on death of recipient.)

Order of the Thistle-K.T.

9.Collar	rare
10.Collar badge	rare
11.Star-metal	2500.00-6000.00
12.Star-embroidered-excellent condition	1200.00
13.Star-embroidered-worn condition	500.00
14.Sash badge	8000.00-15,000.00

(Insignia returnable on death.)

Order of St Patrick-1783-1974-obsolete-K.P.

15.Collar	rare
16.Collar badge	12,000.00-22,000.00
17.Sash badge	8000.00-12,500.00
18.Star-metal	4000.00
19.Star-embroidered-excellent condition	1000.00
20.Star-embroidered-worn condition	400.00

(Insignia returnable on death.)

Order of the Bath-1725-1815-K.B.

21.Collar	rare
22.Collar badge	rare
23.Star-metal	4000.00-6000.00
24.Star-embroidered-excellent condition	800.00
25.Star-embroidered-worn condition	250.00
26.Sash badge-oval-gold-similar to later civil	4000.00-7000.00

Order of the Bath-type II-military-1815

27.Collar	rare
28.Collar badge	6750.00
29.Grand Cross badge-gold	3500.00-5000.00
30.Grand Cross badge-silver/gilt	1200.00-1800.00
31.Grand Cross breast star	1000.00-1800.00

32.Knight Commander-neck badge-gold	1000.00-2000.00
33.Knight Commander-neck badge-silver/gilt	800.00
34.Knight Commander-breast star	650.00
35.Companion-breast badge-gold	1000.00-2000.00
36.Companion-breast badge-silver/gilt	700.00
37.Companion-neck badge-silver/gilt	500.00

(Note: Insignia hallmarked for 1815 command a premium, as an early issue, most likely for the Battle of Waterloo.)

Order of the Bath-type II-civil-1815

38.Collar	rare
39.Grand Cross badge-gold	2000.00
40.Grand Cross badge-silver/gilt	850.00
41.Grand Cross breast star	800.00
42.Knight Commander-neck badge-gold	900.00
43.Knight Commander-neck badge-silver/gilt	400.00
44.Knight Commander-breast star	500.00
45.Companion-breast badge-gold	700.00
46.Companion-breast badge-silver/gilt	450.00
47.Companion-neck badge-silver/gilt	350.00

Order of St Michael & St George-1818

48.Collar-returnable after 1948	2750.00
49.Grand Cross badge-gold	6500.00
50.Grand Cross badge-silver/gilt	1200.00
51.Grand Cross breast star	950.00
52.Knight Commander-neck badge-gold	1900.00
53.Knight Commander-neck badge-silver/gilt	700.00
54.Knight Commander-breast star	700.00
55.Companion-breast badge-gold	1200.00
56.Companion-breast badge-silver/gilt	700.00
57.Companion-breast badge-late issue-World War I	750.00
58.Companion-neck badge	700.00

Royal Guelphic Order-1815-1837

59.Collar-gold	10,000.00-15,000.00
60.Collar-silver/gilt	8000.00
61.Collar badge	6500.00
62.Collar badge-with swords	8000.00
63.Grand Cross badge	6000.00
64.Grand Cross badge-with swords	10,000.00
65.Grand Cross breast star	1000.00-1800.00
66.Grand Cross breast star-with swords	2000.00-3500.00
67.Knight Commander-neck badge	1800.00
68.Knight Commander-neck badge-with swords	3500.00
69.Knight Commander-breast star	900.00
70.Knight Commander-breast star-with swords	1850.00
71.Knight	950.00
72.Knight-with swords	1800.00

(Note: See also Hannover under the German States section. This Order was also known as the Hanoverian Order. The badges of this Order are all in genuine gold & enamels. With swords denotes a military award. Values are for British made insignia. After 1837 this Order became a purely Hannoverian (German) award. Hanover is the English spelling of the German name Hannover.)

Order of the Star of India-1861-1947

73.Collar	rare
74. & 75.Knight Grand Commander-badge & breast star	48,000.00
76. & 77.Knight Commander-neck badge & breast star	10,000.00
78.Companion-breast badge	4000.00
79.Companion-neck badge	2750.00

Order of the Indian Empire-1878-1947

80.Collar	rare
81. & 82.Knight Grand Commander-badge & breast star	6400.00-9000.00
83. & 84.Knight Commander-neck badge & breast star	2800.00-3800.00
85.Companion-type I-breast badge-large-marked INDIA	1800.00
86.same-type II-but without marking	1000.00
87.same-type III-smaller breast badge	800.00
88.same-type IV-neck badge	600.00

(Note: The badges of this Order are all genuine gold & enamels.)

The Royal Order of Victoria & Albert

89.First Class	40,000.00
90.Second Class	30,000.00
91.Third Class	18,000.00
92.Fourth Class	8000.00

(Note: Insignia are returnable on death.)

93.Order of the Crown of India-1878-1947	15,000.00

The Order of Merit

94.Edward VII-civil	6500.00
95.Edward VII-military-with swords	9000.00
96.George V-civil	5000.00
97.George V-military-with swords	9500.00
98.George VI-civil	5500.00
99.George VI-military-with swords	rare
100.Elizabeth II-civil	5000.00
101.Elizabeth II-military-with swords	rare

(Note: Returnable since 1991. Copies of this Order are known to exist.)

The Royal Victorian Chain

102.Gentlemen's collar-1902-1921	rare
103.Ladies' bow style	rare
104.Gentlemen's collar-1921-with diamonds	rare
105.Ladies' bow style	rare

The Royal Victorian Order-1896

106.Collar-gentlemen's	10,000.00
107.Collar-ladies'	12,000.00
108. & 109.Grand Cross badge and breast star	1800.00
110. & 111.same-Dame Grand Cross-ladies	2250.00
112. & 113.Knight Commander-neck badge & star	1100.00
114. & 115.same-Dame Commander-ladies	1500.00
116.Commander	500.00
117.same-ladies	800.00
118.IV Class-Lieutenant	500.00
119.same-ladies	500.00
120.V Class-Member	400.00
121.same-ladies	450.00

(Note: Awards to British recipients are numbered on the reverse with class indication. The Knight Commander (II Class) and the Commander (III Class) badges are identical, but the former is marked K for Knight Commander, and the latter is marked C for Commander. A matched set of badge and star must have the same numbers. Awards to foreigners are considered honorary, and therefore are not numbered. Cases for the Order should have the matching number for the insignia inside. Ladies badges are worn on bows. A low number does not necessarily signify an early recipient, as on promotion in this Order insignia are returned for later distribution.)

The Royal Victorian Medal

122.Victoria-silver	200.00
123.Victoria-bronze	125.00
124.Edward VII-silver	225.00
125.Edward VII-bronze	175.00
126.George V-silver/gilt	275.00
127.George V-silver	150.00
128.George V-bronze	125.00
129.George VI-silver/gilt	200.00
130.George VI-silver	200.00
131.George VI-bronze	rare
132.Elizabeth II-silver/gilt	275.00
133.Elizabeth II-silver	225.00
134.Elizabeth II-bronze	200.00

(Two silver medals issued for Edward VIII.)

Order of the British Empire-1917

Type I-1917-1935-obverse centre bears Britannia-Gentlemen

135.Collar-returnable	rare
136. & 137. Grand Cross badge & breast star	1500.00
138. & 139. Knight Commander-neck badge & breast star	700.00
140.Commander-neck badge	250.00
141.Officer	100.00
142.Member	100.00

Type I-Ladies'-badges worn on bow ribbon on the left chest
143. & 144. Dame Grand Cross badge & breast star	2000.00
145. & 146. Dame Commander badge & breast star	750.00
147. Commander	300.00
148. Officer	150.00
149. Member	150.00

Type II-George V & Queen Mary on obverse centre-Gentlemen
150. Collar-returnable	rare
151. & 152. Grand Cross badge & breast star	1600.00
153. & 154. Knight Commander badge & breast star	750.00
155. Commander-neck badge	250.00
156. Officer	100.00
157. Member	100.00

Type II-Ladies'-badges worn on bow ribbons on the left chest
158. & 159. Dame Grand Cross badge & breast star	1900.00
160. & 161. Dame Commander badge & breast star	800.00
162. Commander	250.00
163. Officer	150.00
164. Member	150.00

(Note: Can be worn with the civil or military ribbon which does not affect values. The type II ribbon can be worn with type I insignia, but not the opposite.)

British Empire Medal-1917
165. Type I-1917-22-small type-usually not named	175.00
Type II-1922-larger size-officially named	
166. George V-For Gallantry-Empire Gallantry Medal	5000.00
167. George V-For Meritorious Service	250.00
168. George VI-For Gallantry-Empire Gallantry Medal	5000.00
169. George VI-For Meritorious Service	150.00
170. Elizabeth II-For Meritorious Service	200.00
171. same-but with gallantry emblem on ribbon-civil	500.00
172. same-but with gallantry emblem on ribbon-military	1000.00

(Values for military awards are 50% to 100% higher.)

Baronet's Badges (worn on neck ribbon)
173. Nova Scotia-17th century	rare
174. Nova Scotia-18th/19th century-gold	4000.00
175. Nova Scotia-19th century-silver/gilt	3000.00
176. England-gold	2000.00
177. England-silver/gilt	1500.00
178. Ireland-gold	2500.00
179. Ireland--silver/gilt	1000.00
180. Great Britain-gold	2000.00
181. Great Britain-silver/gilt	1000.00
182. United Kingdom-gold	1500.00
183. United Kingdom-silver/gilt	1000.00

Knight Bachelor Badges

184.Type I-small breast badge-pinback	350.00
185.Type II-larger breast badge	300.00
186.Type III-neck badge	350.00

187.Order of the Companions of Honor-1917   3500.00
(Neck badge for gentlemen; bow badge for ladies.)

Order of St John-1888 & 1926

188.Bailiff Grand Cross-badge & breast star	1250.00
189.Dame Grand Cross-badge & breast star	900.00
190.Knight of Justice-neck badge & breast star	400.00
191.Dame of Justice-breast badge & breast star	400.00
192.Knight of Grace-neck badge & breast star	400.00
193.Dame of Grace-breast badge & breast star	400.00
194.Commander-Brother-neck badge	200.00
195.Commander-Sister-breast badge	200.00
196.Officer-Brother	85.00
197.Officer-Sister	85.00
198.Serving Brother	100.00
199.Serving Sister	100.00

(Note: Values based on silver & silver/gilt & enameled insignia. Ladies' badges are worn on a bow ribbon. The ribbon for this order is black. The badges are Maltese Crosses. This Order is descended from the Order of St John of Jerusalem, Rhodes & Malta. See also similar insignia from Austria, Prussia, Vatican, etc.)

Order of the Dooranie Empire-1839-obsolete

200.Grand Cross-badge & breast star	14,000.00
201.Knight Commander-neck badge & breast star	7000.00
202.Commander	2500.00

(This Afghan Order was created in 1839, and was awarded to a number of British Officers for their services to the then ruler.)

DECORATIONS-for Gallantry awards see-Abbott & Tamplin-**BRITISH GALLANTRY AWARDS.**

203.Victoria Cross
The value of this item is difficult to establish. Rank, citation, branch of service, time and area of action, such as D-Day June 6th, 1944, can all have significant bearing on its value. Finally, auctions, where most are sold, show great variations.
A minimum reasonable value would be at least   40,000.00

New Zealand Cross-1869

204.Awarded piece	32,500.00
205.Unnamed Specimen	5000.00

George Cross-1940
206.Armed Forces Awards pre-1940 (exchanges for the
Empire Gallantry Medal & Albert Medal)   5000.00

207.Civilian Awards pre-1940-exchanges	4000.00
208.Armed Forces Awards from 1940	12,500.00
209.Civilian Awards from 1940	6000.00

(Note: As citations vary, so can values.)

George Medal-1940

210.George VI-military-type I	1500.00
211.George VI-civil-type I	1200.00
212.Elizabeth II-military-type I	2200.00
213.Elizabeth II-civil-type I	1250.00

Distinguished Service Order-1884

214.Victoria-gold-1884-1887	3200.00
215.Victoria-silver/gilt-1887	1200.00
216.Edward VII	2000.00
217.George V	800.00
218.George VI-type I-GRI	1000.00
219.George VI-type II-GVI	1500.00
220.Elizabeth II	1600.00

(Note: Values are based on an unattributed item. Attributed awards, in a group with named medals, are worth 50% higher or more based on the nature of the award, including the citation if any.)

Imperial Service Order

221.Edward VII-gentlemen	195.00
222.Edward VII-ladies	rare
223.George V-gentlemen	200.00
224.George V-ladies	rare
225.George VI-gentlemen	200.00
226.George VI-ladies	rare
227.Elizabeth II-gentlemen	200.00
228,Elizabeth II-ladies	500.00

(Note: The gentlemen's insignia is composed of a silver star with a gold centre with the monarch's cypher. The ladies' a silver wreath around the circular gold centre, and worn on a bow ribbon.)

Imperial Service Medal

229.Edward VII-gentlemen(bronze/silver like 221)	50.00
230.Edward VII-ladies(bronze/silver like 222)	150.00
231.George V-gentlemen-type I(bronze/silver like 223)	40.00
232.George V-ladies-type I(bronze/silver like 224)	140.00
233.George V-type II-silver medal-coin head	25.00
234.George V-type II-silver medal-crowned head	25.00
235.George VI-type I-Ind Imp	25.00
236.George VI-type II-no Ind Imp	25.00
237.Elizabeth II-long legend	25.00
238.Elizabeth II-short legend	25.00

Royal Red Cross-1883
First Class-R.R.C.

239. Victoria-gold	1500.00
240. Victoria-silver/gilt	800.00
241. Edward VII	1000.00
242. George V	250.00
243. George VI	200.00-400.00
244. Elizabeth II	400.00

Second Class-A.R.R.C.

245. Victoria-not issued	
246. Edward VII-not issued	
247. George V	150.00
248. George VI	200.00
249. Elizabeth II	200.00

(Note:Since this award was instituted for ladies it is properly worn from a bow ribbon.)

Distinguished Service Cross-1901 & 1914-Royal Navy-Officers

250. Edward VII (Conspicuous Service Cross)	rare
251. George V	550.00
252. George VI-GRI	650.00
253. George VI-GVI	rare
254. Elizabeth II	rare

(Note: The values above are for unattributed awards. Attributed awards may command values 50% more or higher than the above, depending on action, rank and citation if any; primarily an officers' award.)

Distinguished Service Medal-1914-Royal Navy-enlisted men

255. George V-type I-uncrowned head-1914-30	350.00
256. George V-type II-crowned head-1930-37	2200.00
257. George VI-type I-GRI reverse-Ind Imp	500.00
258. George VI-type II-GVIR reverse-no Ind Imp	2200.00
259. Elizabeth II-long legend	5000.00
260. Elizabeth II-short legend	5000.00

(Citations, if any, can cause values to rise.)

Military Cross-1914-Army-Officers

261. George V	400.00
262. George VI-type I-GRI	500.00
263. George VI-type II-GVI	rare
264. Elizabeth II	rare

(Note: The above values are for unattributed awards. Attributed awards may command values 50% more or higher than the above; primarily an officers' award, now awarded to all ranks.)

Military Medal-1916-enlisted men

265. George V-corps	150.00
266. George V-line regiments	200.00
267. George V-Royal Flying Corps	3000.00

268.George V-Royal Air Force	rare
269.George V-Royal Naval Division	550.00
270.George V-Australians	600.00
271.George V-Canadians	400.00
272.George V-New Zealanders	550.00
273.George V-South Africans	550.00
274.George V-French Army	rare
275.George V-Italian Army	rare
276.George V-United States Army	rare

(Note: While I have never seen any others so inscribed, there may have been others to Allied Soldiers. It has been suggested that awards to foreign recipients were not named. This is possible, but then it would not explain those that were.)

277.George V-type II-crowned head-1930-38	4500.00
278.George VI-type I-Ind Imp-reverse GRI	750.00
279.same-but to Indian Army	500.00
280.George VI-type II-no Ind Imp-reverse GVI	2000.00
281.Elizabeth II-type I-long legend	2500.00
282.Elizabeth II-type II-short legend	3000.00

(Note: This award for enlisted men is always named. Although primarily an army award it can be granted to other branches of the armed forces under certain conditions. Copies of the George V type exist; thinner, non-swivel suspension, unnamed, king has a pained expression on his face. Copies of the George VI type are without naming, and do not have the designer's initials under bust. However, there are some unnamed specimens of the George VI type I which came from the Canadian War Museum. Replaced by the Military Cross in 1993.)

Distinguished Flying Cross-1918-Combat Heroism

283.George V	800.00
284.George VI-type I-GRI	650.00
285.George VI-type II-GVI	rare
286.Elizabeth II	rare

(Note: These values are for unattributed awards. Attributed awards may be 50% more or higher than above values. Copies exist, some of which are very difficult to detect. An officers' award until 1993.)

Distinguished Flying Medal-1918-Enlisted Men-combat heroism

287.George V-type I-uncrowned head-1918-30	1800.00
288.George V-type II-crowned head-1930-38	3500.00
289.George VI-type I-Ind Imp obverse legend	800.00
290.George VI-type II-no Ind Imp in legend	1500.00
291.Elizabeth II	1500.00

(Note: Always issued named. Copies exist. Some awarded to foreign recipients for World War II & Korea. Now replaced by the Distinguished Flying Cross.)

Air Force Cross-1918-non-combat heroism

292.George V	850.00
293.George VI-type I-GVIRI	850.00

294.George VI-type II-GVIR	1000.00
295.Elizabeth II	1000.00

(Note: These values are for unattributed awards. Attributed awards may be 50% more or higher than the above values. Copies of this decoration exist. Care must be taken that the monarch's cyphers match on the obverse & reverse, and that the designer's initials are on the obverse centre. An officers' award until 1993.)

Air Force Medal-1918-Enlisted Men-non-combat heroism
296.George V-type I-uncrowned head-1918-30	1300.00
297.George V-type II-crowned head-1930-38	4000.00
298.George VI-type I-Ind Imp in obverse legend	1000.00
299.George VI-type II-no Ind Imp	1200.00
300.Elizabeth II	1250.00

(Note: This decoration is always issued named. Replaced by the Air Force Cross since 1993. Copies exist.)

Conspicuous Gallantry Medal-Royal Navy-enlisted men
301.Victoria	4000.00-8000.00
302.Edward VII	two
303.George V	4000.00
304.George VI	6000.00
305.Elizabeth II	one

(Note: This decoration is always issued named. Some unnamed specimens exist. Replaced by the Conspicuous Gallantry Cross since 1993.)

Conspicuous Gallantry Medal-Flying (Royal Air Force)-enlisted men
306.George VI	5200.00
307.Elizabeth II	one

(Note: This decoration is always issued named.)

Distinguished Conduct Medal-Army-enlisted men
308.Victoria-Crimea-Light Brigade	3500.00
309.Victoria-Crimea-Heavy Brigade	2000.00
310.Victoria-Crimea-other issues	1000.00
311.Victoria-Indian Mutiny	8000.00
312.Victoria-Indian Campaigns 1854-95	4500.00
313.Victoria-Abyssinia 1867-68	4000.00
314.Victoria-Ashantee 1873-74	3000.00
315.Victoria-South Africa 1877-79	6000.00
316.Victoria-Afghanistan 1878-80	3000.00
317.Victoria-Egypt 1882	3000.00
318.Victoria-Indian Campaigns 1895-1901	3000.00
319.Victoria-Sudan 1896-97	3000.00
320.Victoria-South Africa 1899-1902	1200.00
321.Edward VII-South Africa 1899-1902	1500.00
322.Edward VII-other issues	rare
323.George V-type I-uncrowned head	450.00
324.George V-type II-crowned head 1930-37	3500.00
325.George VI-type I-Ind Imp in obverse legend	2000.00

326.George VI-type II-no Ind Imp in legend	2500.00
327.Elizabeth II-type I-long legend	4000.00-6500.00
328.Elizabeth II-type II-short legend	4000.00-9500.00

(Note: Values for this decoration can vary considerably according to rank, and citation. Always issued named. Some unnamed specimens of the George VI type I exist, apparently from the Canadian War Museum. Since 1993 replaced by the Conspicuous Gallantry Cross.)

Distinguished Conduct Medal-colonial varieties

329.King's African Rifles-George V	750.00
330.West African Frontier Force-Edward VII	rare
331.West African Frontier Force-GeoV	800.00
332.Canada-all issues	rare
333.Cape of Good Hope-all issues	rare
334.Natal-all issues	rare
335.New Zealand-all issues	rare

(Note: Unnamed specimens of the last four items exist, and are probably the only pieces that collectors will come across.)

Queen's Gallantry Medal-non-combat gallantry

336.Military award	2800.00
337.Civilian award	1200.00

338.Constabulary Medal-Ireland	1800.00

Albert Medal
Military - Sea

339.Gold	8000.00
340.Bronze	5000.00

Military - Land

341.Gold	6500.00
342.Bronze	3500.00

Civil - Sea

343.Gold	6500.00
344.Bronze	3500.00

Civil - Land

345.Gold	5000.00
346.Bronze	3000.00

(Note: Sea - Edward VII -2 gold awarded; George VI -3 gold awarded; Elizabeth II no gold awarded. Land - Edward VII -7 gold awarded; George VI -3 gold awarded and 3 bronze awarded; Ellizabeth II no gold awarded. The gold medal was abolished in 1949, and the bronze in 1971. Living recipients were invited to replace their medals with the George Cross (see above). Most did so.)

Edward Medal
Mine Service Issue

347.Edward VII-silver	1250.00
348.Bronze	850.00

349.George V-silver-type I	1250.00
350.Bronze-type I	850.00
351.George V-silver-type II	2000.00
352.Bronze-type II	850.00
353.George VI-silver-type I	2500.00
354.Bronze	2000.00
355.Bronze-type II	rare
356.Elizabeth II-silver	none issued
357.Bronze	from 3000.00

Industrial Issue

358.Edward VII-silver	rare
359.Bronze	rare
360.George V-silver-type I	not issued
361.Bronze-type I	3000.00
362.George V-silver-type II	2200.00
363.Bronze-type II	1000.00
364.George V-silver-type III	rare
365.Bronze-type IIII	2000.00
366.George VI-silver-type I	not issued
367.Bronze-type I	1800.00
368.George VI-silver-type II	not issued
369.Bronze-type II	rare
370.Elizabeth II-silver	none awarded
371.Bronze	rare

Sea Gallantry Medal-For Lifesaving

372.Edward VII-silver	900.00
373.Bronze	800.00
374.George V-silver	1000.00
375.Bronze	950.00
376.George VI-silver-type I	800.00
377.Bronze-type I	800.00
378.Silver-type II	none awarded
379.Bronze-type II	550.00
380.Elizabeth II-silver	1000.00
381.Bronze	1100.00

382.Order of Burma	rare

383.Burma Gallantry Medal	4000.00

(In Glendining's Auction of 13 December 1989 the above awarded to a member of
the Burma Hospital Corps sold for £2200; unique to the unit.)

Order of British India

384.First Class-gold & enamels	750.00
385.Second Class-gold & enamels	600.00

(There are color variations in the obverse centre blue enamel; sometimes found
named on the reverse.)

Indian Order of Merit-1837-1947
Military 1837-1912-obverse-Reward of Valour
386.First Class-gold star	2200.00
387.Second Class-silver star & gold wreath	1000.00
388.Third Class-silver star & silver wreath	500.00

Military 1912-1939-obverse Reward of Valour
389.First Class-silver star & large gold wreath	1300.00
390.Second Class	600.00

Military 1939-45-obverse Reward of Gallantry
391.First Class-silver star & gold wreath	two
392.Second Class-silver star & silver wreath	1000.00

Military 1945-47-obverse Reward of Gallantry
393.First Class-silver star with gold wreath & crown	1500.00

Civil
394.1939-1947-one class only-For Bravery	1500.00

Indian Distinguished Service Medal
395.Edward VII	950.00
396.George V	300.00
397.George V-type II	600.00
398.George VI	350.00

(Note: A medal roll now exists for this award.)

Kaisar-I-Hind Medal-For Public Service in India
399.Victoria-I Class-gold	1000.00
400.II Class-silver	275.00
401.Edward VII-I Class-gold	1000.00
402.II Class-silver	300.00
403.George V-type I-hollow-I Class-gold	1000.00
404.II Class-silver	250.00
405.type II-solid-small-I Class-gold	850.00
406.II Class-silver	200.00
407.III Class-bronze	175.00
408.George VI-I Class-gold	1000.00
409.II Class-silver	275.00
410.III Class-bronze	175.00

Union of South Africa-King's/Queen's Bravery Medal
411.Gold	one awarded
412.Silver	1250.00

King's Police Medal (King's & Queen's Police & Fire Services Medal)
413.Edward VII	1000.00
414.George V-type I-coinage head	450.00
415.George V-type II-crowned head	500.00
416.George V-For Gallantry	750.00
417.George V-For Distinguished Service	350.00
418.George VI-For Gallantry-type I	900.00
419.George VI-For Gallantry-type II	1500.00

420.George VI-For Distinguished Service-type I	350.00
421.George VI-For Distinguished Service-type II	350.00

(Values for the Police or Fire Service recipients can vary according to circumstances.)

Queen's Police Medal-1954

422.For Gallantry	1000.00
423.For Distinguished Service	600.00

Queen's Fire Service Medal-1954

424.For Gallantry	rare
425.For Distinguished Service	650.00

Burma Police Medal-1937

426.For Distinguished Conduct-bronze	1250.00
427.For Meritorious Service	800.00

Colonial Police/Fire Medal
For Gallantry

428.George VI-police-type I	1200.00
429.George VI-fire-type I	rare
430.George VI-police-type II	1000.00
431.George VI-fire-type II	rare
432.Elizabeth II-police-type I	1000.00
433.Elizabeth II-fire-type I	1200.00
434.Elizabeth II-police-type II	1000.00
435.Elizabeth II-fire-type II	1000.00

For Meritorious Service

436.George VI-police-type I	450.00
437.George VI-fire-type I	450.00
438.George VI-police-type II	rare
439.George VI-fire-type II	500.00
440.Elizabeth II-police type I	450.00
441.Elizabeth II-fire-type I	500.00
442.Elizabeth II-police-type II	450.00
443.Elizabeth II-fire-type II	450.00

Foreign Office Medal for Lifesaving

444.Gold	1000.00
445.Silver	350.00

Indian Police/Fire Medal-1932-1947

446.George V-For Distinguished Conduct	450.00
447.George VI-For Distinguished Conduct	450.00
448.George VI-For Gallantry-1945	650.00
449.George VI-For Meritorious Service-1945	400.00

Awards to Foreign Citizens for Wartime Activities

450.Allied Subjects Medal-1914-18-silver-named	1250.00
451.same-Bronze	550.00
452.King's Medal for Courage in the Cause of Freedom-1939-45 (awarded mainly to members of the European Resistance movement for gallantry against the Nazi Occupation)	650.00
453.King's Medal for Service in the Cause of Freedom-1939-45 (awarded to foreign citizens who made a significant contribution to the war effort.)	350.00
454.Medal for Science, Art & Music-Edward VII	1500.00

CAMPAIGN MEDALS

To properly appreciate this series you are recommended to read **BRITISH BATTLES & MEDALS**-6th edition, by L.L.Gordon (as revised by E.C. Joslin & A. Litherland, and B. Simkin; London 1988.) Values on medals are only for original strikings, to the most common units, when named, and in VF-EF condition.

455.Battle of Dunbar-1650 (restrikes exist)	1500.00
456.Royalist Award Badges for the Civil War-silver/gilt-usually looped at top-thin	750.00
457.Culloden-1746	5000.00

Louisburg 1758

458.Gold	four
459.Silver	5000.00
460.Bronze	1300.00
461.Carib War Medal-1773	1550.00

Germantown 1777

462.Gilt	rare
463.Silver	rare
464.Bronze	rare

Deccan Medal-1778-1784

465.Gold- 40.5mm	8000.00
466.Silver- 40.5mm	1200.00
467.Silver- 32mm	750.00

Defence of Gibraltar-1779-1783

468.General Picton's	900.00
469.General Elliott's	750.00

GREAT BRITAIN

Mysore Campaigns-1790-1792-copies exist
470.Gold- 43mm   8500.00
471.Silver- 43mm   1600.00
472.Silver- 38mm   900.00

473.Isle of St Vincent Medal-1795   1000.00

Capture of Ceylon-1795-1796
474.Gold   two
475.Silver   1200.00

Naval Gold Medals-1795-1815
476.Large gold (23)   45,000.00
477.Small gold (116)   14,000.00

Davison's Nile Medal-1798
478.Gold   9500.00
479.Silver   750.00
480.Bronze/gilt   350.00
481.Bronze   200.00

Seringapatam-1799-English struck 1.9"; Calcutta struck 1.8".
482.Gold- 48mm   5500.00
483.Gold- 45mm   5200.00
484.Silver/gilt- 48mm   700.00
485.Silver- 48mm   650.00
486.Bronze- 48mm   325.00
487.Pewter- 48mm   200.00
488.Silver- 45mm   450.00

Earl St Vincents's Medal-1800
489.Gold-specimens   rare
490.Silver   750.00

Egypt 1801-East India Co.'s Medal
491.Gold   rare
492.Silver   750.00

Egypt 1801-Sultan of Turkey's Award (Order of the Crescent)
493.Gold- 54mm-with jewels   rare
494.Gold- 54mm   4000.00
495.Gold- 48mm   2800.00
496.Gold- 45mm   2000.00
497.Gold- 36mm   850.00
498.Silver- 36mm   750.00

Egypt 1801-Highland Society's Medal
499.Silver   1100.00
500.Bronze   450.00

501.Davison's Medal-Trafalgar 1805   100.00

Bolton's Medal-Trafalgar 1805
502.Gold   one
503.Silver   1300.00
504.Bronze   350.00
505.Bronze/gilt   500.00
506.White Metal   450.00
(Attributed pieces.)

507.Maida Gold Medal(1806)   rare

Army Gold Medals-1806-1814
508.Large gold-for General officers   18,000.00
509.Large gold-for the West Indies   12,000.00
510.Large gold-one campaign bar   rare
511.Large gold-two campaign bars   rare
512.Small gold-for Field Officers   6000.00
513.Small gold-for the West Indies   5000.00
514.Small gold-one campaign bar   rare
515.Small gold-two campaign bars   rare
(Large medals- 54mm diameter;small gold- 33mm diameter.)

Peninsular Gold Cross-1808-1814
516.Gold Cross-four campaigns   18,000.00
517.Gold Cross-with additional bars   rare
(Maximum number of campaign bars awarded was nine, to the Duke of Wellington. Most crosses appear in a senior officer's group with other awards, making a firm value difficult.)

Capture of Rodrigues, Bourbon & Isle of France-1809-1810
518.Gold   8000.00
519.Silver   1100.00

Bagur & Palamos Medal-1810
520.Gold   6000.00
521.Silver   1000.00

Java Medal-1811
522.Gold   6000.00
523.Silver   800.00

Naval General Service 1793-1840-issued 1848
Over 230 campaign bars were struck for this medal, many given in small numbers, others not actually at all. Values listed below are for a representative number of bars, as most rarely come on the market making an accurate value difficult to establish.
524.1st of June 1794 (540)   1000.00
525.14th March 1795 (95)   1200.00

526.23rd June 1795 (177)	1300.00
527.St Vincent (348)	1100.00
528.Camperdown (298)	1000.00
529.Mars 21st April 1798 (26)	1500.00
530.Lion 15th July 1798 (23)	1600.00
531.Isle St Marcou 6 May 1798	three
532.Nile (326)	1000.00
533.12 Octr 1798 (78)	1100.00
534.Acre 30 May 1799 (41)	1400.00
535.Egypt (618)	600.00
536.Copenhagen (555)	1100.00
537.Gut of Gibraltar 12 July 1801 (142)	1100.00
538.Acheron 3 Feby 1805	two
539.Trafalgar (1710)	1500.00
540.4 Novr 1805 (296)	1100.00
541.St Domingo (396)	700.00
542.Amazon 13 March 1806	1400.00
543.Curacao 1st January 1807 (65)	1100.00
544.Hydra 6 Augt 1807	2000.00
545.Comus 15 Aug 1807	2200.00
546.Stately 22 March 1808 (31)	1400.00
547.Redwing 7 May 1808	seven
548.Seahorse Wh Badere Zaffere	2000.00
549.Martinique (486)	600.00
550.Basque Roads 1809 (529)	700.00
551.Pompee 17 June 1809(usually as a multi-bar medal)	1750.00
552.Guadaloupe (483)	600.00
553.Lissa (124)	1000.00
554.Java (665)	600.00
555.Victorious with Rivoli	1400.00
556.St Sebastian (293)	600.00
557.Shannon Wh Chesapeake (42)	5000.00
558.Gluckstadt 5 Jany 1814 (44)	1500.00
559.Gaieta 24 July 1815 (88)	1000.00
560.Algiers (1328)	500.00
561.Navarino (1142)	600.00
562.Syria	350.00

Boat Service Bars

563.16 July 1806 (51)	1150.00	564.1 Nov 1809 (110)	1000.00
565.28 June 1810 (25)	1450.00	566.29 Sep 1812 (25)	1800.00
567.Ap & May 1813 (57)	3000.00	568.2 May 1813 (48)	1350.00
569.8 April 1814 (24)	3000.00	570.24 May 1814 (12)	1750.00
571.14 December 1814			1500.00

(Note: Values for the above are based on several factors, rarity being only one of the. Collector interest in Trafalgar and the N. American actions have made associated medals much more valuable and desirable than others awarded in smaller numbers. Multi-bar medals must be addressed by the value of the rarest bar with an additional percentage(10-20%) per bar. This medal is easy to verify as there are several published rolls of recipients, including for the bar Syria, over

7000 recipients. It is with the latter that there occurs the most problems. Some rare bar medals are sold with comment about recipients of the same name on the Syria roll. Some medals may be genuine, but the "rare" bar is a fake, the name being listed for a rare bar recipient, and for the Syria bar. Despite this not being a common problem prudence is always worthwhile.)

Military General Service Medal-1793-1814-issued 1848

572.Egypt	600.00	573.Maida	600.00
574.Roleia	1000.00	575.Vimiera	600.00
576.Sahagun	1000.00	577.Benevente	8000.00
578.Sahgun & Benevente	800.00	579.Corunna	500.00
580.Martinique (Army)	600.00	581.Talavera	600.00
582.Guadaloupe (Army)	600.00	583.Busaco	500.00
584.Barrosa	550.00	585.Fuentes D'Onor	550.00
586.Albuhuera	700.00	587.Java (Army)	600.00
588.Ciudad Rodrigo	600.00	589.Badajoz	600.00
590.Salamanca	500.00	591.Ft Detroit	2600.00
592.Chateauguay	2600.00	593.Chrystler's Farm	2600.00
594.Vittoria	500.00	595.Pyrenees	500.00
596.St Sebastian	550.00	597.Nivelle	500.00
598.Nive	500.00	599.Orthes	500.00
600.Toulouse	550.00	601.two bar medal	600.00
602.three bars	650.00	603.four bars	750.00
604.five bars	800.00	605.six bars	1000.00
606.seven bars	1200.00	607.eight bars	1400.00
608.nine bars	1800.00	609.ten bars	2000.00
610.eleven bars	2500.00	611.twelve bars	3200.00
612.thirteen bars	rare	613.fourteen bars	rare

(Note: Values for single bar medals are for the most commonly found regiments. Values of multi-bar medals are based on a combination of the most common bars to the most common regiments. See also Spain for campaign medals complementary to some of the above. Bars marked (Army) were also awarded to the RN & RM-approximately five times the Army values.)

Waterloo-1815

614.Heavy Cavalry	1000.00
615.Light Cavalry	1200.00
616.Scot Greys	2200.00
617.Foot Guards	1000.00
618.Infantry Regiments	1000.00-2000.00
619.Corps-Royal Artillery etc	750.00
620.King's German Legion	1000.00
621.General Colville's reserve units	750.00

(Note: The special interest in this medal is heightened by the fact that it was struck & awarded soon after the battle. It does not bear the head of the reigning monarch (George III), but that of the Prince Regent (later George IV. Several of the German states issued medals for Waterloo: Brunswick, Hannover, Nassau, Saxe-Gotha-Altenburg & Prussia [campaign medal dated 1815]. The Netherlands issued a plain 5 armed "star" dated 1813 on the obverse & 1815 on the reverse.)

Army of India Medal-1799-1826

622.Allighur (2 bar medal) (66)	3750.00
623.Battle of Dehli (3 bar medal) (40)	4500.00
624.Assye (3 bar medal) (87)	4000.00
625.Asseerghur (2 bar medal) (48)	4000.00
626.Laswarree (3 bar medal) (100)	1750.00
627.Gawilghur (3 bar medal) (110)	4000.00
628.Argaum (3 bar medal) (126)	4000.00
629.Defence of Dehli (N) (5)	rare
630.Battle of Deig (2 bar medal) (47)	4500.00
631.Capture of Deig (2 bar medal) (103)	3000.00
632.Nepaul (505)	1000.00
633.Kirkee (N) (5)	1200.00
634.Poona (75)	rare
635.Kirkee & Poona (88)	1800.00
636.Seetabuldee (N) (2)	rare
637.Nagpore (155)	1500.00
638.Seetabuldee & Nagpore (N) (21)	rare
639.Maheidpoor (75)	1800.00
640.Corygaum (N) (4)	rare
641.Ava (2325)	750.00
642.Bhurtpoor (1059)	750.00

(Note: Values listed above are based on issues to Europeans (privates), unless otherwise stated by the (N) for native issue. Europeans' medals are impressed, natives' are engraved. There are two strikings for the reverse with a long & short hyphen. Medals with two or more bars are rare.)

643.Nepal War Medal-1814-1816-silver (see also 632)	800.00
644.Ceylon War Medal-1818-silver (45)	2800.00

Burma War Medal-1824-1826 (see also 641)

645.Gold (750)	3500.00
646.Silver (24,000)	700.00

Coorg Medal-1837

647.Gold-original (44)	8000.00
648.Gold-restrike	2000.00
649.Silver-original (300)	1000.00
650.Silver-restrike	450.00

Ghuznee-1839

651.named to British troops	500.00
652.named to Indian troops	300.00
653.unnamed as issued	250.00

Candahar, Ghuznee & Cabul Medals-1841-1842

654.Candahar-named	700.00
655.Candahar-unnamed	400.00

656.Cabul-named   500.00
657.Cabul-unnamed   300.00
658.Ghuznee & Cabul-named   750.00
659.Ghuznee & Cabul-unnamed   450.00
660.Candahar, Ghuznee & Cabul-named   600.00
661.Candahar, Ghuznee & Cabul-unnamed   350.00
662.Victoria Regina obverse-named-Cabvl reverse (15)   rare
663.Victoria Regina obverse-unnamed-Cabvl reverse   rare
(Values are for European recipients, natives are 50-60%.)

Turkish Medal for Acre-1840
664.Gold   950.00   665.Silver/gilt   350.00
666.Silver   200.00   667.Bronze   100.00
(Note: See also number 562.)

Jellalabad Medal-1841-1842
Type I-obverse Jellalbad & Mural Crown
668.named   800.00   669.unnamed   500.00
Type II-obverse-bust of Victoria
670.named   1100.00   671.unnamed   700.00
(Values are for European recipients, natives are 50-60%.)

Defence of Kelat-I-Ghilzie-1842
672.named to Europeans   7500.00
673.named to Indians   3000.00
674.unnamed   1100.00

China-1842
675.Army   400.00   676.Navy   400.00
677.Natives   300.00

Scinde Campaigns-1843
678.Meeanee-British   1200.00
679.Meeanee-native   500.00
680.Meeanee-East India Co. Navy   1800.00
681.Hyderabad-British   850.00
682.Hyderabad-native   250.00
683.Hyderabad-East India Co. Navy   1800.00
684.Meeanee-Hyderabad-British   550.00
685.Meeanee-Hyderabad-native   295.00

Gwalior Campaign Stars-1843
686.Maharajpoor Star-British   450.00
687.Maharajpoor Star-natives   250.00
688.Punniar Star-British   550.00
689.Punniar Star-native   250.00
(Beware of copies to natives. Some unnamed specimens exist.)

GREAT BRITAIN

Sutlej Campaign Medal-1845-1846
Reverse Moodkee
690. no bar-British   300.00
691. no bar-native   200.00
692. one bar-British   350.00
693. one bar-native   250.00
694. two bars-British   500.00
695. two bars-native   350.00
696. three bars-British   750.00
697. three bars-native   450.00
Reverse Ferozeshuhur
698. no bar-British   275.00
699. no bar-native   200.00
700. one bar-British   450.00
701. one bar-native   300.00
702. two bars-British   500.00
703. two bars-native   300.00
Reverse Aliwal
704. no bar-British   275.00
705. no bar-native   200.00
706. one bar-British   350.00
707. one bar-native   200.00
Reverse Sobraon
708. no bar-British   300.00
709. no bar-native   160.00
(For European recipients in native regiments deduct 10% from values to British units.)

Punjab Campaign Medal-1848-1849
Three campaign bars awarded: Mooltan, Chilianwala, Goojerat
710. no bar-British   200.00
711. no bar-Indian   125.00
712. Mooltan-British   300.00
713. Mooltan-Indian   175.00
714. Chilianwala-24th Foot   300.00
715. Chilianwala-casualty   550.00
716. Goojerat-British   300.00
717. Goojerat-Indian   250.00
718. two bars-British   300.00
719. two bars-Indian   225.00

South African Campaign Medal-1834-1853-all dated 1853
720. Army   450.00
721. Navy   400.00
722. Colonial units   300.00

Sir Harry Smith's Medal for Gallantry-1851
723. named   4500.00   724. unnamed   2500.00

Baltic Medal-1854-1855

725.unnamed as issued	100.00	726.engraved naming	150.00
727.impressed naming	250.00	728.R. Sappers & Miners	1100.00

Crimean War Medal-1854-1856

729.no bar	150.00
730.Alma	200.00
731.Inkerman	225.00
732.Azoff	200.00
733.Balaklava	250.00
734.Balaklava-93rd Foot (Thin Red Line)	1000.00
735.Balaklava-Heavy Brigade	1000.00
736.Balaklava-Light Brigade (proven charger)	6000.00
737.Sebastopol	150.00
738.two bars	275.00
739.three bars	350.00
740.four bars	700.00

(Values are for officially impressed to enlisted men in the British Army. Medals, unnamed, privately or regimentally named have lesser values. Bars to French recipients are usually unattached to the medal or each other. Unofficial bars such as TRAKTIR, MALAKOFF, KINBURN and others are also found sometimes on medals to French recipients. Impressed medals to the Light Brigade should be verified. The bar AZOFF was awarded to the Royal Navy.)

Turkish Crimea Medals-1855
British Issue-Crimea 1855

741.unnamed	75.00	742.named	100.00

French Issue-La Crimee 1855

743.unnamed	110.00	744.named	200.00

Sardinian Issue-La Crimea 1855

745.unnamed	50.00	746.named	85.00

(Note: Awarded by the Sultan of Turkey to his allies, the British, French & Sardinians. Most British recipients were given the Sardinian issue.)

India General Service Medal-1854-1895
Silver Medals-Combattent issues

British Recipients		Native Recipients	
747.Pegu	150.00	748.Pegu	---
749.Persia	150.00	750.Persia	100.00
751.N.W. Frontier	150.00	752.N.W. Frontier	100.00
753.Umbeyla	200.00	754.Umbeyla	100.00
755.Bhootan	200.00	756.Bhootan	100.00
757.Looshai	350.00	758.Looshai	175.00
759.Perak	150.00	760.Perak	125.00
761.Jowaki 1877-8	150.00	762.Jowaki 1877-8	110.00
763.Naga 1879-80	1000.00	764.Naga 1879-90	250.00
765.Burma 1885-7	125.00	766.Burma 1885-7	100.00
767.Burma 1887-89	125.00	768.Burma 1887-89	85.00
769.Sikkim 1888	225.00	770.Sikkim 1888	120.00

771.Hazara 1888	150.00	772.Hazara 1888	125.00
773.Chin-Lushai	200.00	774.Chin-Lushai	95.00
775.Lushai-1889-92	500.00	776.Lushai-1889-92	250.00
777.Burma 1889-92	150.00	778.Burma 1889-92	100.00
779.Samana 1891	160.00	780.Samana 1891	100.00
781.Hazara 1891	160.00	782.Hazara 1891	100.00
783.N.E. Frontier	175.00	784.N.E. Frontier	100.00
785.Hunza 1891	rare	786.Hunza 1891	300.00
788.Chin Hills	425.00	788.Chin Hills	200.00
789.Kachin Hills	850.00	790.Kachin Hills	325.00
791.Waziristan 1894-5	150.00	792.Waziristan 1894-5	100.00

Bronze Issues-non-combattent natives

793.Burma 1885-7	100.00	794.Burma 1887-89	100.00
795.Sikkim 1888	150.00	796.Hazara 1888	100.00
797.Chin Lushai	200.00	798.Lushai 1889-92	300.00
799.Burma 1889-92	100.00	800.Samana 1891	120.00
801.Hazara 1891	100.00	802.N.E. Frontier	150.00
803.Hunza 1891	600.00	804.Chin Hills 1892-93	500.00
805.Kachin Hills	1100.00	806.Waziristan 1894-5	85.00

807.<u>Hunza Naga Badge</u>-1891   800.00
(Note: The ribbon for the badge is much rarer.)

<u>Indian Mutiny Medal</u>-1857-1858

808.no bar	150.00	809.Dehli	275.00
810.Defence of Lucknow-original defender			875.00
811.Defence of Lucknow-first relief force			525.00
812.Relief of Lucknow			275.00
813.Lucknow	225.00	814.Central India	225.00
815.two bars-excluding Defence of Lucknow			400.00
816.three bars-excluding Defence of Lucknow			800.00
817.four bars-excluding Defence of Lucknow			1500.00

(Above values for Privates in British Army.)
Royal Navy

818.no bar	600.00	819.Lucknow	800.00
820.Relief of Lucknow			800.00
821.two bars-Relief of Lucknow & Lucknow			1000.00

<u>China</u>-1857-60
Bars awarded: China 1842, Canton 1857, Fatshan 1857 (only to R.N.), Taku Forts 1858, Taku Forts 1860, Pekin 1860.
Unnamed as issued to the Royal Navy

822.no bar	85.00	823.China 1842	rare
824.Fatshan 1857	95.00	825.Canton 1857	120.00
826.Taku Forts 1858	110.00	827.Taku Forts 1860	90.00
828.Pekin 1860	95.00	829.two bars	110.00
830.three bars	150.00	831.four bars	210.00
832.five bars-specimen			400.00

Engraved to the Royal Navy

833.no bar	95.00	834.China 1842	rare
835.Fatshan 1857	150.00	836.Canton 1857	140.00
837.Taku Forts 1858	150.00	838.Taku Forts 1860	135.00
839.Pekin 1860	135.00	840.two bars	135.00
841.three bars	175.00	842.four bars	280.00

Officially Impressed-Army

843.no bar	120.00	844.Canton 1857	240.00
845.Taku Forts 1860	175.00	846.Pekin 1860	200.00
847.two bars	200.00	848.three bars	280.00

New Zealand-First War 1845-1847; Second 1860-1866. Army & Navy-to most common ship or unit.

849.undated-First war			325.00
850.undated-Second war			250.00
851.1845-46	450.00	852.1845-47	550.00
853.1846-47	550.00	854.1846	1000.00
855.1847	750.00	856.1848	rare
857.1860	1000.00	858.1860-61	350.00
859.1860-63	2500.00	860.1860-64	350.00
861.1860-65	350.00	862.1860-66	325.00
863.1861	rare	864.1861-63	rare
865.1861-64	350.00	866.1861-65	rare
867.1861-66	275.00	868.1862-66	rare
869.1863	800.00	870.1863-64	350.00
871.1863-65	325.00	872.1863-66	325.00
873.1864	350.00	874.1864-65	325.00
875.1864-66	300.00	876.1865	550.00
877.1865-66	300.00	878.1866	300.00

(Note: Some of the above dated issues are much rarer to the Royal Navy than the Army. Also some of the Colonial issues are quite rare. Thus, values may vary considerably,as the above must be considered a simplified chart.)

Canada General Service Medal-1866-1870

Bar Fenian Raid 1866

879.British Army	300.00	880.Canadian	275.00
881.Royal Navy			325.00

Bar Fenian Raid 1870

882.British	300.00	883.Canadian	250.00

Bar Red River 1870

884.British	1000.00	885.Canadian	800.00

Multiple bars

886.Fenian Raid 1866 & Fenian Raid 1870-Canadian	300.00
887.Fenian Raid 1866 & Red River 1870	rare
888.Fenian Raid 1866, Fenian Raid 1870 & Red River 1870	rare

(Note: Most of the Canadian recipients belonged to small militia units which saw little or no fighting. This medal is easy to verify as an extensive roll of recipients has been published. Awards to the Royal Navy are much scarcer than to the army. Specimens of the medal, released from the Canadian War Museum and not so marked, exist. Care must be taken that a rare item is named correctly, and not that since the recipient is on the roll the medal must be OK.)

Abyssinia-1867-68

889.British Army	275.00	890.Indian Army	180.00
891.Royal Navy	250.00	892.R.N. Rocket Brigade	475.00

Ashantee War Medal-1873-74

893.no bar-Army	250.00	894.no bar-Royal Navy	200.00
895.no bar-Army-native contingents			150.00
896.Coomassie-Army	400.00	897.Coomassie-Royal Navy	350.00
898.Coomassie-Army-West India Regiment			250.00

(Note: This medal, struck on a thinner planchet, was used for the East & West Africa Medal. Recipients of the Ashantee War Medal who earned bars for East & West Africa had it (them) placed above the Coomassie bar; but rarely seen.)

South Africa Medal-1877-1879
British Army

899.no bar	200.00	900.bar 1877	rare
901.bar 1877-8	325.00	902.bar 1877-9	one
903.bar 1877-8-9	425.00	904.bar 1878	450.00
905.bar 1878-9	450.00	906.bar 1879	350.00
907.Casualty at Isandhlwana (bar 1877-8-9 or 1879)			3000.00
908.Rorke's Drift combattent, including Colonials (bar 1877-8-9)			12,000.00

Royal Navy

909.no bar	225.00		
910.bar 1877-8	650.00	911.bar 1877-8-9	750.00
912.bar 1878-9	450.00	913.bar 1879	300.00

Colonial Troops

914.no bar	175.00	915.bar 1877	2150.00
916.bar 1877-8	300.00	917.bar 1877-9	rare
918.bar 1877-8-9	300.00	919.bar 1878	325.00
920.bar 1878-9	325.00	921.bar 1879	300.00

(Note: A complete roll for the 24th Foot exists for Isandhlwana & Rorke's Drift. Not all members of the 1st & 2nd Bns who received the bars 1877-8-9 & 1879 are listed as present for these two actions. However, even medals to the 24th Foot not present would still command a small premium above other units. Also awarded to the Royal Navy & numerous S. African units, both European & native. This medal without bar is identical to the S. Africa 1853 medal except that it is undated on the reverse.)

Afghanistan-1878-1880

British troops-silver		Native Troops-bronze	
922.no bar	85.00	923.no bar	300.00
924.Ali Musjid	200.00	925.Ali Musjid	85.00
926.Peiwar Kotal	225.00	927.Peiwar Kotal	85.00
928.Charasia	225.00	929.Charasia	85.00
930.Kabul	200.00	931.Kabul	85.00
932.Ahmed Khel	200.00	933.Ahmed Khel	85.00

934.Kandahar	200.00	935.Kandahar	85.00
936.two bars	275.00	937.two bars	125.00
938.three bars	400.00	939.three bars	200.00
940.four bars	650.00	941.four bars	300.00
942.no bars-66th Foot-casualty at Maiwand			700.00
943.E.Btry B. Brigade-R.H.A.-casualty at Maiwand			650.00

Kabul to Kandahar Star-1880 (referred to as the "Roberts Star")

944.British Army	300.00	945.Indian Army	175.00
946.unnamed specimen with maker's name Jenkins on reverse			125.00

(Note: Care must be taken with this piece, especially those named to the Indian Army. Very clever fakes exist.)

Cape of Good Hope General Service Medal-1880-1897

947.no bar	rare	948.Transkei	400.00
949.Basutoland	250.00	950.Bechuanaland	250.00
951.two bars	325.00	952.three bars	rare

Egypt-1882-1889

953.no bar-dated	75.00	954.no bar-undated	85.00
955.Alexandria 11th July (Royal Navy)			175.00
956.Tel-El-Kebir	200.00	957.El Teb	200.00
958.Tamaai	225.00	959.El Teb-Tamaai	200.00
960.Suakin 1884	150.00	961.The Nile 1884-85	150.00
962.The Nile 1884-85-to Canadian recipients			1700.00
963.The Nile 1884-85 & Abu Klea			800.00
964.The Nile 1884-85 & Kirbekan			300.00
965.same-to Canadian recipients			1700.00
966.Suakin 1885			165.00
967.Suakin 1885-to Australian recipients			1200.00
968. Suakin 1885 & Tofrek			275.00
969.Gemaizah 1888	225.00	970.Toski(natives)	300.00
971.two bars	225.00	972.three bars	350.00
973.four bars	475.00	974.five bars	900.00

Khedive of Egypt's Bronze Stars-1882-1889

975.dated 1882	65.00	976.dated 1884	85.00
977.dated 1884-6	85.00	978.undated	100.00
979.undated-with bar for Tokar			200.00

(Note: These stars were originally issued with a black lacquer. From being cleaned most stars show their bronze appearance. Some pieces may have the initials of the name or regiment of the recipient on the reverse. Occasionally the whole naming may be seen. Add 10%.)

Northwest Canada-1885

980.no bar-unnamed	200.00	981.no bar-named	300.00
982.Saskatchewan-unnamed			300.00
983.Saskatchewan-named			700.00
984.Saskatchewan-named to the Steamer Northcote			1000.00

Royal Niger Company's Medal-1886-1897

985.Silver-Nigeria 1886-97-named	3000.00
986.Silver-Nigeria 1886-97-unnamed specimen	200.00
987.Bronze-Nigeria-numbered or named	800.00
988.Bronze-Nigeria-unnumbered or unnamed	150.00

East & West Africa Medal-1887-1900

989.1887-8-R.N.	600.00	990.1887-8-native	225.00
991.Witu 1890-R.N.	225.00	992.1891-92-R.N.	300.00
993.1892-native	200.00	994.Witu-August 1893 RN	300.00
995.Liwondi 1893-R.N.	3000.00	996.Juba River 1893-R.N.	3000.00
997.Lake Nyassa 1893	3000.00	998.1893-94-native	225.00
999.Gambia 1894-R.N.	225.00	1000.Benin River 1894-R.N.	225.00
1001.Brass River 1895-RN	300.00		

1002.no bar-M'wele 1895-96 impressed on edge-native			150.00
1003.1896-98-native	300.00	1004.Niger 1987-native	300.00
1005.Benin 1897-R.N.	200.00	1006.Dawkita 1897-native	rare
1007.1897-98-native	225.00	1008.1898-native	225.00
1009.Sierra Leone 1898-99-British			300.00
1010.Sierra Leone 1898-99-native			200.00
1011.1899-native	300.00	1012.1900-native	300.00

(Note: Verified medals to Europeans for some of the native listings would be 50% to 100% higher.)

British South Africa Company's Medals-1890-1897

1013.bar Mashonaland 1890-no battle reverse	1000.00
1014.reverse Matabeleland 1893-no bar	300.00
1015.reverse Matabeleland 1893-one bar	425.00
1016.reverse Matabeleland 1893-two bars	700.00
1017.reverse Rhodesia 1896-no bar	250.00
1018.reverse Rhodesia 1896-one bar	425.00
1019.reverse Mashonaland 1897	300.00

(Values are for colonial units.)

Central Africa Medal-1891-1898

1020.no bar-ring suspension-silver-native	450.00
1021.Central Africa 1894-98-native	800.00

(Note: Also awarded in bronze- rare)

Hong Kong Plague Medal-1894 (Unofficial)

1022.Gold Medal-between 40-50 awarded	5000.00
1023.Silver Medal-to the Shropshire Light Infantry	1000.00
1024.Silver Medal-to the Royal Navy & Royal Engineers	1250.00

India General Service-1895-1902

Silver-combat troops		Bronze-non-combattents	
1025.Defence of		1026.Defence of	
Chitral-native	1250.00	Chitral	1500.00
1027.Relief of Chitral	125.00	1028.Relief of Chitral	100.00

1029.Punjab Frontier		1030.Punjab Frontier	
1897-98	100.00	1897-98	85.00
1031.Punjab Frontier &		1032.Punjab Frontier &	
Malakand 1897	150.00	Malakand 1897	100.00
1033.Punjab Frontier &		1034.Punjab Frontier &	
Samana 1897	150.00	Samana 1897	125.00
1035.Punjab Frontier &		1036.Punjab Frontier &	
Tirah 1897-98	175.00	Tirah 1897-98	100.00
1037.Waziristan 1901-2	125.00	1038.Waziristan 1901-2	100.00
1039.three bars	225.00	1040.three bars	175.00
1041.four bars	175.00	1042.four bars	---

(Note: For the silver issue 1025, 1033, 1037 and 1041are to natives. Other silver medals to natives are about 60% of values to British recipients. Waziristan 1901-2 was an Edward VII issue; all others being Victoria.)

Ashanti Star-1896

1043.unnamed	200.00	1044.named	350.00

Queen's Sudan Medal-1896-1898

1045.named-silver	200.00	1046.named-bronze	250.00
1047.unnamed-silver	100.00	1048.unnamed-bronze	150.00
1049.named to 21st Lancers-Charged at Omdurman- verified			1000.00

Khedive's Sudan Medal-1896-98

1050.no bar-silver-Army	100.00	1051.no bar-bronze	125.00
1052.Firket	185.00	1053.Hafir	185.00
1054.Abu Hamed	185.00	1055.Sudan 1897	185.00
1056.The Atbara*	175.00	1057.Khartoum*	200.00
1058.Gedaref	175.00	1059.Gedid	175.00
1060.Sudan 1899	175.00	1061.Bahr-el-Ghazal	250.00
1062.Jerok	225.00	1063.Nyam-Nyam	225.00
1064.Talodi	225.00	1065.Katfia	240.00
1066.Nyima	200.00	1067.two bars	200.00
1068.three bars	225.00	1069.four bars	250.00
1070.five bars	275.00	1071.six bars	300.00
1072.seven bars	325.00	1073.eight bars	400.00

(Note: Bars marked * are to British troops; most other bars were awarded to native troops, and usually inscribed in Arabic with the unit designation; values of multi-bars for unnamed medals.)

East & Central Africa-1897-1899-values given for native awards

1074.no bar	300.00
1075.Uganda 1897-98	400.00
1076.Uganda 1898-silver	400.00
1077.Uganda 1898-bronze	650.00
1078.Uganda 1899	400.00
1079.Lubwa's & Uganda 1897-98	475.00

Queen's South Africa Medal-1899-1902

1080.no bar Army	65.00	1081.no bar navy	150.00
1082.no bar-bronze	165.00	1083.Cape Colony	65.00
1084.Rhodesia*	165.00	1085.Orange Free State	65.00
1086.Defence of Mafeking*			1000.00
1087.Relief of Mafeking			250.00
1088.Defence of Kimberly*			200.00
1089.Relief of Kimberly			85.00
1090.Talana	200.00	1091.Elandslaagte	200.00
1092.Defence of Ladysmith			150.00
1093.Relief of Ladysmith			85.00
1094.Tugela Heights			85.00
1095.Belmont	100.00	1096.Modder River	100.00
1097.Natal	150.00	1098.Paardeberg	100.00
1099.Driefontein	85.00	1100.Wepener*	300.00
1101.Transvaal	70.00	1102.Johannesburg	85.00
1103.Laing's Nek	140.00	1104.Diamond Hill	85.00
1105.Wittebergen	85.00	1106.Belfast	100.00
1107.S.Africa 1901	85.00	1108.S.Africa 1902	85.00
1109.two bars	85.00	1110.three bars	95.00
1111.four bars	100.00	1112.five bars	85.00
1113.six bars	110.00	1114.seven bars	300.00
1115.eight bars	500.00	1116.nine bars	rare

1117.reverse raised dates 1899-1900-to Canadians   3850.00

(Note: Values given above for single bar medals, unless stated otherwise, to the most common units of the British army, except as indicated. Items marked * are to local, S.African Units. On multi-bar medals which include both bars S.Africa 1901 & 1902, care must be taken to examine the rivets of the last two bars to make sure that they are the same as the others. If the rivets are different it could mean that these two bars were taken off the King's S. Africa Medal, and that entitlement is possibly lacking. Values for multi-bar medals are based on the most common bars to the most common units. Medals to Canadians, Australians & New Zealanders, as well as to many S.African units are to be found. Values to non-British recipients are likely to be higher and lower.In many cases single bar medals are worth more than multi-bar ones. Because of the very complicated combinations of bars, and units, values for the above may be considered "rougher" than some other series.)

1118.Queen's Mediterranean Medal-1899-1900   200.00

King's South Africa Medal-1901-1902
1119.no bars-as awarded to nurses   150.00
1120.two date bars-S.Africa 1901 & S.Africa 1902-Army   50.00
1121.two date bars-S.Africa 1901 & S.Africa 1902-Navy   150.00
(Note: Awarded only in conjunction with the Queen's Medal.)

Cape Copper Co. Medal-1902-Defense of Ookiep
1122.Silver   rare
1123.Bronze   1000.00

1124.St. John Ambulance Brigade Medal for S. Africa   250.00

1125.Defence of Kimberly Medal-1899-1900   1000.00
1126.Defence of Kimberly Star-1899-1900-date letter "a"   200.00
1127.Defence of Kimberly Star-1899-1900-other letters   150.00

Transport Medal-1899-1902
1128.South Africa 1899-1902   400.00
1129.China 1900   600.00
1130.S.Africa 1899-1902 & China 1900   800.00

Imperial Yeomanry-Yorkshire Medal
1131.3rd Imperial Yeomanry S.Africa 1900-01   125.00
1132.3rd Imperial Yeomanry S.Africa 1901-02   150.00
1133.66th Imperial Yeomanry S.Africa 1900-01   225.00

British North Borneo Company's Medals-1897-1937
Original issues-silver
1134.Punitive Expedition   rare
1135.Punitive Expeditions   rare
1136.Tambunam   rare
1137.Rundum   rare
1138.General Service Medal   rare
Original issues-bronze
1139.Punitive Expedition   1000.00
1140.Punitive Expeditions   1000.00
1141.Tambunam   1000.00
Restruck Specimens-silver
1142.Punitive Expedition   150.00
1143.Punitive Expeditions   150.00
1144.Tambunam   150.00
1145.Rundum   150.00
Restruck Specimens-bronze
1146.Punitive Expedition   85.00
1147.Punitive Expeditions   85.00
1148.Tambunam   85.00

Ashanti Medal-1900
1149.no bar-silver   250.00   1150.no bar-bronze   475.00
1151.bar Kumassi-silver   450.00
(Note: Values for above are to natives; awards to British recipients are much rarer.)

China 1900-Boxer Rebellion
1152.no bar-silver-British   165.00
1153.no bar-silver-native   85.00   1154.no bar-bronze   125.00
1155.Relief of Pekin-silver-Royal Navy   300.00
1156.Relief of Pekin-silver-Royal Welsh Fusiliers   350.00
1157.Relief of Pekin-silver-Indian Army/Native   200.00

1158.Relief of Pekin-bronze			250.00
1159.Taku Forts-Royal Navy			500.00
1160.Taku Forts & Relief of Pekin-Royal Navy			700.00
1161.Defence of Legations			6500.00

Africa General Service Medal-1902-1956

1162.N.Nigeria	250.00	1163.N.Nigeria 1902	225.00
1164.N.Nigeria 1903	225.00	1165.N.Nigeria 1903-04	300.00
1166.N.Nigeria 1903-04-bronze			250.00
1167.N.Nigeria 1904	300.00	1168.N.Nigeria 1906	325.00
1169.S.Nigeria	350.00	1170.S.Nigeria 1902	300.00
1171.S.Nigeria 1902-03	300.00	1172.S.Nigeria 1903	280.00
1173.S.Nigeria 1903-04	300.00	1174.S.Nigeria 1904	250.00
1175.S.Nigeria 1904-05	300.00	1176.S.Nigeria 1905	500.00
1177.S.Nigeria 1905-06	300.00	1178.Nigeria 1918	225.00
1179.E.Africa 1902	600.00	1180.E.Africa 1904	350.00
1181.E.Africa 1905	350.00	1182.E.Africa 1906	325.00
1183.E.Africa 1913	475.00	1184.E.Africa 1914	450.00
1185.E.Africa 1913-14	350.00	1186.E.Africa 1915	400.00
1187.E.Africa 1918	400.00	1188.W.Africa 1906	325.00
1189.W.Africa 1908	375.00	1190.W.Africa 1909-10	350.00
1191.Somaliland 1901	500.00	1192.Somaliland 1902-04 RN	150.00
1193.Somaliland 1902-04	100.00	1194.Somaliland 1908-10 RN	150.00
1195.Somaliland 1908-10	125.00	1196.Somaliland 1920-RAF	450.00
1197.Somaliland 1920-RN	300.00	1198.Somaliland 1920	150.00
1199.Somaliland 1902-04 & Jidballi-British recipient			275.00
1200.Uganda 1900	300.00	1201.B.C.A. 1899-1900	250.00
1202.Jubaland-R.N.	325.00	1203.Jubaland	175.00
1204.Jubaland-bronze	500.00	1205.Jubaland 1917-18	300.00
1206.Gambia	265.00	1207.Gambia-R.N.	400.00
1208.Aro 1901-02	280.00	1209.Aro 1901-02-R.N.	500.00
1210.Lango 1901	400.00	1211.Kissi 1905	650.00
1212.Nandi 1905-06	250.00	1213.Nyasaland 1915	300.00
1214.Shimber Berris 1914-15			350.00
1215.Kenya-British	125.00	1216.Kenya	85.00

(Note: Values for above based on African or Indian recipients except as noted. Care must be taken with other than common multi- bar medals to British recipients, especially officers. There are a number of fake or copy bars to the latter.)

Tibet-1903-04

1217.Silver-no bar-British			300.00
1218.Silver-no bar-native			200.00
1219.Silver-bar Gyantse-native			225.00
1220.Silver-bar Gyantse-British recipients			750.00
1221.Bronze-no bar	125.00	1222.Bronze-bar Gyantse	250.00

Natal Native Rebellion-1906

1223.no bar	175.00	1224.bar 1906	225.00
1225.Natal Naval Corps			400.00

India General Service Medal-1908-1935

1226. N.W.Frontier 1908-British	100.00
1227. N.W.Frontier 1908-native	65.00
1228. N.W.Frontier 1908-native-bronze	100.00
1229. Abor 1911-12-British	600.00
1230. Abor 1911-12-native	300.00
1231. Abor 1911-12-native-bronze	350.00
1232. Afghanistan NWF 1919-British	60.00
1233. Afghanistan NWF 1919-R.A.F.	200.00
1234. Afghanistan NWF 1919-native	35.00
1235. Mahsud 1919-20 & Waziristan 1919-21-British	125.00
1236. Mahsud 1919-20 & Waziristan 1919-21-R.A.F.	225.00
1237. Mahsud 1919-20 & Waziristan 1919-21-native	65.00
1238. Waziristan 1919-21-British	60.00
1239. Waziristan 1919-21-native	50.00
1240. Malabar 1921-22-British	150.00
1241. Malabar 1921-22-native	60.00
1242. Waziristan 1921-24-British	60.00
1243. Waziristan 1921-24-R.A.F.	150.00
1244. Waziristan 1921-24-native	50.00
1245. Waziristan 1925-to the R.A.F. only	900.00
1246. N.W.Frontier 1930-31-British	75.00
1247. N.W.Frontier 1930-31-R.A.F.	125.00
1248. N.W.Frontier 1930-31-native	35.00
1249. Burma 1930-32-British	85.00
1250. Burma 1930-32-R.A.F.	850.00
1251. Burma 1930-32-native	50.00
1252. Mohmand 1933-British	200.00
1253. Mohmand 1933-R.A.F.	300.00
1254. Mohmand 1933-native	50.00
1255. N.W. Frontier 1935-British	85.00
1256. N.W. Frontier 1935-RAF	100.00
1257. N.W. Frontier 1935-native	45.00

Khedive's Sudan Medal-1910-18 & 1918-22

1258. no bar-silver-type I	200.00	1259. no bar-bronze-type I	700.00
1260. no bar-silver-type II	250.00	1261. no bar-bronze-type II	300.00
1262. Atwot	325.00	1263. S.Kordofan 1910	325.00
1264. Sudan 1912	400.00	1265. Zeraf 19113-14	425.00
1266. Mandal	425.00	1267. Miri	425.00
1268. Mongalla 1915-16	425.00	1269. Darfur 1916	400.00
1270. Fasher	400.00	1271. Lua Nuer	450.00
1272. Nyima 1917-18	400.00	1273. Atwot 1918	400.00
1274. Garjak Nuer	400.00	1275. Aliab Dinka	450.00
1276. Nyala	450.00	1277. Darfur 1921	500.00

(Note: As this medal was issued unnamed the value of one of these in a verifiable group would be greater.)

WORLD WAR I

1278.1914 Star-British-line regiment	40.00
1279.1914 Star-British-corps (R.E.,R.A. etc.)	25.00
1280.1914 Star-British-RN or RM	85.00
1281.1914 Star-British-with bar	65.00
1282.1914 Star-Indian recipient	25.00
1283.1914-15 Star	15.00
1284.1914-15 Star-commonwealth or colonial	20.00
1285.War Medal-silver-British	10.00
1286.War Medal-silver-commonwealth or colonial	15.00
1287.War Medal-bronze	85.00
1288.Victory Medal-British	10.00
1289.Victory Medal-S.African-bilingual issue	75.00
1290.Victory Medal-other commonwealth or colonial	15.00
1291.Mercantile Marine	25.00
1292.Territorial Force War Medal-R.A. or Corps	85.00

(Values reflect most common units.)

Naval General Service Medal-1915-62

1293.Persian Gulf 1909-14	125.00
1294.Iraq 1919-20	1500.00
1295.N.W. Persia 1919-1920 or 1920	rare
1296.Palestine 1936-39	100.00
1297.S.E.Asia 1945-46	150.00
1298.Minesweeping 1945-51	150.00
1299.Palestine 1945-48	100.00
1300.Malaya-George VI	100.00
1301.Malaya-EIIR	125.00
1302.Yangtze 1949-HMS Amethyst	1000.00
1303.Yangtze 1949-HMS London & Black Swan	700.00
1304.Yangtze 1949-other ships	500.00
1305.Bomb & Mine Clearance 1945-53	750.00
1306.Bomb & Mine Clearance 1945-56	rare
1307.Bomb & Mine Clearance, Mediterranean	1600.00
1308.Cyprus	100.00
1309.Near East	85.00
1310.Arabian Peninsula	275.00
1311.Brunei	225.00

(Note: Medals to the Royal Marines will command a small premium on the above listed values.)

General Service Medal-1918-62-Army & Royal Air Force

1312.S.Persia-R.A.F.	rare	1313.S.Persia-native	75.00
1314.Kurdistan-British	85.00	1315.Kurdistan-R.A.F.	185.00
1316.Kurdistan-native	50.00	1317.Iraq-British	75.00
1318.Iraq-R.A.F.	185.00	1319.Iraq-native	40.00
1320.N.W.Persia-British	85.00	1321.N.W.Persia-R.A.F.	350.00
1322.N.W.Persia-native	60.00	1323.S.Desert Iraq-R.A.F.	500.00

1324.N.Kurdistan-R.A.F.	1000.00	1325.Palestine (1936-39)	65.00
1326.S.E.Asia 1945-46			35.00
1327.S.E.Asia 1945-46-named			100.00
1328.Bomb & Mine Clearance 1945-49-Army & RAF			500.00
1329.Bomb & Mine Clearance 1945-56-Army & RAF			750.00
1330.Palestine 1945-48			50.00
1331.Malaya-George VI	50.00	1332.Malaya-EIIR	50.00
1333.Cyprus			50.00
1334.Near East			85.00
1335.Arabian Peninsula			65.00
1336.Brunei-Army	250.00	1337.Brunei-RAF	200.00

India General Service Medal-1936-39

1338.NWF 1936-37-British	85.00	1339.NWF 1936-37-Indian	45.00
1340.NWF 1937-39-British	100.00	1341.NWF 1937-39-Indian	50.00
1342.two bars-British	120.00	1343.two bars-native	65.00

WORLD WAR II

Stars

1344.1939-45	10.00	1345.Atlantic	50.00
1346.Air Crew Europe	200.00	1347.Africa	20.00
1348.Italy	15.00	1349.Pacific	60.00
1350.Burma	40.00	1351.France & Germany	35.00

Medals

1352.Defence	20.00	1353.Defence-silver	25.00
1354.War	15.00	1355.War-silver	25.00
1356.India Service	20.00	1357.Canadian Volunteer	25.00
1358.Africa Service	20.00	1359.S.Africa-Home Service	45.00
1360.Australian Service	50.00	1361.New Zealand Service	30.00
1362.S.Rhodesia	300.00	1363.Newfoundland	700.00

(Note: For the Canadian Volunteer Medal-add $5.00 for the overseas bar. Although there were eight stars, the maximum number that could be worn was five. Authorization for any others were to be expressed by the addition of a bar sewn on the medal ribbon. Thus, the recipient of a Burma Star would have to have the Pacific bar sewn on his medal ribbon in lieu of the Pacific Star. For genuine bars add $15.00, except for the Battle of Britain, where entitlement, and the recipient will help to determine values. Except for Australian & S. African, these issues were awarded unnamed.)

Korean Service-1950-53

1364.British-type I	100.00	1365.British-type II	200.00
1366.Canadian-silver			125.00
1367.Australian/New Zealand award			150.00
1368.British-to Gloucester Regt at Imjin river			450.00
1369.S.African Medal-one Air Force Squadron present			600.00
1370.United Nations Korean Service-English			25.00
1371.same-but named to a Canadian			40.00
1372.same-but French language type-named to a Canadian			150.00

GREAT BRITAIN

Campaign Service Medal-1962

1373.Borneo	65.00	1374.Radfan	85.00
1375.South Arabia	65.00	1376.Malay Peninsula	65.00
1377.South Vietnam-to Australians only			1500.00
1378.N.Ireland	50.00	1379.Dhofar	225.00
1380.Lebanon	800.00	1381.Mine Clearance	1350.00
1382.Gulf	650.00	1383.Kuwait	1350.00
1384.N.Iraq + S.Turkey	1000.00	1385.two bars	100.00
1386.three bars	175.00	1387.four bars	225.00

(Note: Multi-bar medals are with the most common bars to the most common units.)

Vietnam Service-1964

1388.Australian	250.00	1389.New Zealander	275.00

Republic of Vietnam Campaign Star-bar 1960

1390.named	50.00	1391.unnamed	25.00

1392.Rhodesia Medal-1980	450.00

South Atlantic Medal-1982

1393.Royal Navy	275.00	1394.R.N.-ship in action	400.00
1395.Infantry	300.00	1396.Merchant Navy	200.00

(Note: In as much as over 20,000 medals have been awarded, the values listed above can vary considerably according to the recipient, and other factors.)

Gulf War Medal-1991

1397.no bar	200.00
1398.bar 2 Aug 1990	2500.00
1399.bar 16 Jan-28 Feb 1991	300.00

(Copies of this medal exist. They are unnamed and without the designer's initials.)

Independence Medals (in alphabetical order)

1400.Fiji	125.00	1401.India-Armed Forces	25.00
1402.India-police	20.00	1403.Jamaica	125.00
1404.Malawi	85.00	1405.Nigeria	35.00
1406.Pakistan	15.00	1407.Papua-New Guinea	125.00
1408.Solomon Islands	125.00	1409.Zimbabwe	35.00

LONG SERVICE & GOOD CONDUCT MEDALS

Royal Navy

1410.William IV-anchor on reverse	650.00
1411.Victoria-wide suspender	300.00
1412.Victoria-wide suspender-dated 1848	rare
1413.Victoria-narrow suspender-engraved	100.00
1414.Victoria-narrow suspender-impressed	85.00
1415.Edward VII	50.00
1416.George V-admiral's bust	35.00

1417.George V-coinage bust		40.00
1418.George VI-type I-Ind Imp		50.00
1419.George VI-type II-without Ind Imp		75.00
1420.Elizabeth II-type I-fixed suspender		60.00
1421.Elizabeth II-type II-swivel suspender		40.00

(Note: William IV type also awarded in early part of Victoria's reign; some may be observed to have come from a cracked die! Medals to the Coast Guard are valued less than those to the R.N. Medals to the Royal Marines may vary according as to whether the a ship is included in the naming. From 1920 on the suspension does not swivel.)

Royal Naval Reserve Decoration-1908-for officers

1422.Edward VII	175.00	1423.George V	150.00
1424.George VI-GRI	150.00	1425.George VI-GVIR	175.00
1426.Elizabeth II			200.00

Royal Naval Reserve Long Service & Good Conduct Medal

1427.Edward VII	60.00	1428.George V-Admiral's bus	85.00
1429.George V-coinage	45.00	1430.George VI-Ind Imp	45.00
1431.George VI-type II-without Ind Imp			50.00
1432.Elizabeth II-fixed suspender			85.00
1433.Elizabeth II-swivel suspender			60.00

Royal Naval Volunteer Reserve Decoration-1908-1966

1434.Edward VII	200.00	1435.George V	150.00
1436.George VI-GRI	125.00	1437.George VI-GVIR	150.00
1438.Elizabeth II			200.00

Royal Naval Volunteer Reserve Long Service & Good Conduct-1908-56

1439.Edward VII	rare	1440.George V-(admiral)	75.00
1441.George V-coinage	85.00	1442.George VI-Ind Imp	75.00
1443.George VI-type II	75.00	1444.Elizabeth II	120.00

Royal Naval Auxiliary Sick Berth Reserve L.S.G.C. Medal-1919-49

1445.George V-Admiral's bust	150.00
1446.George V-coinage bust	175.00
1447.George VI	125.00

Royal Naval Wireless Auxiliary Reserve L.S.G.C. Medal-1939-57

1448.George VI-Ind Imp	250.00
1449.Elizabeth II	250.00

Royal Naval Auxiliary Services Long Service & Good Conduct Medal

1450.Elizabeth II	250.00

Royal Fleet Reserve Long Service & Good Conduct Medal

1451.George V-Admiral	35.00	1452.George V-coinage bust	45.00
1453.George VI-Ind Imp	40.00	1454.George VI-no Ind Imp	50.00
1455.Elizabeth II-type I	85.00	1456.Elizabeth II-type II	65.00

Rocket Apparatus Volunteers Long Service Medal-1911
1457.George V-coinage bust	75.00
1458.GeoVI-Ind Imp	80.00
1459.George VI-no Ind Imp	85.00
1460.Elizabeth II-Coast Lifesaving	125.00
1461.Elizabeth II-Coastguard Auziliary	100.00

Royal Naval Dockyard Police (Hong Kong) L.S.G.C. Medal
1462.George V-coinage bust	400.00
1463.George VI-type I-Ind Imp	300.00
1464.George VI-type II-no Ind Imp	400.00
1465.Elizabeth II	400.00

Meritorious Service Medal-Royal Navy-1919-1928; 1977-
1466.George V-Admiral's bust	400.00
1467.Elizabeth II-short legend	450.00

Meritorious Service Medal-Royal Marines
1468.George V	350.00	1469.Elizabeth II	450.00

Army Long Service & Good Conduct-1830-
1470.William IV-1830-1831-small ring	750.00
1471.William IV-1831-1837-large ring	700.00
1472.Victoria-1837-55-steel clip & ring-dated	200.00
1473.Victoria-1855-74-scroll suspender-large letters on the reverse	150.00
1474.Victoria-1874-1901-numbered regiments	125.00
1475.Victoria-1874-1901-titled regiments	100.00
1476.Edward VII	65.00
1477.George V-Field Marshal's bust	50.00
1478.George V-crowned head-bar Regular Army	50.00
1479.George VI-type I-Ind Imp-bar Regular Army	50.00
1480.George VI-type II-no Ind Imp-bar Regular Army	60.00
1481.Elizabeth II-type I-long legend-bar Regular Army	85.00
1482.Elizabeth II-type II-short legend-bar Regular Army	85.00

(Note: George V, George VI & Elizabeth II issues may be found with various commonwealth & colonial bars, e.g. India, Canada etc. These issues are worth up to several times more than above.)

Volunteer Decoration-1892-1908-officers
1483.Victoria-British issue-VR cypher	100.00
1484.Victoria-Indian issue-VRI cypher	350.00
1485.Victoria-Colonial issue	300.00
1486.Edward VII	125.00

Volunteer Force Long Service Medal
1487.Victoria-British issue	65.00
1488.Victoria-British issue-unnamed	40.00
1489.Victoria-India & colonies	125.00

1490.Edward VII-British issue	75.00
1491.Edward VII-British issue-unnamed	40.00
1492.Edward VII-India	125.00
1493.Edward VII-colonial issues	85.00
1494.George V-India	50.00

Territorial Decoration-1908-1930-officers
1495.Edward VII	125.00
1496.George V	125.00

Territorial (Force) Efficiency Medal-1908-1930
1497.Edward VII	100.00
1498.George V-Territorial Force Efficiency Medal	50.00
1499.George V-Territorial Efficiency Medal	50.00

Efficiency Decoration-1930-officers
1500.George V-bar Territorial	100.00
1501.George V-bar India	100.00
1502.George VI-bar Territorial-type I-GRI	100.00
1503.George VI-bar Territorial-type II-GVIR	125.00
1504.George VI-bar India-type I	100.00
1505.George VI-colonial/commonwealth bar-starting from	150.00
1506.Elizabeth II-bar Territorial	125.00
1507.Elizabeth II-bar Army Emergency Reserve	200.00
1508.Elizabeth II-bar Territorial & Army Volunteer Reserve 160.00	

Efficiency Medal-1930
1509.George V-crowned & robed-bar Territorial	50.00
1510.George V-with colonial or commonwealth bar	from 125.00
1511.George V-bar Militia	85.00
1512.George VI-type I-bar Territorial	35.00
1513.George VI-type I-bar India	125.00
1514.George VI-type I-bar Militia	85.00
1515.George VI-type II-bar Territorial	35.00
1516.George VI-type II-bar Militia	85.00
1517.George VI-with colonial or commonwealth bar	from 175.00
1518.Elizabeth II-type I-bar Territorial	85.00
1519.Elizabeth II-type II-bar Territorial	85.00
1520.Elizabeth II-type II-bar Army Emergency Reserve	250.00
1521.Elizabeth II-type II-bar T. & A.V.R.	150.00

Other Reserve Long Service & Good Conduct Medals
1522.Imperial Yeomanry-Edward VII-1904-08	300.00
1523.Militia-Edward VII	200.00
1524.Militia-George V	250.00
1525.Special Reserve-Edward VII	250.00
1526.Special Reserve-George V	275.00

Meritorious Service Medal-Army-1845
1527.Victoria-dated 1847 on rim	600.00
1528.Victoria-dated 1848 on reverse	rare
1529.Victoria-standard issue	300.00
1530.Edward VII	250.00
1531.George V-immediate award	275.00
1532.George V-non-immediate award	125.00
1533.George V-coinage head	250.00
1534.George VI-type I	150.00
1535.George VI-crowned head	1300.00
1536.George VI-type II	125.00
1537.Elizabeth II-type I	275.00
1538.Elizabeth II-type II	225.00

Royal Air Force Long Service & Good Conduct Medal-1919
1539.George V			100.00
1540.George VI-type I	50.00	1541.George VI-type II	65.00
1542.Elizabeth II-type I	65.00	1543.Elizabeth II-type II	50.00

Air Efficiency Award-1942-officers & enlisted men
1544.George VI-type I	115.00	1545.George VI-type II	125.00
1546.Elizabeth II-type I	150.00	1547.Elizabeth II-type II	130.00

Royal Air Force Levies Iraq Long Service & Good Conduct Medal
1548.George VI--1949-1955	2000.00	1549.Elizabeth II	2800.00

Royal Air Force Meritorious Service Medal-1919-28; 1977
1550.George V	350.00	1551.Elizabeth II	350.00

Indian Army Long Service & Good Conduct Medal
1552.East India Company Arms obverse	650.00
1553.Victoria-anchor reverse	700.00
1554.Victoria-standard issue	150.00
1555.Edward VII	85.00
1556.George V-Kaisar-I-Hind	45.00
1557.George V-Ind Imp	65.00
1558.George VI-Ind Imp	50.00

Indian Army Meritorious Service Medal
1559.Victoria-East India Company reverse 1848-1873	450.00
1560.Victoria-standard issue 1888	200.00
1561.Edward VII	85.00
1562.George V-Kaisar-I-Hind	75.00
1563.George V-Ind Imp	85.00
1564.George VI-Ind Imp	60.00

Indian Volunteer Decoration-1899-1900-officers
1565.Victoria (same as British Volunteer Decoration)			140.00
1566.Edward VII	225.00	1567.George V	250.00

Colonial Auxiliary Forces Decoration-1899-1930-officers
1568.Victoria			325.00
1569.Edward VII-ERI	300.00	1570.George V-GRI	200.00

Colonial Auxiliary Forces Long Service Medal-1899-1930
1571.Victoria			160.00
1572.Edward VII	140.00	1573.George V	125.00

Permanent Forces of the Empire Beyond the Seas Long Service
& Good Conduct Medal-1909-1930
1574.Edward VII	rare	1575.George V	160.00

(Note: The above values are based on awards to Canadians; values to other dominions or colonies are higher.)

Canadian Forces Decoration
1576.George VI	85.00	1577.Elizabeth II	65.00

South African Permanent Force Long Service & Good Conduct
1578.George VI-type I-Ind Imp	250.00
1579.George VI-type II-no Ind Imp	350.00

Police Long Service-1951
1508.George VI-type II	50.00
1581.Elizabeth II-type I-long legend	85.00
1582.Elizabeth II-type II-short legend	50.00

Special Constabulary Long Service Medal-1919
1583.George V-robed	50.00	1584.George V-coinage	20.00
1585.George VI-type I	20.00	1586.George VI-type II	120.00
1587.Elizabeth II-type I	35.00	1588.Elizabeth II-type II	35.00
1589.Elizabeth II-Ulster issue			200.00
1590.Elizabeth II-Colonial issue			250.00

(Note: Sew on Long Service or War Service Bars are sometimes found on the ribbon of these medals-add $5.00 to $10.00.)

Colonial Police Long Service Medal-1934
1591.George V			150.00
1592.George VI-type I	100.00	1593.George VI-type II	100.00
1594.EIIR-type I	100.00	1595.EIIR-type II	100.00

Colonial Police Meritorious Service Medal-1938
1596.George VI-type I	100.00	1597.George VI-type II	100.00
1598.EIIR-type I	125.00	1599.EIIR-type II	125.00

Colonial Prison Service Long Service Medal-1955
1600.Elizabeth II-type II-short legend	400.00

GREAT BRITAIN

African Police Meritorious Service Medal-1915-1938

1601.George V			600.00
1602.George VI-type I	550.00	1603.George VI-type II	rare

Ceylon Police Long Service Medal

1604.George V-coinage issue			500.00
1605.George VI	500.00	1606.Elizabeth II	425.00

Cyprus Military Police Long Service & Good Conduct-1929

1607.George V	rare

Malta Police Long Service & Good Conduct-1921-1934

1608.George V-robed	rare	1609.George V-coinage	rare

Colonial Fire Brigade Long Service Medal-1934

1610.George V			450.00
1611.George VI-type I	400.00	1612.George VI-type II	400.00
1613.EIIR-type I	400.00	1614.EIIR-type II	400.00

Cadet Forces Long Service & Good Conduct Medal-1950

1615.George VI-type II			85.00
1616.EIIR-type I	95.00	1617.EIIR-type II	75.00

Civil Defence Long Service Medal-1961

1618.EIIR-standard issue	35.00	1619.EIIR-Ulster issue	150.00

Royal Observer Corps Long Service Medal-1950

1620.EIIR-type I	100.00	1621.EIIR-type II	75.00

1622.Women's Voluntary Services Long Service Medal	35.00

Ulster Defence Regiment Medal-1970

1623.Officers	90.00	1624.Enlisted Men	75.00
1625.For Long Service & Good Conduct			150.00

Royal Household Faithful Service Medal

1626.Victoria	850.00	1627.Edward VII	rare
1628.George V	350.00	1629.Edward VIII	rare
1630.George VI	400.00	1631.Elizabeth II	rare

(Note: Extra service bars may be found on these medals-add 50% to 100%.)

ROYAL COMMEMORATIVE, CORONATION & JUBILEE MEDALS

Empress of India Medal-1877

1632.Gold	10,000.00	1633.Silver	400.00

Jubilee Medal-1887-standard issue

1634.Gold-to royalty & royal household	2000.00

1635.Gold-with bar 1897			rare
1636.Silver	125.00	1637.Silver-bar 1897	200.00
1638.Bronze	100.00	1639.Bronze-bar 1897	125.00

Jubilee Medal-1887-Police Issue
Metropolitan Police

1640.Bronze	35.00	1641.same-bar 1897	30.00

City of London Police

1642.Bronze	85.00	1643.same-bar 1897	95.00

Police Ambulance Service

1644.Bronze	rare	1645.same-bar 1897	rare

Jubilee Medal-1897-standard issue

1646.Gold-to royalty & royal household			1500.00
1647.Silver	125.00	1648.Bronze	100.00

Jubilee Medal-1897-Mayor & Provost Issue

1649.Gold	rare	1650.Silver	450.00

Jubilee Medal-1897-Police Issue-all bronze

1651.Metropolitan Police	25.00
1652.City of London Police	85.00
1653.Police Ambulance Service	300.00
1654.St John Ambulance Brigade	110.00
1655.L.C.C. (London County Council) Metropolitan Fire Brigade	100.00

1656.Visit to Ireland-1900	100.00

Coronation Medal-Edward VII-1902-standard issue

1657.Silver	100.00	1658.Bronze	65.00

Coronation Medal-1902-Mayor & Provost Issue

1659.Silver	225.00

Coronation Medal-1902-Police Issue
Metropolitan Police

1660.Silver	375.00	1661.Bronze	25.00

City of London Police

1662.Silver	1000.00	1663.Bronze	50.00

L.C.C. Metropolitan Fire Brigade

1664.Silver	600.00	1665.Bronze	85.00

St John Ambulance Brigade

1666.Silver	---	1667.Bronze	85.00

Police Ambulance Service

1668.Silver	---	1669.Bronze	225.00

1670.Visit to Scotland-Edward VII-1903	85.00

1671.Visit to Ireland-Edward VII-1903	100.00

Dehli Durbar-1903

1672.Gold	1500.00	1673.Silver	150.00

1674.Coronation Medal-George V-1911-standard issue   50.00

Coronation Medal-1911-Police & Miscellaneous Issues-all silver

1675.City of London Police	85.00
1676.Metropolitan Police	25.00
1677.County & Borough Police	100.00
1678.Scottish Police	150.00
1679.Royal Irish Constabulary	125.00
1680.Police Ambulance Service	500.00
1681.London Fire Brigade	85.00
1682.St John Ambulance Brigade	85.00
1683.St Andrew's Ambulance Brigade	260.00
1684.Royal Parks	450.00
1685.Visit to Ireland 1911 (unnamed)	85.00

Dehli Durbar-1911

1686.Gold	1500.00	1687.Silver	50.00

(Silver issue sometimes found named-add 15%.)

1688.Jubilee-1935	35.00
1689.Coronation-1937-GeoVI	35.00
1690.Coronation-1953-Elizabeth II	50.00

Jubilee-1977

1691.British issue	250.00
1692.Canadian issue	150.00

ARCTIC & POLAR MEDALS

1693.Arctic-Victoria-1818-1855-unnamed as issued			450.00
1694.same-but privately named			600.00
1695.Arctic-Victoria-1875-76-named			2000.00
Edward VII			
1696.Silver	from 2000.00	1697.Bronze	from 1500.00
George V			
1698.Silver	from 1500.00	1699.Bronze	from 1100.00
George VI			
1700.Silver	from 1200.00	1701.Bronze	from 1100.00
Elizabeth II			
1702.Silver			from 1200.00

(Note: The above values do not apply to the smaller Antarctic Expeditions 1902-04; 1907-09; 1910-13 & the Capt Scott, which are much rarer, and very difficult to estimate.)

NAVAL ENGINEER'S MEDAL-1842-46

1703.Issued Medal-named (eight)	rare
1704.Unnamed specimen	200.00

6

37

88

116

201

255   45 & 46   214 - 220

251   210 & 211

242   265 - 276

323   247

283 - 286 292 - 295

261 289

562 634

849 - 878 732

1152 & 1153   975   732

922 & 923   955

765 & 767   882 & 883

1009 & 1010   1188

1126 & 1127   1043 & 1044

1232 - 1234   1112

1346   1350   1351

1352 & 1353   1357

1326 & 1327   1364

1378   1393 - 1396

1473 - 1475   1510   1577

1688   1690

GREECE

Kingdom till 1924
Republic 1924-1936
Kingdom 1936-1973

The awards of this country are handsome and well made. The Orders in particular reflect the religious struggle which took place against the Turks for centuries. The awards to the armed forces and the police have been generous, as witnessed by the great variety of items struck.

Many of the insignia of Greek Orders have been made by foreign firms. Some of the early 19th century material was made in Imperial Russia, and consequently of very high quality. During and after World War II the London, England, firm of Spink was the official purveyor, and displayed their usual fine quality manufacture.

For the most part there is no problem with copies of Greek awards. The two notable exceptions seem to be the World War I Service Cross, and the World War I Victory Medal. The Service Cross in its genuine form has a hinged suspension on the reverse for the ribbon. The copy has a bar attached on the reverse for the ribbon to go through. The Victory Medal to be genuine must have the designer's name Henry Nocq on the rim, otherwise it is a copy.

Order of the Redeemer-1833-1973
Type I-head of King Otto on obverse center-1833-1862
1.Grand Cross badge	1200.00
2.Grand Cross breast star	750.00
3.Commander Cross I Class	750.00
4.Commander Cross I Class breast star	500.00
5.Commander Cross II Class	750.00
6.Officer-gold	350.00
7.Knight-silver	300.00

Type II-with Christ on the obverse center-1862-1924;1936-1973
8.Grand Cross badge	600.00
9.Grand Cross breast star	500.00
10.Commander Cross I Class	400.00
11.Commander Cross I Class breast star	400.00
12.Commander Cross II Class	400.00
13.Officer-gold	275.00
14.Officer-silver/gilt	150.00
15.Knight-silver	125.00

Order of George I-1915-1924; 1936-1973 (See also 149-154.)
16.Grand Cross badge	550.00
17.Grand Cross badge with swords	600.00
18.Grand Cross breast star	500.00
19.Grand Cross breast star with swords	550.00
20.Commander Cross I Class	350.00
21.Commander Cross I Class with swords	400.00
22.Commander Cross I Class breast star	350.00
23.Commander Cross I Class breast star with swords	400.00
24.Commander Cross II Class	350.00
25.Commander Cross II Class with swords	400.00

26.Officer	150.00
27.Officer with swords	200.00
28.Knight	150.00
29.Knight with swords	175.00

Order of the Phoenix-1926-1973
Type I-1926-1935-without crown suspension

30.Grand Cross badge	500.00
31.Grand Cross breast star	450.00
32.Commander Cross I Class	300.00
33.Commander Cross I Class breast star	300.00
34.Commander Cross II Class	300.00
35.Officer	150.00
36.Knight	125.00

Type II-1936-with crown-reverse monogram of George II
Type III-with crown-star on top arm obverse-reverse monogram of
Paul. Values for these two type are approximately the same.

37.Grand Cross badge	500.00
38.Grand Cross badge with swords	550.00
39.Grand Cross breast star	450.00
40.Grand Cross breast star with swords	500.00
41.Commander Cross I Class	300.00
42.Commander Cross I Class with swords	350.00
43.Commander Cross I Class breast star	300.00
44.Commander Cross I Class breast star with swords	350.00
45.Commander Cross II Class	300.00
46.Commander Cross II Class with swords	350.00
47.Officer	150.00
48.Officer with swords	200.00
49.Knight	125.00
50.Knight with swords	150.00

Royal Family Order of Sts George & Constantine

51.Collar	5000.00
52.Collar with swords	rare
53.Grand Cross badge	800.00
54.Grand Cross badge with swords	850.00
55.Grand Cross breast star	750.00
56.Grand Cross breast star with swords	800.00
57.Commander Cross I Class	500.00
58.Commander Cross I Class with swords	550.00
59.Commander Cross I Class breast star	500.00
60.Commander Cross I Class breast star with swords	500.00
61.Commander Cross II Class	500.00
62.Commander Cross II Class with swords	550.00
63.Officer	350.00
64.Officer with swords	400.00
65.Knight	300.00
66.Knight with swords	325.00

Order of Sts Olga & Sophia-1936-1973
67.Grand Cross badge	1000.00
68.Grand Cross breast star	800.00
69.II Class badge-on bow ribbon	700.00
70.II Class breast star	600.00
71.III Class-gold medal	350.00
72.IV Class-silver medal	175.00

Order of Good Deeds (or Charity)-1948-1973
73.Grand Cross badge	700.00
74.Grand Cross breast star	700.00
75.Grand Officer Cross	625.00
76.Grand Officer breast star	625.00
77.Commander Cross	625.00
78.Officer	450.00
79.Knight	350.00

Miscellaneous Decorations & Campaign Medals

Cross of Valor-1913; 1940
80.I Class-gold & enamel cross	350.00
81.II Class-silver cross	250.00
82.III Class-bronze cross	125.00

Cross of Valor for the Gendarmerie-1946
83.I Class-neck badge	rare
84.II Class-gold cross	250.00
85.III Class-silver cross	150.00

86.Decoration for Arts, Science & Letters-1914	rare
87.Commemorative Medal-I National Assembly Members-1822	rare
88.Commemorative Medal-Guard of Missalongi	rare
89.Commemorative Cross for Bavarian Auxiliary Corps-1833	350.00
90.Commemorative Cross for Bavarian Volunteers	350.00

Commemorative Cross for the War of Independence 1821-1829
91.Silver-Officers	rare
92.Bronze-N.C.O.'s	rare
93.Iron-for enlisted soldiers & sailors	rare

94.Commemorative Cross-Revolution of 1843-Athens	rare
95.same-but for all other provinces	rare

96.Seamen's Pension Fund Medal-Lifesaving	275.00

97.I Balkan War Medal-1912-1913   45.00
(With 13 campaign bars; a wounded bar, and a killed in action
bar. Add $15.00 each campaign bar, and $25.00 for the others.)
98.II Balkan War Medal-1913   35.00
(With 5 campaign bars; a wounded bar, and a killed in action bar. Add $15.00 for
the campaign bars, and $25.00 for the others.)

GREECE

War Cross 1914-1917
99.I Class-bronze palm on ribbon   45.00
100.II Class-bronze star on ribbon   40.00
101.III Class-no device on ribbon   35.00
(Note: Copies of this award have a straight bar soldered on the reverse for the ribbon to go around, instead of the correct movable suspension device with a ring at top for the ribbon.)

Military Merit Medal-for Officers of the Army & Navy
102.I Class-gilt wreath on ribbon-generals/admirals   50.00
103.II Class-silver wreath-colonels & captains   45.00
104.III Class-bronze wreath-Lt Colonels, Major, Commanders,
       Lt Commanders   35.00
105.IV Class-no wreath-captains & naval lieuts   25.00

106.World War I Victory Medal-Henry NOCQ on rim   150.00

Merchant Marine Service Medal-1925
107.I Class   35.00
108.II Class   25.00

Naval Good Shooting Medal
109.Presidential type-1925   50.00
110.Royal type-1935   65.00

Commemorative Medal of the Macedonian Struggle-(1903-1909)
Type I-Presidential Issue-1925
111.I Class-silver laurel on ribbon   75.00
112.II Class-silver star on ribbon   65.00
113.III Class-no device on ribbon   50.00
Type II-Royal Issue-1935
114.I Class-silver laurel on ribbon   75.00
115.II Class-silver star on ribbon   65.00
116.III Class-no device on ribbon   50.00

Commemorative Medal for Northern Epirus-(1914)-1935
117.I Class-silver laurel wreath on ribbon   75.00
118.II Class-silver star on ribbon   65.00
119.III Class-no device on ribbon   50.00

Long Service & Good Conduct Medal-1937 & 1940
120.I Class-gilt-20 years   35.00
121.II Class-silvered-15 years   25.00
122.III Class-bronze-10 years   20.00

Agricultural Merit Medal
123.I Class-gilt   65.00
124.II Class-silver   45.00
125.III Class-bronze   35.00

World War II Decorations
126.Medal for Outstanding Acts-1940	85.00
127.Royal Navy Cross-1943	85.00
128.Valor Cross in Flight-1945 & 1953	225.00
129.Distinguished Flying Cross-1945-combat	225.00
130.Air Force Cross-1945-non-combat	175.00
131.Air Force Medal-1945-non-combat-N.C.O.'s	175.00
132.Air Force Merit Medal-1945	125.00
133.Distinguished Service Medal-Air Force	175.00
134.Convoy Escort Medal-1945	150.00

Commemorative Medal-1940-1941
135.Army-Albania, Macedonia, Thrace, Crete	25.00
136.Navy-Aegean, Ionian, Mytroon, Adriatic Seas	25.00

Commemorative Medal-1941-1945
137.Army-Albania, Italy, Aegean Isles	25.00
138.Navy-Mediterranean Sea, Atlantic & Indian Oceans	25.00

War Cross-1940
139.I Class-bronze with gilt crown	45.00
140.II Class-with silver crown	35.00
141.III Class-all bronze	25.00

Police Awards

142.Police Cross-1946	75.00

Police Long Service Medals-1946
143.I Class-gilt	35.00
144.II Class-silvered	25.00
145.III Class-bronze	20.00

Royal Household Decorations
146.George I-1881	rare
147.Constantine II-1914	rare
148.Alexander	rare
George II	
149.I Class-gilt	60.00
150.I Class-gilt-with swords	85.00
151.II Class-silver	50.00
152.II Class-silver-with swords	60.00
153.III Class-bronze	35.00
154.III Class-bronze-with swords	45.00

(Note: Items 149-154 are also considered to be the VI-VIII Classes of the Order of George I, but are included here because of their being used as Royal Household awards.)

26   6 & 7   149, 151, 153

13 - 15

89   80   127

82

GULF WAR-1990-91
(Kuwait Liberation)

This war between Iraq and a United Nations coalition of many countries produced a series of medals from the various countries; thus providing for the collector another topical area around which to collect. Unfortunately, it also produced a fake medal. The British medal has been copied. The copy is unnamed, in distinction to originals which are officially named to the recipient.

1.Bahrain	25.00
2.Canada	200.00
3.Canada-with maple leaf bar	225.00
4.Great Britain-no bar	200.00
5.Great Britain-bar 2 Aug 1990	2500.00
6.Great Britain-bar 16 Jan-28 Feb 1991	300.00
7.Italy	25.00
8.Kuwait	25.00
9.Norway	250.00
10.Saudi Arabia	25.00
11.Singapore (30 man medical detachment)	rare
12.United Arab Emirates	25.00
13.United Nations Service Medal	25.00
14.United States of America-S.W.Asia Medal-military	25.00
15.United States of America-Desert Shield/Desert Storm- civilian medal-Department of State	25.00

(Several states of the U.S.A. have also issued medals for this conflict.)

10   12   14

1   8   7

HUNGARY

Associated with Austria until 1918 (Holy Roman Empire till 1806; Austrian Empire till 1867; Austro-Hungarian Empire 1867-1918).
Republic 1918-1922
Titular Monarchy under the Regent, Admiral Horthy, 1922-1944

Properly speaking, the awards system between 1922 and 1944 can be considered a continuation of that of the Austro-Hungarian Empire. The Order of St Stephen, although issued under the Empire, was regarded as a strictly Hungarian award, and thus is included under this country. The intricacy and style of the Hungarian awards system follows directly the Austrian manner, even including the practice of wearing a device on the ribbon of a lower class of an Order to denote possession of higher class, yet obviating the necessity of wearing it.

The Order of St Stephen offers a number of problems to the collector. There are many unmarked pieces of insignia for sale; some of them recently made, and offered to the collector as "genuine". My feeling is that unmarked pieces are to be avoided, as they are almost certain to be copies. This is also the feeling of collectors with whom I discussed the matter. None of the other Hungarian items seem to offer any difficulties with the exception of the Officer's Cross with swords of the Order of Merit. This comes in a German variation without the war decoration. Whether this is a copy or a variation is open to dispute. However, one Hungarian collector told me that "if it doesn't have the War Decoration on it then it is not correct."

The World War I Commemorative Medal, combat type, is frequently found in German medal groups. The collector of III Reich awards also has some interest in Hungarian items, as many Germans received them during World War II.

Order of St Stephen-1764-1918
1.Collar	rare
2.Grand Cross badge-with diamonds	rare
3.Grand Cross badge	rare
4.Grand Cross breast star-with diamonds	rare
5.Grand Cross breast star	2500.00
6.Commander-neck badge	2500.00
7.Knight	750.00
8.Kleine Dekoration of the Grand Cross	1500.00
9.Kleine Dekoration of the Commander Cross	1250.00

(Note: Many excellent copies of this Order exist. They are not hallmarked, and the ribbon suspension ring is not fused closed.)

10.Order of the Golden Spur-1918	rare
11.Vitez Order-1920-1944	300.00

Order of Merit-1922-1944
12.Collar	rare
13.Grand Cross badge with crown	2000.00
14.Grand Cross badge with crown & swords	2800.00
15.Grand Cross badge	1000.00
16.Grand Cross badge with swords	1200.00

17.Grand Cross badge with swords & war decoration	1300.00
18.Grand Cross breast star with crown	2000.00
19.Grand Cross breast star with crown & swords	2250.00
20.Grand Cross breast star	700.00
21.Grand Cross breast star with swords	800.00
22.Grand Cross breast star with swords & war decoration	850.00
23.Commander-neck badge	300.00
24.Commander with swords	350.00
25.Commander with swords & war decoration	400.00
26.Commander breast star	300.00
27.Commander breast star with swords	350.00
28.Commander breast star with swords & war decoration	400.00
29.Officer-pinback cross	300.00
30.Officer-with swords	350.00
31.Officer with swords & war decoration	400.00
32.Knight	150.00
33.Knight with swords	200.00
34.Knight with swords & war decoration	250.00
35.Silver Merit Cross	150.00
36.Kleine Dekoration of the Grand Cross	300.00
37.same-with swords	350.00
38.same-with swords & war decoration	400.00
39.Kleine Dekoration of the Commander Cross	250.00
40.same-with swords	300.00
41.same-with swords & war decoration	350.00
42.Kleine Dekoration of the Officer Cross	250.00
43.same-with swords	300.00
44.same-with swords & war decoration	350.00

Order of the Holy Crown-1943-1944

45.Grand Cross badge	1000.00
46.Grand Cross badge with swords	1100.00
47.Grand Cross badge with swords & war decoration	1200.00
48.Grand Cross breast star	800.00
49.Grand Cross breast star with swords	900.00
50.Grand Cross breast star with swords & war decoration	1100.00
51.Commander-neck badge	750.00
52.Commander with swords	800.00
53.Commander with swords & war decoration	850.00
54.Commander breast star	700.00
55.Commander breast star with swords	750.00
56.Commander breast star with swords & war decoration	800.00
57.Officer-pinback cross	400.00
58.Officer with swords	450.00
59.Officer with swords & war decoration	500.00
60.Knight	300.00
61.Knight with swords	350.00
62.Knight with swords & war decoration	400.00
63.Gold Merit Cross	250.00
64.Gold Merit Cross with swords	300.00
65.Gold Merit Cross with swords & war decoration	350.00

66.Silver Merit Cross	150.00
67.Silver Merit Cross with swords	175.00
68.Silver Merit Cross with swords & war decoration	225.00
69.Bronze Merit Cross	125.00
70.Bronze Merit Cross with swords	150.00
71.Bronze Merit Cross with swords & war decoration	175.00

Honor Decoration of the Hungarian Red Cross-1922-1944

72.Breast Star	700.00
73.Breast Star with war decoration	750.00
74.Merit Cross-pinback	300.00
75.Merit Cross with war decoration	350.00
76.Merit Medal-enameled	300.00
77.Merit Medal with war decoration	325.00
78.Silver Medal	125.00
79.Silver Medal with war decoration	150.00
80.Bronze Medal	75.00
81.Bronze Medal with war decoration	85.00
82.Honor Commemorative Decoration	200.00

83.War Invalid Decoration-1931	75.00

Matthias Corvin Decoration-1930-1944

84.I Class-decoration on a collar chain	5500.00
85.II Class-wreath with shield-pinback	1500.00
86.III Class-Honor Decoration-breast star	1250.00

Merit Medal-1922-1944-"A HAZAERT"

87.Silver Medal	75.00
88.Bronze Medal	45.00

Large Golden Merit Medal with Crown (Signum Laudis)-1922-1939

89.Medal with crown	200.00
90.Medal with crown & swords	250.00
91.Medal with shield suspension	300.00
92.Medal with shield suspension & swords	350.00
93.Medal with shield suspension & wreath	450.00
94.Medal with shield suspension & wreath & swords	500.00

Small Merit Medal (Signum Laudis)-1922-1939

95.Small Golden Medal	85.00
96.Silver Medal	75.00
97.Bronze Medal	60.00

98.Lifesaving Medal-1922-1929	125.00

99.National Defense Service Cross-1940	35.00

Medal for Bravery-1939-1944
Obverse: Admiral Horthy Reverse: VITEZSEGERT

100.Golden Medal	300.00

101.Large Silver Medal	150.00
102.Small Silver Medal	100.00
103.Bronze Medal	75.00

Frontline Combat Cross-1941-1944
104.I Class with swords & wreath	45.00
105.same-dated 1941	45.00
106.same-dated 1942	45.00
107.same-dated 1943	45.00
108.same-with extra award bar	75.00
109.II Class with wreath	35.00
110.same-dated 1941	35.00
111.same-dated 1942	35.00
112.same-dated 1943	35.00
113.same-with extra award bar	45.00
114.III Class	25.00
115.same-dated 1941	25.00
116.same-dated 1942	25.00
117.same-dated 1943	25.00

Civil Merit Cross-1944
118.Golden Cross	95.00
119.Silver Cross	60.00
120.Bronze Cross	50.00

Toldi Miklos Merit Medal-1936
121.Golden Medal-silver/gilt-37mm	95.00
122.Silver Medal-32.5mm	60.00
123.Bronze Medal	35.00

Officers' Long Service Decorations-1923-1944
124.I Class-35-40 years	75.00
125.II Class-25-30 years	60.00
126.III Class-15-20 years	50.00

Enlisted Men's Long Service Awards
127.I Class Cross-20 years	35.00
128.II Class-10 years	25.00
129.III Class-6 years	20.00
130.Honor Medal-35 years service	85.00

Reserve Honor Medals-1923
131.Officers' Medal	60.00
132.Enlisted Men's Medal	50.00

Commemorative Medals
133.World War I-1914-18-combat	25.00
134.World War I-1914-18-non-combat	50.00
135.Upper Hungary Medal-1938	35.00
136.Siebenburgen Medal-1938	35.00
137.South Hungary Medal-1941	35.00

23
29

118 & 119   32   120

51
57

61 48 87 & 88

72   82

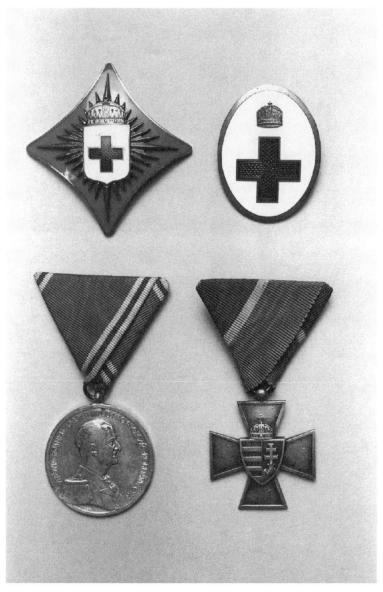

100 & 101   99

133   134

137   104 - 107

ICELAND

Colony of Denmark till 1944
Republic since 1944

As a small country with a long, but uncomplicated history, Iceland's awards are few. The sole Order can be seen in two types, with and without crown, reflecting its change in status.

French made insignia do exist, of poorer quality, and they command at most half of the values listed. I have seen only a French made Commander's badge, but there may be others.

Order of the Falcon

Type I-with royal crown-1921-1944
1.Collar	rare
2.Grand Cross badge	2500.00
3.Grand Cross breast star	950.00
4.Commander-neck badge	750.00
5.Commander breast star	550.00
6.Knight	450.00

Type II-without royal crown-1944-
7.Collar	rare
8.Grand Cross badge	2000.00
9.Grand Cross breast star	850.00
10.Commander-neck badge	500.00
11.Commander breast star	500.00
12.Knight	350.00

Lifesaving Medal
13.I Class-gold	1500.00
14.II Class-silver	500.00

15.President of Iceland's Medal	550.00

4

15

IRELAND

Republic

As a republic which struggled hard to break away from the British Empire, Ireland has shown its independence in its awards system also. This country has no Orders; only awards for gallantry, merit, long service and the like. With the exception of the War for Independence and World War II, Irish awards have been granted sparingly, and thus are quite rare. While there does not seem to be a problem with Irish pieces being copied, it should be noted that they are not of a very high quality.

For the collector of Irish interest who might become frustrated by the lack of material I can recommend the campaign medals of Great Britain, awarded to Irish Regiments. On rare occasions the collector might come across a group which has medals from both the British & Republican periods.

The collector should also be aware that the Irish Army has qualified for a number of U.N. Service Medals, other than for the Korean War.

1.Easter Rising Medal	350.00
2.Easter Rising Medal-privately named	450.00
3.General Service Medal-1917-1921-with combat bar	85.00
4.same-privately named	300.00
5.same-without combat bar	60.00
6.same-privately named	200.00
7.Military Medal for Gallantry-1964	rare

Distinguished Service Medal-1964

8.I Class-silver	rare
9.II Class-bronze	rare
10.III Class-bronze	rare

Emergency Service Medal-1939-1946-obverse same-different reverses

11.NA FORSAI COSANTA-The Defense Forces	25.00
12.AN SLUA AUIRI-Naval Reserve	125.00
13.26u CATHLAN-26th Battalion (I.R.A. members)	250.00
14.AN FORSA COSANTA AITIUIL-Local Defense Force	25.00
15.FORSA NA NOGLACH 2u LINE-Second Line Volunteer Reserve	25.00
16.SEIRBHIS ALTRANAIS AN AIRM (Army Nursing Service)	200.00
17.RANNA CABHAIR DEONTACA CUMANN CROISE DEIRGE H-EIREANN-Volunteer Air Division-Red Cross	95.00
18.RANNA CEAD-CABHRAC CUMANN CROISE DEIRGE NA H-EIREANN-First Aid Division-Irish Red Cross	95.00
19.NA SEIRBISE REAMHCURAIM IN AGHAIDGH AER-RUATHAR-Air Raid Precautions Organization	25.00
20.CAOMNOIRI AITULA-Local Security Force	20.00
21.AN SEIRBHIS SEIPLINEACHTA-Chaplaincy Service	250.00
22.AN SEIRBHIS MUIR-TRACALA-Merchant Navy Service	300.00

(Note: Extra service bars are to be found on the above medals-add $5.00 per bar except for the rare items.)

23.Long Service Medal-An Bonn Seirbhise	65.00
24.Reserve Long Service Medal	25.00
25.1916 Survivor's Medal-gilt-1916-1966	250.00

Civilian Awards-all are rare; listed for information purposes.
26.For Bravery-An Bonn Gniomh Gaile-gold
27.same-bronze
28.Scott Medal-Police Valor Decoration-gold
29.same-silver
30.same-bronze
31.President's Award-Irish Red Cross Society-1959
32.Irish Red Cross Merit Medal-1960
33.St John Ambulance Medal-Irish Brigade-gilt

34.St John Ambulance Medal-silver	350.00

35.Order of Malta-Ambulance Corps Merit Medal

Foreign Awards to Irish Troops

36.Papal States-Cross of Mentana	300.00
37.Medal for Castelfiardo	300.00
38.U.N. Observers Medal-various ribbons	$25.00 - 45.00

ITALY

Group of Independent States until 1860
Kingdom 1860-1946

In a smaller sense the awards of Italy are like those of Germany prior to unification in 1871. A group of independent states awarded their own decorations, and one dominant state, in the case of Italy, Piedmont-Sardinia, united the country under its control.

The awards of Italy also reflect its historical associations with other countries, as the dynasties of the various states had family ties with other nations.

The Orders of the pre-unified states were given sparingly, primarily to army officers, nobles, high government officials, and sometimes to the higher clergy. Unlike those of the German states, they ceased to be given out officially after Piedmont- Sardinia had taken them over. Some of the former ruling families did continue to grant some Orders on a personal basis, as a family award. The status of these awards is difficult to decide from the position of the collector. The original awarding authority, a royal family, did not continue to have the political authority, as the rulers of a country, to award such items! Therefore, to the collector the value of an Italian state order given out after unification of Italy in 1860 should have different status to that of such awarded before that date. Of course this is a matter of opinion. However, I have found that collectors place more value on items where there is no question of legitimacy.

Upon unification, the awards of the King of Piedmont-Sardinia became those of the Kingdom of Italy, replacing those of the other states. While there appear to be a great variety of Italian medals in reality this is not so. Many of these varieties may be only of a different designer's name or initials, with no real difference in value. The specialist Italian collector therefore will not find all the designer differences listed herein, as this would have complicated things very greatly.

There have appeared a series of restrikes or copies of common Italian medals in recent years. The medal for Military Valor (Al Valore Militare [royal type]) in its post-World War II restrike lacks the initials of the designer. Some collectors consider it to be copy. I have had in my possession a cast copy of the World War I Commemorative Medal, and the World War I Victory Medal. While these items are cheap looking, and very low in price so are many of the originals.

One piece which is not cheap, and copied very well, is the Order of the Roman Eagle, a fascist era item. While the workmanship on the copies is not as good as that of the originals it is difficult to tell without having another for purposes of comparison. This Order, especially when with swords, should be examined very carefully before buying, with a powerful magnifier in a good light.

Otherwise, the Orders, decorations and medals of Italy can afford much pleasure to the collector. For the most part they are well designed, and well struck.

Finally, mention should be made of a large number of unofficial medal issued by various military units; armies, divisions, regiments and battalions. Many were struck for World War I, and the campaigns in Ethiopia in 1935-1936. They have no official standing, and are not included herein, but nevertheless of interest.

ITALY

FORMER ITALIAN STATES

DUCHY OF LUCCA-1805-1847

Military Order of St George-1833-1847
1.I Class-with diamonds	rare
2.I Class-gold cross-for Household service	rare
3.II Class-silver cross-enameled-for Officers	1800.00
4.III Class-unenameled silver cross-enlisted men	900.00

Civil Merit Order of St Louis-1836-1847
5.I Class-gold-enameled cross	rare
6.II Class-silver cross-enameled center	1500.00
7.III Class-silver cross-unenameled	900.00

8.Military Service Medal-1833-1847-for Officers	750.00

Civil Merit Medal
9.Silver Medal	450.00
10.Bronze Medal	175.00

DUCHY OF MODENA-1452-1860

Order of the Eagle of Este-1855-1875
Military Division-trophy of arms suspension
11.Grand Cross badge	rare
12.Grand Cross breast star	rare
13.Commander	4000.00
14.Knight	3000.00

Civil Division-oak wreath suspension
15.Grand Cross badge	rare
16.Grand Cross breast star	rare
17.Commander	4000.00
18.Knight	3000.00

19.Military Medal for Loyalty-1831	550.00
20.Officers' Service Cross-1832	450.00
21.Military Merit Medal-1852	400.00
22.Medal of Fidelity-1863	175.00

DUCHY OF PARMA-1545-1859

Order of Constantine of St George-1814-1847
23.Collar of Senator Grand Cross	rare
24.Senator Grand Cross badge	3000.00
25.Senator Grand Cross breast star	2500.00
26.Commander	1500.00
27.Commander breast star	1500.00
28.Knight I Class-pinback	800.00
29.Knight II Class	600.00

(Note: Later insignia of this Order exist. It appears to have been continued as a royal family order.)

Order of St Louis-1849-1907 (See also Lucca.)
30.Grand Cross badge	2500.00
31.Grand Cross breast star	2000.00
32.Commander	1750.00
33.Commander breast star	1750.00
34.Knight I Class-with crown	1100.00
35.Knight II Class	850.00

36.Medal of Merit	rare

KINGDOM OF THE TWO SICILIES (NAPLES)-1735-1860

Order of St Januarius-1738
37.Collar	rare
38.Badge	rare
39.Breast Star-early	2500.00
40.Breast Star-late 19th century	1100.00

(Note: There are many variations of this Order. Don't be surprised if the picture in a book looks different from your piece. It doesn't mean that yours is a fake.)

Order of St Ferdinand
41.Collar	rare
42.Grand Cross badge-with diamonds	rare
43.Grand Cross breast star-with diamonds	rare
44.Grand Cross badge	rare
45.Grand Cross breast star	3500.00
46.Commander	4500.00
47.Knight	3000.00

Order of the Two Sicilies-1808-1819
Type I-name of King Joseph-no crown-all classes extremely rare.

Type II-name of King Joseph-with crown-1809-1810
48.Grand Cross badge	rare
49.Grand Cross breast star	rare
50.Commander	rare
51.Knight	5000.00

Type III-name of King Joachim Murat-3 leg device-1810-1811
52.Collar	rare
53.Grand Cross badge	rare
54.Grand Cross breast star	4500.00
55.Commander	rare
56.Knight	4500.00

Type IV-head of Joachim Murat-1811-1815
57.Grand Cross badge	rare
58.Grand Cross breast star	4500.00
59.Commander	rare
60.Knight	5000.00

Type V-Bourbon Restoration-1815-all classes rare.

ITALY

Order of St George of the Reunion
61.Collar	rare
62 Grand Cross badge	5000.00
63..Grand Cross breast star	3500.00
64.Commander	2500.00
65.Knight I Class	1500.00
66.Knight II Class	800.00
67.Gold Merit Medal	1100.00
68.Silver Merit Medal	500.00

Order of Francis I-1829-1860
69.Grand Cross badge	4000.00
70.Grand Cross breast star	2500.00
71.Commander	3000.00
72.Knight	900.00
73.Gold Merit Medal	1100.00
74.Silver Merit Medal	550.00

(Note: This award was continued after 1860 as a Royal Family Order.)

Medal of Honor for the Provincial Legion-1809
75.Silver	1500.00
76.Bronze	600.00

Medal of Honor for Naples-1814
77.Gold	rare
78.Silver	1100.00

Medal of Honor for the Restoration-1815
79.Gold	rare
80.Silver	900.00
81.Bronze (Sicily)	600.00

Security Medal-1816
82.Gold	rare
83.Silver	750.00

Civil Merit Medal-1757-1859 (several types)
84.Gold	rare
85.Silver	900.00

Medals for the Revolution of 1848-1849
86.Defense of Messina-1848	400.00
87.Siege of Messina-1848	150.00
88.Reconquest of Sicily-1848-1849	150.00

Medals for the War of Reunification of Italy-1860-1861
89.Campaign of 1860	150.00
90.Eastern Sicily	150.00
91.Defense of Catania	300.00
92.Gaeta-silver	400.00

93.Army 25 Year Long Service Medal	150.00

GRAND DUCHY OF TUSCANY

Order of St Stephen-1817-1859
94.I Class neck badge-trophy of arms suspender	3000.00
95.II Class neck badge	1500.00
96.Breast Star for the I & II Classes	1750.00
97.III Class-knight-trophy of arms suspender	1500.00
98.IV Class knight	900.00

Order of St Joseph-1814-1908
99.Grand Cross badge	5000.00
100.Grand Cross breast star	2500.00
101.Commander	2500.00
102.Knight	1000.00

Military Merit Order-1853-1860
103.Grand Cross badge	2500.00
104.Grand Cross breast star	1100.00
105.Commander	1000.00
106.Knight	750.00

Civil Merit Order-1853-1860
107.Grand Cross badge	2500.00
108.Grand Cross breast star	1100.00
109.Commander	1000.00
110.Knight	700.00

111.Military Medal for Bravery-1815-silver	550.00
112.Long Service Medal-1816-bronze	150.00
113.Military Merit Medal-1841	400.00
114.Medal of 1848	400.00

Medal of Merit-Ferdinand IV
115.I Class-gold-40mm	1000.00
116.II Class-gold-30mm	750.00
117.III Class-silver-49mm	450.00
118.IV Class-silver-30mm	350.00
119.V Class-bronze-45mm	150.00

120.Long Service Cross-1850-gilt-for officers	300.00

REPUBLIC OF VENICE

Medals for the Defense of Venice-1848
121.Silver	400.00
122.Bronze	150.00

Bravery Medal-1848
123.Silver	350.00
124.Bronze	150.00

125.Civil Guard Medal-1849	300.00

ITALY

DUCHY OF SAVOY
KINGDOM OF PIEDMONT-SARDINIA
KINGDOM OF ITALY

Order of the Annunciation (Annunziata)-1360-1944
Awards till 1860
126.Large Collar	rare
127.Small Collar	rare
128.Breast star	5000.00

Awards from 1860-1944
129.Large Collar	rare
130.Small Collar	20,000.00
131.Breast star	5000.00

(Note: Some excellent copies of this Order exist-usually not hallmarked.)

Order of Sts Maurice & Lazarus-1434-1946
Type of 1816-1860
132.Grand Cross badge	1800.00
133.Grand Cross breast star	1800.00
134.Commander I Class	800.00
135.Commander I Class breast star	800.00
136.Commander	800.00
137.Knight	400.00
138.Gold Medal-55mm	1100.00
139.Gold Medal-39mm	850.00

Type of 1860-1946
140.Grand Cross badge	1100.00
141.Grand Cross breast star	850.00
142.Commander I Class	550.00
143.Commander I Class breast star	550.00
144.Commander II Class	550.00
145.Officer (breast badge with crown)	400.00
146.Knight (breast badge without crown)	300.00

(Note: Values above are for gold insignia; for silver/gilt deduct 30%.)

Military Order of Savoy-1815-1946
Type I-1815-1855
147.Grand Cross badge	rare
148.Grand Cross breast star	rare
149.Commander	rare
150.Officer	rare
151.Knight	rare

Type II-1855-1946
152.Grand Cross badge	3000.00
153.Grand Cross breast star	2000.00
154.Commander I Class	1100.00
155.Commander I Class breast star	1100.00
156.Commander II Class	1100.00
157.Officer	750.00
158.Knight	500.00

(Note: This Order in modified form was continued by the Republic after 1946, as the Military Order of Italy. Restrikes of this Order, in poorer quality than the originals, have been made.)

Civil Merit Order or Civil Order of Savoy-1831-1946
Type I-1831-1860
159.Badge of the Order   rare
Type II-1860-1946
160.Badge of the Order   500.00

Order of the Crown of Italy-1860-1946
161.Grand Cross badge   550.00
162.Grand Cross breast star   500.00
163.Grand Officer (neck badge)   400.00
164.Grand Officer breast star   300.00
165.Commander (same as Grand Officer badge 163)   400.00
166.Officer-breast badge with rosette   175.00
167.Knight-breast badge without rosette   150.00
(Note: The above values are for gold insignia; silver/gilt pieces would be worth about 35% less. See also the Order of the Iron Crown of Austria.)

Order of Merit in Labor-1901-1946
168.Badge of the Order   350.00

Colonial Merit Order-1914-1946
169.Grand Cross badge   500.00
170.Grand Cross breast star   500.00
171.Grand Officer neck badge   350.00
172.Grand Officer breast star   350.00
173.Commander (same as 171)   350.00
174.Officer   150.00
175.Knight   110.00

Order of the Roman Eagle-1942-1944
176.Grand Cross badge   850.00
177.Grand Cross badge with swords   900.00
178.Grand Cross golden breast star   rare
179.Grand Cross gold breast star with swords   rare
180.Grand Cross silver breast star   800.00
181.Grand Cross silver breast star with swords   850.00
182.Grand Officer badge   650.00
183.Grand Officer badge with swords   700.00
184.Grand Officer breast star   550.00
185.Grand Officer breast star with swords   650.00
186.Commander (same as 182)   650.00
187.Commander with swords (same as 183)   700.00
188.Officer   400.00
189.Officer with swords   450.00
190.Knight   250.00
191.Knight with swords   300.00
192.Medal   150.00
193.Medal with swords   200.00
(Note: Excellent copies of this Order are known to exist.)

ITALY

Military Valor Medal (Al Valore Militare)-1793-1946
Type I-1793-bust of Victor Amadeus II
194.Gold   rare
195.Silver   1500.00

Type II-1796-bust of Charles Emanuel IV
196.Gold   rare
197.Silver   1500.00

Type III-1815-Victor Emanuel I
198.Gold   rare
199.Silver   1500.00

Type IV-1833-obverse royal arms-initials F.G. (any example of this type without
the initials F.G. is a restrike.)
200.Gold (silver/gilt)   450.00
201.Silver   300.00
202.Bronze-1887   150.00

203.Silver-named to an Italian-19th century   750.00
204.Silver-named to a Briton-Crimean War   800.00
205.Silver-named to a Frenchman-Crimean War   750.00
206.Silver-named to a Frenchman-Austrian War 1859   850.00
207.Silver-named to an Italian-World War I   700.00
208.Silver-named to an Allied Soldier-World War I   600.00
209.Bronze-named to an Italian-World War I   350.00
210.Bronze-named to an Allied Soldier-World War I   350.00
211.Gold-gilt restrike without initials   50.00
212.Silver-restrike without initials   25.00
213.Bronze-restrike without initials   20.00
(Note: There are many different styles of this award, including naming styles,
especially for the 19th century. The above is only a representative sample of what
a collector might come across.)

Civil Valor Medal-1851-1946
Type I-designer's name G.Ferrari F. on obverse
214.Gold   rare
215.Silver   350.00
216.Bronze-1888   250.00
(Above values for unnamed awards.)

Type II-no designer's name on obverse-1900-many restrikes
217.Gold (silver/gilt)   25.00
218.Silver   20.00
219.Bronze   15.00

Naval Valor Medal-Al Valore di Marina-1836; 1847; 1860
220.Gold   rare
221.Silver   450.00
222.Bronze-1888   200.00

Aeronautical Valor Medal-Al Valore Aeronautico-1927-1944
223.Gold (silver/gilt)	50.00
224.Silver	40.00
225.Bronze	25.00

Cross of Merit-Bronze-1918-1946
226.Merito Di Guerra-(War Merit)1918 & 1922	20.00
227.Croce Al Valor Militare-(Military Valor Cross)-1941	35.00
228.Al Valore Militare-(Military Valor)-1942	35.00

(Gallantry awards were denoted by a bronze Roman sword placed horizontally on the ribbon.

Lifesaving Medal-1888
229.Silver	400.00
230.Bronze	200.00

Medal of Merit for Public Safety-1854
231.Gold	rare
232.Silver	200.00
233.Bronze	100.00

234.Medal for Veteran Guards of the Royal Tombs	125.00

Messina Earthquake Medals-1908
235.Gold	rare
236.Silver	100.00
237.Bronze	50.00

(Note: A number of the Silver Medals were given to sailors of the British Royal Navy.)

CAMPAIGN & SERVICE MEDALS

238.Crimean War Medal-1855-1856	800.00
239.Turkish Crimean War Medal-Sardinian version	75.00

Liberation of Sicily-1860
240.Silver	200.00
241.Bronze	100.00

Medal for Marsala-1865
242.Silver	350.00
243.Bronze	175.00

Independence Medal-1862
244.with no campaign bar	85.00
245.bar 1848-1849 (War with Austria)	250.00
246.bar 1855-1856 (Crimean War)	350.00
247.bar 1859 (War with Austria)	300.00
248.bar 1860-1861 (Garibaldi's expeditions)	250.00
249.bar 1866 (War with Austria)	350.00
250.bar 1870 (Capture of Rome)	300.00

ITALY

United Italy Medal-1883

251.Silver-1848-1870	60.00
252.Bronze-1848-1870	35.00
253.Bronze-1848-1918	20.00
254.Bronze-1848-1922	25.00

255.African Campaign Medal-1894   100.00

Boxer Rebellion & China Occupation Service-1901

256.Boxer Rebellion-reverse CINA 1900-1901	1000.00
257.China Occupation Service Medal-reverse CINA	800.00

Italo-Turkish War-1911-1912

258.Medal-silver	60.00
259.Campaign bar 1911	100.00
260.Campaign bar 1912	100.00

World War I Issues

261.Campaign Medal-1915-18	15.00
262.with one campaign bar 1915,1916,1917,1918	20.00
263.with two campaign bars	30.00
264.with three campaign bars	45.00
265.with four campaign bars	60.00
266.Volunteers Medal	25.00
267.Victory Medal (various makers)	25.00
268.Medal of National Gratitude-1919	35.00

269.Libyan Campaigns   35.00

270.Occupation of Fiume-1919-(unofficial)   100.00

271.March on Rome-1922   100.00

272.Ethiopian Campaigns-1936   35.00
(Note: There are a number of unit medals found for the Ethiopian campaigns, which are unofficial.)

Spanish Civil War-1936-1939

273.Campaign Cross	35.00
274.Volunteers Medal	35.00
275.Fascist Volunteers Medal	35.00
276.Spanish Victory Medal	35.00

World War II Awards

277.Albania-1939-obverse soldiers	35.00
278.Albania-1939-obverse-Victor Emanuel III-uniformed bust	35.00
279.Albania-1939-obverse-Victor Emanuel III-coin bust	35.00
280.French Campaign Medal-1940-Prince Umberto	rare
281.French Campaign Medal-soldier & mountain	rare
282.Occupation of Greece-1941	75.00
283.North Africa Service Medal-several variations-in both German & Italian languages	45.00

Long Service Crosses
284.Gold Cross with crown-XL years-civil   50.00
285.Gold Cross without crown-XXV years-civil   35.00
286.Silver Cross with crown-XXV years military   25.00
287.Silver Cross without crown-XVI years-military   15.00

Customs Officials Long Service Crosses-1905
288.Gold Cross with crown   50.00
289.Gold Cross without crown   35.00
290.Silver Cross with crown   25.00
291.Silver Cross without crown   15.00

Police Long Service Medal-1907
292.Gold   35.00
293.Silver   25.00

Colonial Military Merit Medal-1923
294.Silver Star with crown   45.00
295.Silver Star without crown   25.00

296.National Fire Service Medal-silver-1942   25.00

Fascist Militia Long Service Crosses-1933
297.XXV Years   50.00
298.X Years   35.00

Colonial Police Long Service Crosses-Africa-1941
299.Gold Cross with crown-XL years   45.00
300.Gold Cross without crown-XXV years   30.00
301.Silver Cross with crown-XXV years   25.00
302.Silver Cross without crown-XVI years   20.00
303.Bronze Cross with crown-XX years   15.00
304.Bronze Cross without crown-X years   10.00

305.Fire Service XV Year Cross-bronze-1942   15.00

Navy Long Service Medals-1904; 1945-1946
306.Silver Medal-1905-22 years service   50.00
307.Gold Medal(silver/gilt)-20 years service   45.00
308.Silver Medal-15 years service   25.00
309.Bronze Medal-10 years service   15.00

Air Force Long Service-1926-1946
310.Gold Medal(silver/gilt)-30 years service   50.00
311.Silver Medal-15 years service   25.00
312.Bronze Medal-10 years service   15.00

Army Long Service (Al Lungo Commando)-1935-1946
313.Gold Medal(silver/gilt)-30 years service   40.00
314.Silver Medal-20 years service   25.00
315.Bronze Medal-15 years service   15.00

ITALY

Customs Long Service Medal-1936-1946
316.Gold Medal(silver/gilt)-30 years service   35.00
317.Silver Medal-20 years service   20.00
318.Bronze Medal-10 years service   10.00

Earthquake Medal-1915
319.Gold Medal   450.00
320.Silver Medal   200.00
321.Bronze Medal   100.00

Medal of Social Redemption-1923
322.Gold Medal (silver/gilt)   45.00
323.Silver Medal   25.00
324.Bronze Medal   15.00

Merit Medal for War Orphans Aid-1929
325.Gold Medal (silver/gilt)   40.00
326.Silver Medal   25.00
327.Bronze Medal   15.00

328.Medal of the Italian Family-1939   15.00
(Devices on the ribbon indicated for how many children it was being awarded.)

329.Medal for Aeronautical Pioneers-1941   25.00

Agricultural & Labor Awards
330.Agricultural Merit Medal-silver/gilt-1898   35.00
331.Industrial Merit Medal-silver/gilt-1898   35.00
332.Honor to Workers Medal-silver-1898   20.00
333.Honor to Industry & Commerce Medal-silver-1898   20.00
334.Labor Merit Star-silver-1923   25.00
335.Labor Merit Star-white enamel-1925   35.00
336.Rural Merit Star-gold (silver/gilt)-1932   35.00
337.Rural Merit Star-silver   20.00
338.Rural Merit Star-bronze   10.00

Cholera Epidemic Medals
339.Gold Medal-Genoa-1835   450.00
340.Silver Medal   150.00
341.Bronze Medal   100.00
342.Silver/gilt Medal-1854   200.00
343.Silver Medal   100.00

Public Health Merit Medals
Victor Emmanuel II-1867
344.Gold Medal   350.00
345.Silver Medal   200.00
346.Bronze Medal   100.00
Umberto I-1878
347.Gold Medal   350.00
348.Silver Medal   200.00
349.Bronze Medal   100.00

Victor Emmanuel III
350.Gold Medal (silver/gilt)   75.00
351.Silver Medal   50.00
352.Bronze Medal   35.00

Public Sanitation Medal-1918
353.Gold Medal (silver/gilt)   50.00
354.Silver Medal   35.00
355.Bronze Medal   20.00

Education Awards
356.Public School Long Service Medal-1902-for 40 years   35.00
357.Public Instruction Medal-Elementary Schools-Gold Medal   35.00
358.Silver Medal   25.00
359.Bronze Medal   15.00
360.Service to Education-1919-Gold Medal (silver/gilt)   35.00
361.Silver   25.00
362.Bronze   15.00
363.Colonial Education Service-1932-Gold Medal (silver/gilt)   40.00
364.Silver Medal   30.00
365.Bronze Medal   20.00
366.National Education Merit-1936-Gold Medal (silver/gilt)   35.00
367.Silver Medal   25.00
368.Bronze Medal   15.00
369.School Merit-1939-Gold Star (silver/gilt)   35.00
370.Silver Star   25.00
371.Bronze Star   15.00

Arts & Culture Awards
372.Aid to Italian Culture Overseas-1932-Gold Medal   40.00
373.Silver Medal   25.00
374.Bronze Medal   15.00
375.Aid to the Arts-1939-Gold Medal (silver/gilt)   35.00
376.Silver Medal   25.00
377.Bronze Medal   15.00

Medal of Merit for Target Shooting-1930
378.Gold Medal (silver/gilt)   35.00
379.Silver Medal   25.00

Athletic Awards
380.Athletic Valor-1933-Gold Medal (silver/gilt)   75.00
381.Silver Medal-I Class   50.00
382.Silver Medal-II Class   35.00
383.Bronze Medal   20.00
384.Sporting Merit-1933-Gold Star (silver/gilt)   45.00
385.Silver Star   25.00

FACIST PARTY & ASSOCIATED AWARDS

National Balilla Merit Medal-1928
386.Gold Medal (silver/gilt)   75.00

ITALY

387.Silver Medal	50.00
388.Bronze Medal	25.00

Medal of Merit-Fascist Workers Recreation Service-1928
389.Gold Medal (silver/gilt)	35.00
390.Silver Medal	20.00
391.Bronze Medal	15.00

Fascist Youth Merit Medal-1928
392.Gold Medal (silver/gilt)	40.00
393.Silver Medal	25.00
394.Bronze Medal	15.00

Italian Youth Merit Medal-1939
395.Gold Medal (silver/gilt)	35.00
396.Silver Medal	25.00
397.Bronze Medal	15.00

398.Fascist Party Loyalty Medal	35.00

ITALIAN SOCIAL REPUBLIC-1943-1945 (FACIST)

Order of the Roman Eagle
399.Grand Cross badge	rare
400.Grand Cross badge with swords	rare
401.Golden Grand Cross breast star	rare
402.Golden Grand Cross breast star with swords	rare
403.Silver Grand Cross breast star	rare
404.Silver Grand Cross breast star with swords	rare
405.Grand Officer Badge	rare
406.Grand Officer badge with swords	rare
407.Grand Officer breast star	rare
408.Grand Officer breast star with swords	rare
409.Commander	rare
410.Commander with swords	rare
411.Officer	750.00
412.Officer with swords	600.00
413.Knight	500.00
414.Knight with swords	550.00
415.Medal	400.00
416.Medal with swords	450.00

(Note: As the above indicates this Order was awarded very sparingly. Be careful of copies.)

REPUBLIC

In 1946 Italy became a republic. Among many other consequences, the orders, medals and decorations of the monarchy were either abolished, or modified to a republican appearance. The Orders of the Annunciation, Sts Maurice & Lazarus, and the Civil Order of Savoy continued as purely family orders of the House of Savoy.

There appeared the new Orders of Merit, and the Star of Italian Solidarity. The Military Order of Savoy was modified into the Military Order of Italy, and the Order of Labor Merit was similarly "republicanized". Various medals for gallantry and merit were likewise contiued in a republican form. Since most of the collector interest seems to be in pre-Republican issues there will be not a complete listing of all this material.

Order of Merit
417.	Collar	rare
418.	Grand Cross badge	350.00
419.	Grand Cross breast star	300.00
420.	Grand Officer badge-neck badge (see 422)	200.00
421.	Grand Officer breast star	250.00
422.	Commander-neck badge (see 420)	200.00
423.	Officer-breast badge with rosette on ribbon	75.00
424.	Knight-breast badge without rosette on ribbon	70.00

Military Order of Italy (See also Military Order of Savoy)
425.	Grand Cross badge	550.00
426.	Grand Cross breast star	500.00
427.	Grand Officer neck badge	350.00
428.	Grand Officer breast star	400.00
429.	Commander-neck badge	350.00
430.	Officer-breast badge-trophy of arms suspender	150.00
431.	Knight-breast badge-without trophy of arms suspender	100.00

Order of the Star of Italian Solidarity
432.	First Class-breast star-gilt bronze	250.00
433.	Second Class-neck badge-gilt bronze	150.00
434.	Third Class-breast badge-gilt bronze	75.00

Gallantry Awards
435.	Military Valor Medal- I Cl-gilt-unnamed	50.00
436.	same-but an awarded decoration-usually encountered with an inscription for World War II-then they are silver/gilt	250.00
437.	Military Valor Medal -II Cl-silvered	25.00
438.	Military Valor Medal-III Cl-bronze	15.00
439.	Military Valor Cross	25.00
440.	Military Merit Medal	15.00

Miscellaneous Awards
441.	Long Service Medals-I Cl	25.00
442.	Long Service Medals-II Cl	15.00
443.	Long Service Medals-III Cl	10.00
444.	United Nations Korean Service Medal-Italian language	rare
445.	Service Medal 1940-43 (service bars add 5.00)	25.00
446.	Service Medal 1943-45 (service bars add 5.00)	25.00
447.	Volunteers Medal-type I-1940-1945	25.00
448.	Volunteers Medal-type II-MCMXL-MCMXLV	50.00
449.	Sinai Peacekeeping Medal	50.00
450.	Lebanon Peacekeeping Medal	50.00
451.	Gulf War Campaign Medal	25.00

72　　　　　　　　　106　　　　　　　　　29

34

167   146   160

191   175

211 - 213   154 & 156   223 - 225

237   236

266   223 - 225

272   217 - 219

JAPAN

Empire

After being reopened to Western influence in the mid-19th Century, Japan began to adapt its society. In conjunction with this its Orders and decorations were instituted in the third quarter of the 1800's. Having no tradition of knighthood and religious association in the European sense the awards adopted reflected a system of merit only.

For a fuller examination of this subject reference should be made to **ORDERS & MEDALS OF JAPAN AND ASSOCIATED STATES**-by James W. Petersen (Monograph No. 1 of the Orders and Medals Society of America.)

The quality of Japanese Orders has remained very high, in contrast to much of the work of Europeans. The two most common Japanese Orders are the Rising Sun, and the Sacred Treasure; both which come in eight classes. The military Order, the Golden Kite, which came in seven classes, was abolished after World War II. Unlike other countries, Japan did not establish specific awards for gallantry, so that the lower classes of the Golden Kite were used for that purpose.

For the most part Japanese items have not been extensively copied. Reference to some copies does appear in Petersen, such as breast stars of the Rising Sun, and 8th classes of the same Order. Petersen also refers to copies of the World War I Victory Medal stamped "Made in France", with a ball suspension instead of a barrel suspension. I have come across others not so stamped, and thus to be considered more dangerous for the collector.

The Order of the Golden Kite in its two highest grades is very rare. As of 1939 only 41 of the 1st class had been awarded (2 recipients then still living), and 201 of the 2nd class had been conferred (with 13 recipients still living), according to Petersen. However, the collector should be aware that in the past few years 1st class badges and stars have turned up a number of times, which while at first glance look very nice, on closer examination, especially with a good magnifier, appear to be of much poorer quality. Since most collectors have little opportunity to compare items with known genuine material it stands to reason that these items must be treated with the greatest of caution.

Concerning the Order of the Sacred Treasure there is a mystery. For the classes five through eight the ribbon of the Order is in the triangular Austrian style. The only Japanese award with such a ribbon type.

Following the awards of Japan are those of the puppet state/empire of Manchukuo. These awards were based directly on those of the Japanese Empire, with Manchukoan awards having a Japanese counterpart. Copies do not seem to be a problem.

Some note might be made on the cases and boxes for Japanese awards. Orders come in two styles of cases. A lacquer case, hinged at one end and closed by a small flap of metal fitting over a metal post is the type used for domestic awards. Another type was, or is, of a lacquer box with a lid fitting over the top, and closed by having braided cords with tassels tied around. This is sometimes referred to as the diplomatic type of case. Campaign medals are found in three types of containers. Firstly, lacquer cases, secondly, balsa wood boxes, and in the 1920's and 1930's a hard cardboard type. The cover of the container in Japanese characters indicated the nature of the award. The value of an item in its container of issue is greater to some people, and not to others, therefore, I have not attempted to deal with this matter.

Supreme Order of the Chrysanthemum

1.Collar	rare
2.Collar badge	12,000.00
3.Sash badge	12,000.00
4.Breast Star	7000.00

Order of the Rising Sun-Grand Cordon

5.Order Badge	8500.00
6.Breast Star	5500.00
(Copies exist.)	

Order of the Rising Sun

7.I Class badge	3000.00
8.I Class breast star	1750.00
9.II Class badge-neck badge	800.00
10.II Class breast star	1750.00
11.III Class badge-neck badge	800.00
12.IV Class-breast badge	450.00
13.V Class	400.00
14.VI Class	300.00
15.VII Class-enameled both sides	100.00
16.VII Class-enameled one side-World War II issue	75.00
17.VIII Class-silver	50.00
18.VIII Class-aluminum-World War II issue	40.00

(Note: The breast stars for classes I & II are the same. The neck badges for classes II & III are the same. Copies exist.)

Order of the Golden Kite-abolished

19.I Class badge	rare
20.I Class breast star	rare
21.II Class badge-neck badge	5000.00
22.II Class breast star	rare
23.III Class badge-neck badge	5000.00
24.IV Class breast badge	1200.00
25.V Class	750.00
26.VI Class	350.00
27.VII Class	300.00

(Note: Breast stars for the I & II Classes are the same. Neck badges for the II & III Classes are the same. There are obvious collector copies of the I Class badge, and a very dangerous copy of the breast star.

Order of the Sacred Crown-for ladies

28.I Class badge		rare
29.I Class breast star		rare
30.II Class badge		rare
31.III Class badge		rare
32.IV Class badge		rare
33.V Class badge		rare
34.VI Class badge		rare
35.VII Class badge		2500.00
36.VIII Class badge		2000.00

(Note: The only classes which seem to show up are the VII & VIII. They are worn on bow ribbons.)

Order of the Sacred Treasure

37.I Class badge	1750.00
38.I Class breast star	1250.00
39.II Class breast star(same as 38-worn on right chest)	1250.00
40.III Class neck badge	600.00
41.IV Class badge-breast badge	400.00
42.V Class	350.00
43.VI Class	250.00
44.VII Class-silver/gilt-no enamel	75.00
45.VIII Class-silver-no enamel	50.00

Campaign & Commemorative Medals

46.China War Medal 1874	4500.00
47.Constitution Commemorative Medal-gold	rare
48.Constitution Commemorative Medal-silver	900.00
49.25th Wedding Anniversary Medal-1894	1500.00
50.China War Medal 1894-1895	150.00
51.Boxer Rebellion Medal-China 1900	500.00
52.Russo-Japanese War Medal-1904-1905	75.00
53.Crown Prince's Voyage to Korea-1909	1500.00
54.Korean Annexation Medal-1910	150.00
55.Taisho Enthronement Medal-1915	75.00
56.1914-15 Campaign Medal (one line of characters reverse)	125.00
57.1914-20 Campaign Medal (two lines of characters)	75.00
58.World War I Victory Medal	350.00
59.same-but a French copy-ball suspension	75.00
60.First National Census-1920	50.00
61.Showa Enthronement Medal-1928 (Emperor Hirohito)	75.00
62.Capital Earthquake Rehabilitation Medal-1930	300.00
63.Korean National Census-1930	150.00
64.Manchurian Incident Medal-1931	60.00
65.China Incident Medal-1937	50.00
66.2600th Anniversary of the Empire	50.00
67.China Incident Commemorative Medal	1500.00
68.Great East Asia War Medal-1944	3000.00

(Note: Copies of number 68 exist.)

Medals of Merit
69.Medal with red ribbon   425.00
70.Medal with blue ribbon   425.00
71.Medal with green ribbon   425.00
(Subsequent awards are noted by the addition of bars which are placed on the
ribbon, 1-5 silver bars, with a 6th award indicated by a gold bar.
72.Medal with yellow ribbon-gold   rare
73.Medal with yellow ribbon-silver   425.00

Red Cross Awards
74.Order of Merit-silver/gilt/enamels   350.00
75.same-on a bow ribbon for ladies   375.00
76.Order of Merit-silver/enamels   250.00
77.same-on bow ribbon for ladies   275.00
78.same-special non-wearing type as awarded to companies   300.00
79.Membership Medal-silver   35.00
80.same-with special membership rosette   40.00
81.same-with life membership rosette   40.00
82.Membership Medal-aluminum-World War II issue   35.00
83.same-with special membership rosette   40.00
84.same-with life membership rosette   40.00
85.Bronze type-with suspension bar & no ribbon   25.00

Various Badges
86.Field Marshal's badge   rare
87.Wound Badge-combat   250.00
88.Wound Badge-non-combat   225.00
89.Graduate of Staff Academy   225.00
90.Army Officer Pilot's badge   750.00
91.Army Enlisted Men Pilot's badge   500.00
92.Time Expired Soldier's Badge   35.00
93.Women's Auxiliary Patriotic Service Badge-enameled   50.00
93.same-but plain silvered or gilt metal   20.00
(Note: This is only a small sample of the enormous number of Japanese badges
which are outside the scope of this work.)

Lifesaving Medals-unofficial
94.First Class-gold   550.00
95.First Class-silver/gilt   350.00
96.Second Class   275.00

MANCHUKUO-Japanese puppet state 1932-1945

Order of the Illustrious Dragon
97.Badge of the Order   5500.00
98.Breast Star   4000.00

Order of the Auspicious Clouds
99.I Class badge   3000.00
100.I Class breast star   2500.00

JAPAN

101.II Class breast star (same as 100 above)	2500.00
102.II Class badge-neck badge	1250.00
103.III Class badge-neck badge (same as 102 above)	1250.00
104.IV Class-breast badge	800.00
105.V Class	600.00
106.VI Class	500.00
107.VII Class	300.00
108.VIII Class	250.00

Orders of the Pillars of State

109.I Class badge	rare
110.I Class breast star	2500.00
111.II Class breast star (same as 110-worn on right chest)	2500.00
112.III Class-neck badge	2000.00
113.IV Class breast badge-two gold & enamel bars on ribbon	1200.00
114.V Class-one gold & enameled bar on ribbon	850.00
115.VI Class-three silver bars on ribbon	750.00
116.VII Class-two silver bars on ribbon	600.00
117.VIII Class-one silver bar on ribbon	500.00
118.Breast Badge-IV-VIII Classes-no bars on ribbon	350.00

Campaign & Commemorative Medals

119.National Foundation Merit Medal	250.00
120.same-Japanese variation	75.00
121.Enthronement Commemorative Medal	500.00
122.Imperial Visit to Japan	150.00
123.Border Incident War Medal 1939	500.00
124.National Shrine Foundation Medal	300.00
125.National Census Commemorative Medal	250.00
126.Red Cross Merit Decoration-silver	750.00
127.Red Cross Membership Medal	250.00

INNER MONGOLIA

128. Merit Medal	350.00

34

8 & 10   38 & 39

25

14

42 & 43

55   61

64   60 & 63

128   106   118

123   124

KOREAN WAR

The medals of the Korean War offer an opportunity for the collector to work with a theme for a narrow time period, with most of the items affordable. These items may be divided into two separate sections. The medals being awarded by the nations involved, being one part, and those by the United Nations the other.

The medals of the United Nations, with the exceptions of the Belgian and Filipino issue, have the same design. The inscription is in the language of the participating country. Some countries such as Sweden used the English language issue in place of one in their own language.

It should be pointed out also that the involvement of some countries was that of non-combattent or humanitarian service, such as providing ambulance or hospital units. The rarest U.N. issue is the Italian; with something like 100 struck. It is not known how many were actually awarded, or even exist. Thus far, copies do not seem a problem.

The national awards are also an interesting series. Some countries involved did not issue a national award, such as Greece and Turkey, yet played an important role militarily. Other countries played a minor role, do not have a U.N. issue like Greece and Turkey, yet like Norway and India issued their own medals. Copies of the national issues do not seem to be a problem, except for the Danish Red Cross issue, which is identical except for the engraved dates, to the World War II award.

UNITED NATIONS ISSUES

1.English language-for Commonwealth, Denmark, Norway, Sweden, and the U.S.A.	30.00
2.same-but recent strikings	10.00
3.Amharic language-Ethiopia	300.00
4.Dutch language-Netherlands	300.00
5.French/Flemish-Belgium	75.00
6.French language-France, Luxembourg, French Canadian	50.00
7.Greek language	75.00
8.Italian language	3000.00
9.Korean language	50.00
10.Spanish language-Colombia-Corea	300.00
11.Spanish language-Colombia-variation-Korea	300.00
12.Tagalog language-Philippines (several variations)	125.00
13.Thai language-Thailand	400.00
14.Turkish language-Turkey	450.00

NATIONAL ISSUES

15.Belgium-Campaign Medal	75.00
(Belgian issue is also found with campaign bars-add $25.00 each.)	
16.Belgium-Croix de Guerre	75.00
17.Belgium-Volunteers Medal	50.00
18.Canada-named	125.00

19.	China-Commemorative Medal	550.00
20.	China-Large Peace Medal-1953	500.00
21.	China-Small Peace Medal	400.00
22.	China-War Badge for Anti-aircraft defense	350.00
23.	Colombia-Iron Cross for Valor	350.00
24.	Colombia-Distinguished Service Star	300.00
25.	Colombia-Campaign Medal	300.00
26.	Colombia-Capture of Mount Baldy Medal	250.00
27.	Denmark-Jutlandia Hospital Ship Medal	1500.00
28.	Denmark-Red Cross Medal	rare
29.	Ethiopia-Swedish made	350.00
30.	same-native made	300.00
31.	France	50.00
32.	Great Britain-named (common issue)	100.00
33.	same-Australian/New Zealand issue	150.00
34.	India-Foreign Service Medal-Ambulance	600.00
35.	India-General Service Medal-bar Overseas-Korea	500.00
36.	North Korea-Medal of Merit in Combat	350.00
37.	North Korea-Merit Badge for Distinguished Service	275.00
38.	North Korea-Service Badge against the U.S.A.	250.00
39.	South Korea-Campaign Medal-type I-dull finish	50.00
40.	South Korea-Campaign Medal-type II-shiny finish	50.00
41.	South Korea-Defense of Seoul	95.00
42.	Netherlands-Cross for Right & Freedom-bar Korea 1950	200.00
43.	same-but with two bars-second marked 2	250.00
44.	same-but with three bars-third marked 3	350.00
45.	Norway-enameled type	250.00
46.	Norway-unenameled type	250.00
47.	Philippines-several strikings	85.00
48.	South Africa-named (one Air Force Squadron only)	750.00
49.	Sweden-Red Cross Medal-1950-1957	550.00
50.	Sweden-Service Plaque-1950-1957	350.00
51.	Thailand	250.00
52.	U.S.A.-original issue	20.00
53.	same-recent strikings	10.00

31   29   39 & 40

7   9

LATVIA

Republic 1919-1940

As is with the case of Esthonia and Lithuania this country existed as an independent political unit for only a short time before it was reabsorbed into Russia.

The Orders and decorations of this country are very much tied up with its struggle for independence. All of its awards were granted sparingly, and as such are reflected in values shown. Furthermore, since this area underwent a Soviet, then a German, and then a Soviet occupation again, the tendency was to hide or destroy one's awards, lest they be a source of further problems. Most of the Latvian Orders seen abroad are the lower classes of the Three Stars Order. These were brought out by exiles, besides having been awarded to foreign nationals such as diplomatic and governmental personnel.

There does not seem to be a problem of copies with the orders and decorations of this country.

The following values are for pre-1941 issues only.

Order of the Bearslayer-1919-1940

1.Grand Cross badge	2500.00
2.Grand Cross breast star	1750.00
3.Commander	1750.00
4.Knight	1250.00

Order of the Three Stars-1924-1940

5.Collar	rare
6.Grand Cross badge	800.00
7.Grand Cross breast star	700.00
8.Commander I Class neck badge	550.00
9.Commander I Class breast star	550.00
10.Commander	550.00
11.Officer	300.00
12.Knight	250.00
13.Golden Merit Medal	150.00
14.Silver Merit Medal	125.00
15.Bronze Merit Medal	75.00

Order of Vesthardus-1938-1940

16.Grand Cross badge	3000.00
17.Grand Cross badge with swords	3250.00
18.Grand Cross breast star	2500.00
19.Grand Cross breast star with swords	3000.00
20.Commander I Class neck badge	2250.00
21.Commander I Class with swords	2500.00
22.Commander I Class breast star	1800.00
23.Commander I Class breast star with swords	2000.00
24.Commander	2000.00
25.Commander with swords	2250.00
26.Officer	1500.00
27.Officer with swords	1600.00

28.Knight	1100.00
29.Knight with swords	1250.00
30.Golden Merit Medal	350.00
31.Silver Merit Medal	300.00
32.Bronze Merit Medal	275.00

Merit Cross of Recognition-1938-1940

33.I Class-on sash	3000.00
34.II Class-pinback	2000.00
35.III Class-neck badge	1600.00
36.IV Class-breast badge on ribbon-Officer	1250.00
37.V Class-breast badge on ribbon-Knight	1000.00
38.Golden Merit Medal	400.00
39.Silver Merit Medal	300.00
40.Bronze Merit Medal	250.00

Merit Order of the Red Cross-1927-1940

41.I Class-neck badge	750.00
42.II Class-Knight-breast badge	600.00
43.III Class-breast badge	400.00
44.IV Class-stick pin	250.00

45.Independence Medal	150.00
46.Freedom Fighters Commemorative Medal	200.00
47.National Guard Cross of Merit-1929-1939	350.00

37 28

4 11 & 12

LIECHTENSTEIN

Principality

As one of the smallest countries in the world, whose ruler until after World War I usually did not reside in his country, the awards of Liechtenstein have not been extensive.

While rare, they are not necessarily sought after by collectors. Copies do not seem to be a problem.

Princely Merit Order
1.Grand Star badge	1200.00
2.Grand Star breast star-gilt	1000.00
3.Grand Cross badge	850.00
4.Grand Cross breast star	850.00
5.Commander neck badge	750.00
6.Commander breast star	750.00
7.Knight	500.00
8.Golden Merit Cross	400.00
9.Silver Merit Cross	300.00
10.Merit Medal	75.00
11.Prince Johan Jubilee Medal-bronze	75.00

7   11

10   8 & 9

LITHUANIA

Republic 1919-1940

Lithuania along with Esthonia and Latvia was born out of the torment of the Russian Revolution and Civil War. Like those countries its independence was to last only until the U.S.S.R. was able to take advantage of the international situation in 1940 to once more gather this territory to its empire. The Orders of this country honor great figures from the past, for Lithuania was during the 17th century one of the major powers of Europe.

The most common award of this country is the Order of Gedeminas, which is seen even in its highest classes. It would seem that quite a few awards were made to foreign recipients.

The following values are for pre-1941 issues only. Copies do not seem to be a problem.

Order of Vytautus the Great-1930-1940

1.Collar	rare
2.Breast Star for the Collar-gilt-red enamel	rare
3.I Class badge	3000.00
4.I Class breast star-silver-blue enamel	2250.00
5.II Class neck badge	2000.00
6.II Class breast star	1750.00
7.III Class neck badge	2000.00
8.Officer	1200.00
9.Knight	1000.00
10.Golden Medal	350.00
11.Silver Medal	300.00
12.Bronze Medal	275.00

Order of the Cross of Vytis-1920-1940

13.I Class badge	1500.00
14.I Class breast star	1500.00
15.II Class neck badge	1000.00
16.II Class breast star	1000.00
17.III Class neck badge	1000.00
18.IV Class-2 oak leaf branches	750.00
19.V Class-1 oak leaf branch	675.00
20.Vytis Cross-I Class-gilt	600.00
21.Vytis Cross-II Class-silver	500.00
22.Vytis Cross-III Class-bronze	450.00

Order of Gedeminas-1928-1940

23.Grand Cross badge	650.00
24.Grand Cross breast star	600.00
25.Grand Officer badge	550.00
26.Grand Officer breast star	550.00
27.Commander	550.00
28.Officer	300.00

LITHUANIA

29.Knight	250.00
30.Merit Medal-I Class-gilt	200.00
31.Merit Medal-II Class-silver	175.00
32.Merit Medal-III Class-bronze	150.00

Various Decorations

33.Volunteer Combattents Medal	200.00
34.Independence Medal	175.00
35.Lifesaving Cross	400.00
36.Star for Partisan Service	400.00
37.National Guard Merit Cross	300.00

8   29

LUXEMBOURG

Grand Duchy

This country, although one of the smallest in Europe, has for the medal collector an interesting history. The royal house has associations with both the Netherlands and Germany. The Orange Nassau family ruled the Netherlands, with a branch similarly situated in the German State of Nassau, absorbed into Prussia in 1866. Luxembourg subsequently came under the rule of Nassau's last duke, Adolph. Thus, the Order of Adolph of Nassau is both a German and Luxembourgish one.

The Orders of the Oaken Crown and Merit are quite common. The oaken crown in its earlier issue was of gold, and therefore somewhat rarer. The military awards like the 1940 Military Medal and the 1940-1945 Croix de Guerre are very rare. The Order of Resistance of World War II is more often seen.

Copies do not seem to be a problem.

House Order of the Golden Lion of Nassau-1858
Awarded in five classes 1873-1882
Awarded in four classes 1882-1890
Awarded in one class since 1890

1.Grand Cross badge	5000.00
2.Grand Cross breast star	3000.00

(All other classes rare on the market.)

Order of Adolph-Civil & Military Merit-1858

3.Grand Cross badge	2500.00
4.Grand Cross badge with swords	3000.00
5.Grand Cross breast star	1750.00
6.Grand Cross breast star with swords	2000.00
7.Grand Officer badge	1250.00
8.Grand Officer badge with swords	1750.00
9.Grand Officer breast star	1650.00
10.Grand Officer breast star with swords	1850.00
11.Commander	1250.00
12.Commander with swords	1650.00
13.Officer with crown	500.00
14.Officer with crown & swords	550.00
15.Officer without crown	400.00
16.Officer without crown & with swords	450.00
17.Knight with crown	300.00
18.Knight with crown & swords	325.00
19.Knight without crown	250.00
20.Knight without crown & with swords	275.00
21.Honor Cross for Ladies	500.00
22.Golden Merit Cross	200.00
23.Golden Merit Cross with swords	225.00
24.Silver Merit Cross	175.00
25.Silver Merit Cross with swords	200.00
26.Golden Merit Medal	75.00
27.Silver Merit Medal	65.00
28.Bronze Merit Medal	50.00

Order of Oaken Crown-1841
29.Grand Cross badge	500.00
30.Grand Cross breast star	400.00
31.Grand Officer badge	350.00
32.Grand Officer breast star	275.00
33.Commander	300.00
34.Officer (older badges have wreath between arms)	275.00
35.Knight	150.00
36.Golden Merit Medal	85.00
37.Silver Merit Medal	75.00
38.Bronze Merit Medal	50.00

Order of Merit-1961
39.Grand Cross badge	350.00
40.Grand Cross breast star-silver/gilt	275.00
41.Grand Officer badge	250.00
42.Grand Officer breast star-silver	250.00
43.Commander	250.00
44.Officer	150.00
45.Knight	85.00
46.Merit Medal	50.00

Military Awards
47.Military Medal-1945	600.00

Cross of Honor and of Military Merit-1951
48.I Class-silver/gilt-Senior Officers	300.00
49.II Class-silver-Junior Officers & Senior N.C.O.'s	250.00
50.III Class-bronze-Junior N.C.O.'s & Enlisted Men	150.00

Croix de Guerre (War Cross)
51.type I-1940-45	600.00
52.type II-1951	rare

Volunteers Medals
53.type I-1914-1918 - issued 1923	200.00
54.type II-1940-1945- issued 1945	200.00

Volunteer Long Service Cross-1850
55.For Officers-25 years-silver-gold crown	85.00
56.For Officers-15 years-silver-silver crown	75.00
57.Enlisted Men-30 years-silver-silver crown	75.00
58.Enlisted men-20 years-silver	65.00
59.Enlisted Men-10 years-bronze	50.00

Civilian Awards

Resistance Decorations-1946
60.Order of the Resistance	300.00
61.Medal for the Resistance	200.00

LUXEMBOURG

Medal of Sporting Merit-1945
62.I Class-silver/gilt	200.00
63.II Class-silver	175.00
64.III Class-bronze	150.00

65.Medal for Burgomasters-1830; 1855; 1890; 1892	250.00

Medal for Lifesaving
66.Lifesaving Medal-1843-1866	500.00
67.Medal for Lifesaving-1932	rare

Fire Service Medal of Honor-1897; 1913
68.Bronze-15 years	50.00
69.Silver-20 years	100.00
70.Golden-25 years	150.00
71.Golden-with crown-25 years	175.00
72.Golden-with one bar-30 years	200.00
73.Golden-with two bars-50 years	250.00

Merit Medal of the National Music Association-Adolphe
74.16 years-bronze	25.00
75.25 years-silver	35.00
76.40 years-silver/gilt	40.00
77.50 years-silver/gilt with palm	50.00

Musical Society of City of Luxembourg Merit Medal-1925
78.Bronze Medal-20 years	20.00
79.Silver-30 years	30.00
80.Silver/gilt-40 years	40.00

81.Military Veterans Merit Medal-gilt	25.00

35 47 45

51 60

MEXICO

The history of this country is both long and turbulent. Unfortunately, there has not been a great deal of collector interest in its awards. Primarily, focus has been on the items from the Maximilian period, as well as some interest in the Order of the Aztec Eagle because of its very handsome appearance, as well as its rarity.

"EMPIRE OF MEXICO"-1863-1867-Under Maximilian of Hapsburg

Order of Our Lady of Guadalupe-1822;restored 1863-1867
Two reverses exist on the badges-military AL PATRIOTISMO
HEROICO;civil-AL MERITO Y VIRTUDES

1.Grand Cross badge	rare
2.Grand Cross breast star	rare
3.Grand Officer neck badge	2000.00
4.Grand Officer breast star (same as Grand Cross)	rare
5.Commander (same as Grand Officer badge)	2000.00
6.Knight	750.00

(These values are for civil badges; for military add 40-50%.)

7.Order of the Mexican Eagle-1865-1867
Six grades authorized-all rare

8.Order of San Carlos-1865-1867
Two classes-both rare

9.Ladies' Court Badge of Honor-presented by Empress Carlota to her ladies-in-waiting. I know of one which came up for sale in Europe several years ago. Value certainly in excess of $10,000.

Military Merit Medal-1863-1867

10.I Class-enamelled gold	rare
11.II Class-silver	600.00
12.III Class-bronze	500.00

(There are several strikings of this medal. The designers are the same for those of the French China 1860, and the French Mexican 1863 medals. Some may be rarer than others.)

Civil Merit Medal-1863-1867

13.I Class-enamelled gold	rare
14.II Class-silver	500.00
15.III Class-bronze	350.00

(See comments for Military Merit Medal above.)

See also France - Mexican Campaign Medals

REPUBLIC

Order of the Aztec Eagle-1933

16.Collar-to heads of state only	rare
17.First & Second Class badge	850.00
18.First & Second Class breast star	650.00

(The only difference in classes is that the sash for the II Class is narrower than for the I.)

19.Third Class-breast star only	650.00
20.Fourth Class neck badge	450.00
21.Fifth Class breast badge	350.00

There were several awards to the Mexican forces for resisting the French intervention of 1862-1867. The reference in English is **MEDALS OF MEXICO VOL. III** by Frank Grove. The only one I have ever come across is listed below.

22.Bronze Cross of 1867-awarded to those Officers & Soldiers who took up arms in the defense of the Republic before June 1, 1866	250.00

Army Long Service Crosses-1926
Type I-1926-1945

23.I Class-35 years	50.00
24.II Class-30 years	40.00
25.III Class-25 years	30.00
26.IV Class-20 years	25.00
27.V Class-15 years(1936)	20.00
Type II-1945	
28.I Class-30 years	35.00
29.II Class-25 years	25.00
30.III Class-20 years	20.00
31.IV Class-15 years	15.00

Army War Cross-1949

32.I Class	50.00
33.II Class	40.00
34.III Class	35.00

7   3 & 5   20

8

MONACO

Principality

With the exception of the Order of St Charles, the Orders of this country are of recent origin. They are colorful and handsome in appearance, but so far are not avidly sought after by collectors. Since Monaco has not been engaged in any wars it has not issued many awards.

Order of St Charles-1858
1.Grand Cross badge	850.00
2.Grand Cross breast star	700.00
3.Grand Officer badge	700.00
4.Grand Officer breast star	700.00
5.Commander	700.00
6.Officer	350.00
7.Knight	250.00

Order of the Crown-1960
8.Grand Cross badge	350.00
9.Grand Cross breast star	300.00
10.Grand Officer badge	300.00
11.Grand Officer breast star	300.00
12.Commander	300.00
13.Officer	175.00
14.Knight	150.00

Order of Grimaldi-1950
15.Grand Cross badge	350.00
16.Grand Cross breast star	300.00
17.Grand Officer badge	300.00
18.Grand Officer breast star	300.00
19.Commander	300.00
20.Officer	185.00
21.Knight	175.00

Order of Cultural Merit-1952
22.I Class-neck badge-Commander	250.00
23.II Class-breast badge-Officer	175.00
24.III Class breast badge-Knight	150.00

7

21

24

NETHERLANDS

Kingdom of Holland-1806-1811 (Louis Bonaparte)
Kingdom of the Netherlands-1815 (House of Orange)

The awards and decorations of the Netherlands, like those of other countries engaged in an imperial manner in world affairs are many, varied and interesting. This country is also distinguished by some of its awards being part of the Napoleonic era, when as the Kingdom of Holland it was under French control from 1806-1814.

Perhaps the most interesting item is the Expedition Cross of 1869, which has been used as a General Service Medal, with campaign bars for the various actions in the Dutch East Indies, some thirty three in all. Also of special interest is the War Commemorative Cross 1940-1945 which likewise has campaign bars for a number of actions around the world.

The Order of Orange-Nassau and the Royal Family Order of Orange are the most commonly seen.

Copies do not appear to be a problem except for Expedition Cross bars.

Order of the Reunion-1806-1807
1.Grand Cross badge	rare
2.Grand Cross breast star	rare
3.Commander	rare
4.Knight	5500.00

Royal Merit Order-1806-1807
5.Grand Croos badge	rare
6.Grand Cross breast star	rare
7.Commander	rare
8.Knight	5500.00

Royal Order of Holland-1807-1811
9.Collar	rare
10.Grand Cross badge	rare
11.Grand Cross breast star	rare
12.Commander	rare
13.Knight	4500.00

Military Order of William-1815
14.Grand Cross badge	2750.00
15.Grand Cross breast star	1750.00
16.Commmander	1750.00
17.Officer	1100.00
18.Knight	800.00

(Note: There are several strikings or variations of this Order. Values are given as an average. This Order in its lower grades is for military gallantry.)

Civil Merit Order of the Netherlands Lion-1815
19.Grand Cross badge	800.00
20.Grand Cross breast star	700.00
21.Commander	600.00

22.Commander breast star (early issue)   700.00
23.Knight   300.00
24.Merit Medal   200.00
(Note: There several variations of this Order. Values, except as noted, are for the
most common.)

Order of Orange-Nassau-1892
25.Grand Cross badge   650.00
26.Grand Cross badge with swords   700.00
27.Grand Cross breast star   600.00
28.Grand Cross breast star with swords   650.00
29.Grand Officer badge   500.00
30.Grand Officer badge with swords   550.00
31.Grand Officer breast star   500.00
32.Grand Officer breast star with swords   550.00
33.Commander   500.00
34.Commander with swords   550.00
35.Officer   200.00
36.Officer with swords   275.00
37.Knight   175.00
38.Knight with swords   200.00
39.Gold Medal (silver/gilt)   100.00
40.Gold Medal with swords   125.00
41.Silver Medal   75.00
42.Silver Medal with swords   110.00
43.Bronze medal   75.00
44.Bronze Medal with swords   100.00

House Order of Orange-1905
45.Grand Cross badge   450.00
46.Grand Cross breast star   400.00
47.Grand Officer badge   400.00
48.Grand Officer breast star   400.00
49.Commander   400.00
50.Officer   250.00
51.Knight   200.00
52.Honor Cross for Ladies   225.00
53.Golden Merit Cross-gentlemen   125.00
54.Golden Merit Cross-ladies   125.00
55.Silver Merit Cross-gentlemen   100.00
56.Silver Merit Cross-ladies   100.00
57.Golden Merit Medal   100.00
58.Silver Merit Medal   85.00
59.Bronze Merit Medal   65.00

Medal of Honor for Lifesaving
60.Gold Medal   500.00
61.Silver Medal   350.00
62.Bronze Medal   200.00

Gallantry Awards
63.Bronze Lion Decoration-1944   150.00
64.Cross for Merit-1941   100.00
65.Bronze Cross Gallantry-1940   120.00
66.Flying Cross-1941   275.00
(Note: As this decoration was established in Britain during World War II most crosses have the word STERLING impressed on the reverse to indicate silver content.)
67.Medal for Courage and Loyalty-native troops-1839   250.00
68.same-but Silver Cross-1898   300.00
69.Bronze Cross   200.00

Resistance Awards-World War II
70.Resistance Cross-Europe   150.00
71.East Asia Resistance Star   100.00

Campaign Awards
72.Dogger Bank Medal-gold-1871   rare
73.Dogger Bank Medal-silver   rare
74.Hague Volunteers Medal-silver-1813   500.00
75.Dordrecht Volunteers Medal-1813   500.00
76.Siege of Naarden-1814   500.00
77.Rotterdam Medal-1815   500.00
78.Amsterdam Medal-1815   400.00
79.Silver Cross-1813-1815 (1865)-usually referred to as
    the Waterloo Medal, erroneously as the Belgian Water-
    loo Medal, although it was for veterans of all the
    campaigns of 1813-1815, including Waterloo.)   350.00
80.Java War Medal-1825-1830 (1831)   175.00
81.Metal Cross (Hasselt Cross)-1830-1831   75.00
82.Siege of Antwerp-1832   75.00
83.Expedition Cross-1869 (nickel)   35.00
(The Expedition Cross was used as a General Service Medal, with 33 campaign bars from Bali 1846 to Timor 1942. The most common bars are for the late 19th & early 20th centuries for the East Indies, add $25.00 common bar, and $50.00 for the rarer ones. Copies of bars exist.)
84.Guinea Expedition Medal-1869-1870   rare
85.Atjeh Campaign Medal-1873-1874   100.00
86.Lombok Cross-1894   150.00
87.Mobilization Cross-1914-1918 (1924)   25.00
88.Air Raid Service Medal-1940-45   35.00
89.Commemorative Cross-1940-45   25.00
90.War Commemorative Cross-1940-45   25.00
(The World War II campaign award-with twelve campaign bars issued for Europe, Asia, Pacific and Mediterranean, add $20.00 per bar.)
91.Decoration for Order & Peace-1947   25.00
(This award had five campaign bars 1945, 1946, 1947, 1948, 1949-add $20.00 per bar.)

92.Cross for Right and Freedom-bar Korea-1951	250.00
93.same-bar Korea,bar Korea numeral 2	300.00
94.same-but with bars Korea,Korea 2,Korea 3	450.00
95.New Guinea Commemorative Cross-bar 1962	200.00

Red Cross Medal-1910

96.Medal	125.00
97.Medal with bar Balkan 1912-13	300.00
98.Medal with bar Ethopie 1935-36	350.00

Officers' Long Service Decoration-1844

99.XXX Years	200.00
100.XX Years	150.00

Officers' Long Service Cross-1866

101.XL years	125.00
102.XXXV years	75.00
103.XXX years	60.00
104.XXV years	50.00
105.XX years	40.00
106.XV years	30.00
107.X years	25.00
108.Long Service Cross for Officers of the Marine Steam Navigation Service	200.00

Long Service Medals

109.Army-Large Gold Medal-50 years service-1825	700.00
110.Army-Small Gold Medal-35 years service	450.00
111.Army-Silver Medal-24 years	50.00
112.Army-Bronze Medal	40.00
113.Navy Long Service-1845	50.00
114.Coast Guard-Military issue-1903-1946	60.00
115.Coast Guard-Naval issue-1926-1946	75.00
116.Military Pilots-1903-1926	rare
117.Naval Reserve-1906-1925	50.00
118.Militia Long Service-1851-1866	100.00

Medal for Zeal & Loyalty-1877

119.Gold-36 years	300.00
120.Silver-24 years	60.00
121.Bronze-12 years	40.00

Royal Commemorative Medals

122.Enthronement of Queen Wilhelmina-1898	75.00
123.Wedding of Queen Wilhelmina	75.00
124.Silver Wedding Anniversary of Queen Wilhelmina-1926	75.00
125.Wedding of Princess Juliana-1937	75.00
126.Enthronement of Queen Juliana-1948	75.00
127.Wedding of Princess Beatrix-1966	75.00
128.Enthronement of Queen Beatrix-1980	75.00

18 23

37 51

83   63

64   66

76 79

80 85

NORWAY

Attached to the Kingdom of Sweden till 1906
Kingdom since 1906

As a country with a small population, independent only since 1906, and without a rigid social class system or an extensive military establishment the awards of Norway have been few.

Its decorations for World War II are quite sought after by the collector, and are well made, and quietly impressive in appearance. The Order of St Olav is surely one of the most beautiful ever struck, and has been sparingly conferred in the higher grades.

Copies do not seem to be a problem.

Order of St Olav-type I-1847-1906-Under Sweden

1.Collar	rare
2.Grand Cross badge	1750.00
3.Grand Cross badge with swords	2000.00
4.Grand Cross breast star	1250.00
5.Grand Cross breast star with swords	1500.00
6.Commander neck badge	900.00
7.Commander neck badge with swords	1100.00
8.Commander breast star	750.00
9.Commander breast star with swords	900.00
10.Knight I Class	400.00
11.Knight I Class with swords	450.00
12.Knight II Class	300.00
13.Knight II Class with swords	350.00

(This Order is in gold & enamels except for the lowest class.)

Order of St Olav-type II-1906-since independence

14.Collar	rare
15.Grand Cross badge	1250.00
16.Grand Cross badge with swords	1500.00
17.Grand Cross breast star	1000.00
18.Grand Cross breast star with swords	1150.00
19.Commander neck badge	900.00
20.Commander neck badge with swords	1000.00
21.Commander breast star	700.00
22.Commander breast star with swords	800.00
23.Knight I Class	300.00
24.Knight I Class with swords	350.00
25.Knight II Class	200.00
26.Knight II Class with swords	250.00
27.Medal of St Olav-1929	200.00

Commemorative & Campaign Awards

28.South Pole Medal-1912	rare
29.War Cross-1940-45-with combat sword on ribbon	75.00
30.War Cross without swords	60.00
31.War Medal-1940-45	50.00

32.King Haakon VII's Liberty Cross-1940-45	400.00
33.King Haakon VII's Liberty Medal	250.00
34.War Participation Medal-1940-45	85.00
35.King Haakon VII's 70th Anniversary Medal-1942	85.00
36.Korean War Service-enameled type	250.00
37.same-but no enamel	250.00

Outstanding Citizen Service-1819
38.Gold Medal	300.00
39.Silver Medal	200.00

Medal for Heroic Deeds (Lifesaving)-1885
40.Large Gold Medal	1500.00
41.Large Silver Medal	350.00
42.Small Gold Medal	7750.00
43.Small Silver Medal	250.00

(Note: These medals are usually found named; some are from the pre-independence period. Values are for post-independence issues.)

Medal for Civil Services-1908
44.Gold Medal	rare
45.Silver Medal	rare

Coronation of King Haakon VII
46.Silver Medal	100.00
47.Bronze Medal	75.00

King's Commemorative Medal for Court Servants-1906
48.Gold Medal with crown	350.00
49.Silver Medal with crown	200.00
50.Silver Medal without crown	150.00

32   23 & 25

29   31

PHILIPPINES

Spanish colony till 1898
American dependency 1898-1946
Republic 1946

The awards of this country are of interest to many American collectors, through the association of this area as a U.S. colony. Because some of its medals were awarded to Americans after World War II and Independence, they are avidly sought after by both U.S. collectors and eligible recipients.

A major problem with Filipino awards is that there are several variations of these pieces that have been struck by the original firm of El Oro in Manila, later taken over by Jose Tupaz. Some can be found in orange,green, and multicolored boxes. The quality of workmanship varies enormously. This applies to both the items themselves and their ribbons and there are copies. One copy of the Liberation Medal spelled it Libiration. Values listed below are for earlier strikes.
It should also be pointed out that some of the awards established after independence had existed in a slightly different form, and were awarded to the Philippine Constabulary, the colonial defense force. In the interest of space and simplicity it will be pointed out that pre-independence forms of a given award are worth more than later issues; how much more is difficult to say.

For other medals pertaining to the Philippines see also Spain and the U.S.A.

Order of Sikatuna-1951
1.Commander I Class badge-sash badge	650.00
2.Commander I Class breast star	550.00
3.Commander II Class-neck badge	400.00
4.Officer	350.00
5.Companion	250.00

Legion of Honor-1947
6.Chief Commander breast star	500.00
7.Commander	250.00
8.Officer	100.00
9.Legionnaire	75.00

(This award was intended to be similar in nature to the U.S. Legion of Merit.)

Gallantry Awards
10.Medal of Valor-pre 1947	rare
11.Medal of Valor-post independence version	1000.00

(This is the equivalent of the U.S. Medal of Honor.)
12.Distinguished Conduct Star-several types	550.00
13.Bravery Cross for the Air Force	200.00
14.Distinguished Aviation Cross	150.00
15.Gold Cross for valor	75.00

Military Decorations
16.Distinguished Service Star	250.00
17.Military Merit Medal	50.00
18.Silver Wing Medal	45.00

PHILIPPINES

19. Cross for the Wounded	50.00
20. Exemplary Efficiency & Devotion to Duty	35.00
21. Long Service Cross	45.00

Campaign and Service Awards

22. Luzon Service Medal	75.00
23. Philippine Constabulary Service Medal 1917-18	1000.00

(It should be noted that item 23 is often referred to by collectors as the "Philippine Constabulary World War I Victory Medal". This is not correct, as the Philippines was not an independent country.)

24. Visayan Campaigns	75.00
25. Mindanao & Sulu Campaigns	75.00
26. Jolo Campaigns	75.00
27. Resistance Medal	75.00
28. Defense Medal	75.00
29. Liberation Medal	75.00
30. Independence Medal	75.00

(U.S. forces were eligible for the last three items.)

31. Anti-dissidence Medal	45.00
32. Korean Service Medal	85.00
33. Viet Nam Service Medal	85.00

(Note: It should be re-emphasized that some of the above have several versions, and that the values listed are for well struck pieces.)

POLAND

Kingdom till 1795
Divided between Russia, Austria & Prussia (Germany) till 1918
Republic 1918-1944 (under German occupation 1939)

The Orders and decorations of pre-Communist Poland can be divided into three series. First of the independent kingdom prior to 1795; second, of the Russian dominated period between 1795 and 1917, when the Orders were either taken over as in the case of the Virtuti Militari, or actually incorporated into the body of Russian Orders, such as the White Eagle and the St Stanislaus; third, the 1918-1944 types of the Republic. This last type can be further broken down into those made in Poland before World War II, and those produced in exile, such as by Spink in London, England, and Lorioli in Italy.

Thus, the insignia of all classes of the Polonia Restituta Order are quite plentiful of the London variety, but much less so than the Polish made ones. The two lower classes of the Virtuti Militari Order can be seen frequently in their London made style, and in numbered World War II badges apparently made in Italy, after the Polish Brigade of the British 8th Army had been involved in massive fighting, especially in the Battle for Monte Cassino.

Since the first edition of this book appeared, a work on Polish awards by Zdzislaw P. Wesolowski **POLISH ORDERS, MEDALS, BADGES AND INSIGNIA MILITARY AND CIVILIAN DECORATIONS 1705-1985** has been published which covers this country in comprehensive detail, and which has enabled me to list more items. Certainly many Polish items are much rarer than previously believed, and increased values now reflect this important point.

Copies of the Virtuti Militari in the Grand Cross and lower classes have surfaced in recent years. These are not of high quality, but to the unfamiliar they will seem a bargain at $500.00 to $1000.00, which of course they are not. Copies of the White Eagle Order also exist, also of poor quality.

While not in the scope of this book I would alert collectors to the enormous number of copies of Polish Regimental and Military badges. The originals were made before World War II and were generally of high quality. Later pieces are cruder.

The World War II Air Force Active Service Medal exists without the enamel squares on the obverse. It is this author's opinion that this item is a copy because of the poor quality of its appearance.

Except as noted, values listed are for Republic 1918-1944.

Kingdom of Poland till 1795
Order of the White Eagle-1705-1795
1.Collar	rare
2.Badge	rare
3.Breast Star	rare

Order of St Stanislaus-1765-1795 (see also Russia)
4.Badge	rare
5.Breast Star	rare

POLAND

Order of Virtuti Militari (Military Virtue)-1792-1831
Type I-1792
6.Gold Medal	rare
7.Silver Medal	rare

Type II-dated 1792-initials SARP on reverse
8.Grand Cross badge	rare
9.Grand Cross breast star	rare
10.Commander Cross-neck badge	rare
11.Knight-breast badge	6500.00
12.Gold Merit Cross	5500.00
13.Silver Merit Cross	4500.00

Type III-Grand Duchy of Warsaw-Kingdom of Poland-1808-1831
14.Grand Cross badge	rare
15.Grand Cross breast star	rare
16.Commander	rare
17.Knight	rare
18.Gold Merit Cross	5500.00
19.Silver Merit Cross	4500.00

Type IV-Russian Administration-Rex et Patria-dated 1831
20.Grand Cross badge	rare
21.Grand Cross breast star	rare
22.Commander	rare
23.Knight	6500.00
24.Gold Merit Cross	5000.00
25.Silver Merit Cross	4000.00

Republic of Poland-1918-1944

Order of Virtuti Militari-1918-1944
26.Grand Cross badge	rare
27.Grand Cross breast star	rare
28.Commander-neck badge	rare
29.Knight	3250.00
30.Gold Merit Cross-pre-World War II	1600.00
31.Gold Merit Cross-World War II-numbered	800.00
32.Gold Merit Cross-London made & unnumbered	300.00
33.Silver Merit Cross-pre-World War II	500.00
34.Silver Merit Cross-World War II-numbered	400.00
35.Silver Merit Cross-London made & unnumbered	250.00

(Note: As mentioned previously, copies of the Virtuti Militari in the higher grades have appeared. Mainly of the Grand Cross badge and star, they seem at first to be genuine. However, after closer examination they show a cruder quality than would be expected of Poland's highest military award. The "silver" has worn through on some of the pieces and you can see the copper underneath. These may have been made in Warsaw or West Germany. Buy with caution, all you have to lose is your money!)

Order of the White Eagle-1921-1944
36.Badge	3500.00
37.Breast star	3000.00

(Note: These values are for Polish made pieces. Some were made by Spink in

London, during World War II-deduct 20%. Copies of this Order are also on the market. One that I saw had an American Bronze Star ribbon on the badge instead of a sash. Beware!)

Order of Polonia Restituta-1918-1944
Type I-Polish made-pre-World War II
38.Grand Cross badge	700.00
39.Grand Cross and II Class breast star	600.00
40.II Class & Commander neck badge	500.00
41.Officer	300.00
42.Knight	200.00

Type II-London made
43.Grand Cross badge	450.00
44.Grand Cross & II Class breast star	400.00
45.II Class & Commander neck badge	325.00
46.Officer	125.00
47.Knight	100.00

Cross of Merit-1923
48.I Class-silver/gilt/enamel	200.00
49.I Class-with swords	300.00
50.II Class-silver/enamel	150.00
51.II Class-with swords	200.00
52.III Class-bronze	75.00
53.III Class-with swords	100.00

(Note: These values are for pre-World War II issues; for wartime pieces deduct 25%.)

54.Cross of Merit for Bravery-State Police-1928	300.00

Valor Cross-1920-1944
55.1920 issue-undated	rare
56.1920 issue-dated 1920-reverse numbered-45mm	250.00
57.1920 issue-dated 1920-reverse numbered-36mm	125.00
58.1920 issue-dated 1920-unnumbered-45mm or 46mm	75.00
59.1939 issue-dated 1939-unnumbered	100.00
60.1940 issue-dated 1940-unnumbered	100.00
61.World War II issue-dated 1920-variously made in England, Italy or the Middle East-45mm or 46mm	75.00

Independence & Soviet-Polish Campaigns-1918-1921
62.Independence Cross	150.00
63.Independence Cross with swords (Copies exist.)	400.00
64.Independence Medal	50.00
65.Russo-Polish War Medal	35.00

66.Cross of the Central Lithuanian Army	300.00
67.Silesian Uprising Cross-type I-33mm	400.00
68.Silesian Uprising Cross-type II-45mm	400.00

Other Commemorative and Merit Awards

69. 3rd of May Medal-1925	300.00
70. 10th Anniversary of Independence-1928	25.00
71. XXX Year Long Service Medal-1938	not awarded
72. XX Year Long Service Medal-silver	85.00
73. X Year Long Service Medal	50.00
74. Red Cross Decoration-silver/enamel-1923	250.00
75. Volunteers War Cross-1939-struck but not awarded	150.00
76. Volunteers War Medal-1939-struck but not awarded	125.00
77. Polish Army in France Medal-1920-(Haller Medal)	75.00

World War II Awards

78. Army Active Service Medal	50.00
79. Navy Active Service Medal	300.00
80. Air Force Active Service-red/white enamels obverse	150.00
81. Merchant Navy Service Medal	300.00
82. Monte Cassino Cross-reverse numbered (in awarded range)	100.00
83. Red Cross Medal	150.00

Polish Government In Exile-post World War II

84. Home Army Cross	150.00
85. Resistance Medal-France	50.00
86. Polish Army in France	50.00
87. 22nd Argonsky Rifle Regiment Medal-1918-1948	50.00
88. 25th Anniversary of Monte Cassino-1944-1969	25.00
89. 1st Grenadier Division Medal-1940-1970	50.00

The following medals while not marked PRL for the People's Republic are awards of that post-1944 government for World War II. As such collectors have exhibited some interest for them, and they are being included.

90. Oder-Neisse-Baltic Campaign Medal	45.00
91. Liberation of Warsaw	45.00
92. Conquest of Berlin	50.00
93. Victory over Germany	35.00

49 & 51   48 & 50

30-35   41 & 46

63   62

66   82

PORTUGAL

Kingdom till 1910
Republic since 1910

The Orders of Portugal are among the oldest in Europe. With the establishment of the Republic, while the form of some of the Orders may have changed, the practice of awarding them was expanded. The numbers of Orders increased also.

Thus, the Orders of the Republic are quite commonly come across, and not eagerly sought after by collectors, even though their appearance may be handsome. Their values are therefore lower than some comparable items from other countries.

The royal Orders etc are much rarer and generally of better quality than the later material. With the exception of the World War I War Cross and Victory Medal there does not seem to be problem with copies of this country's awards.

Kingdom of Portugal till 1910

Combined Honor Award of the Three Orders
Type I-1850-1910
1.Badge	4000.00
2.Breast star	3500.00

Combined Honor Award of the Christ & Aviz Orders-1850-1910
3.Badge	3500.00
4.Breast star	3000.00

Order of Christ-see also the Vatican
Type I-1789-1910
5.Grand Cross badge	700.00
6.Grand Cross breast star	500.00
7.Commander-neck badge	375.00
8.Commander breast star	375.00
9.Knight	250.00

Military Order of St Benedict of Aviz
Type I-1789-1910
10.Grand Cross badge	700.00
11.Grand Cross breast star	500.00
12.Commander	375.00
13.Knight	250.00

Order of St James of the Sword
Type I-1789-1862
14.Grand Cross badge	850.00
15.Grand Cross breast star	650.00
16.Commander	475.00
17.Knight	300.00
Type II-1862-1910
18.Collar of the Grand Cross & Commander-gilt	2000.00
19.Collar of the Officer Class-silver	1500.00
20.Grand Cross badge	700.00
21.Grand Cross breast star	500.00

22.Commander I Class	375.00
23.Commander I Class breast star	375.00
24.Commander II Class	375.00
25.Officer	250.00
26.Knight	100.00

Order of the Tower & Sword
Type I-1808-1832

27.Grand Cross badge	2500.00
28.Grand Cross breast star	2200.00
29.Commander	1850.00
30.Knight	1600.00

(Note: A number of British Officers received this Order for their services in the Peninsula Campaigns of the Napoleonic Wars.)
Type II-1832-1910

31.Collar of the Grand Cross & Commander-gilt & enamel	3000.00
32.Collar of the Officer Class-gilt-no enamel	2000.00
33.Collar of the Knight Class-silver	1500.00
34.Grand Cross badge	750.00
35.Grand Cross breast star	550.00
36.Commander I Class	400.00
37.Commander I Class breast star	400.00
38.Commander II Class	400.00
39.Officer	275.00
40.Knight	225.00

Order of Villa Vicosa-1819-1910

41.Grand Cross badge-gold	700.00
42.Grand Cross badge-silver/gilt	500.00
43.Grand Cross breast star-gold	700.00
44.Grand Cross breast star-silver/gilt	500.00
45.Commander I Class	400.00
46.Commander I Class breast star	400.00
47.Commander II Class	400.00
48.Officer	250.00
49.Knight	225.00

Ladies' Order of St Isabella-1801-1910

50.Badge	4000.00

Republic-1910

Combined Honor Award of the Three Orders-1910-Type II

51.Badge	2000.00
52.Breast Star	1700.00

Order of the Tower and Sword-Type III-1917

53.Collar of the Grand Cross	3500.00
54.Collar of the Commander & Officer Class	2000.00
55.Collar of the Knight Class	1500.00
56.Grand Cross badge	500.00
57.Grand Cross breast star	450.00

58.Commander I Class	300.00
59.Commander I Class breast star	300.00
60.Commander II Class	300.00
61.Officer	225.00
62.Knight	175.00

Order of Christ-Type II-1910

63.Grand Cross badge	450.00
64.Grand Cross breast star-gilt	400.00
65.Grand Officer-neck badge	350.00
66.Grand Officer star-gilt (as 64)	400.00
67.Commander-neck badge (as 65)	350.00
68.Commander-breast star-silver	350.00
69.Officer	185.00
70.Knight	150.00

Military Order of St Benedict of Aviz-Type II-1910

71.Grand Cross badge	400.00
72.Grand Cross breast star-gilt	350.00
73.Commander I Class	300.00
74.Commander I Class breast star-gilt	350.00
75.Commander II Class	300.00
76.Commander II Class breast star-silver	300.00
77.Officer	200.00
78.Knight	150.00

Order of St James of the Sword-Type II-1910

79.Grand Collar as awarded to Heads of State	4000.00
80.Collar of the Grand Cross, Commander, and Officer	2000.00
81.Collar of the Knight Class-silver	1200.00
82.Grand Cross badge	400.00
83.Grand Cross breast star-gilt	350.00
84.Commander I Class	275.00
85.Commander I Class breast star-silver	275.00
86.Commander II Class	275.00
87.Officer	150.00
88.Knight	125.00

Order of Prince Henry the Navigator-1960

89.Grand Collar as awarded to Heads of State	2000.00
90.Collar	1500.00
91.Grand Cross badge	400.00
92.Grand Cross breast star	350.00
93.Commander I Class	275.00
94.Commander I Class breast star	300.00
95.Commander II Class	275.00
96.Officer	125.00
97.Knight	100.00
98.Golden Medal	75.00
99.Silver Medal	50.00

PORTUGAL

The Imperial Order-1932
100.	Grand Cross badge	400.00
101.	Grand Cross badge	350.00
102.	Commander I Class	250.00
103.	Commander I Class breast star	250.00
104.	Commander II Class	250.00
105.	Officer	150.00
106.	Knight	75.00

Merit Order-1929
107.	Grand Cross badge	350.00
108.	Grand Cross breast star-gilt	325.00
109.	Grand Officer badge	250.00
110.	Grand Officer breast star-gilt	300.00
111.	Commander	250.00
112.	Commander breast star-silver	250.00
113.	Officer	150.00
114.	Knight	75.00

Military Merit Order
115.	Grand Cross badge	350.00
116.	Grand Cross breast star-gilt	300.00
117.	Grand Officer badge	250.00
118.	Grand Officer breast star-gilt	300.00
119.	Commander	250.00
120.	Commander breast star-silver	250.00
121.	Officer	150.00
122.	Knight	75.00

Order of Public Instruction-1919
123.	Grand Cross badge	225.00
124.	Grand Cross breast star-gilt	200.00
125.	Grand Officer badge	150.00
125.	Grand Officer breast star-gilt	200.00
126.	Commander	150.00
127.	Commander breast star-silver	150.00
128.	Officer	60.00
129.	Knight	50.00

Orders of Agricultural & Industrial Merit-1893; 1926; 1963
(Green enamel-Agricultural;Red enamel-Industrial-same design.)
130.	Grand Cross badge	250.00
131.	Grand Cross breast star-gilt	200.00
132.	Grand Officer badge	200.00
133.	Grand Officer breast star-gilt	175.00
134.	Commander	200.00
135.	Commander breast star	150.00
136.	Officer	75.00
137.	Knight	60.00

Peninsular Crosses-Napoleonic Wars-to British Officers
138.Gold Cross	rare
139.Silver Cross	2500.00

Various Awards
140.Capture of Cayenne-1809-silver	450.00
141.Capture of Cayenne-bronze	300.00
142.Overseas Service Medal-Marie II-silver/gilt	250.00
143.same-in silver	125.00
144.Assiduous Service Overseas 1910-silver	50.00
145.Military Merit Medal-I Class-silver/gilt	85.00
146.Military Merit Medal-II Class-silver	50.00
147.Foreign Legion Cross-I Class-silver/gilt	85.00
148.Foreign Legion Cross-II Class-silver	50.00
149.Police Exemplary Service-1926-silver	40.00
150.War Cross 1917	50.00

(Copies of 150 exist.)

151.Army Campaign Medal-1916-gilt-obverse head looks left	50.00
152.Army Campaign Medal-silver	40.00
153.Army Campaign Medal-bronze	20.00
154.Army Campaign Medal-but head looks right-gilt	50.00
155.Army Campaign Medal-silver	40.00
156.Army Campaign Medal-bronze	20.00

(There are several campaign bars for items 151-156-add $20.00 to $50.00;many are scarce or even rare.)

157.World War I Victory-by Joao da Silva	rare
158.same-but no designer's name	250.00

(Beware of recent issues of the Victory Medal chocolate in color, and an earlier one from a cracked die.)

159.Overseas Service Medal (add $10.00 to $25.00 for bars)	40.00
160.Red Cross Decoration	125.00

49   40 & 62

70   105

122   113

137   97

RUMANIA-Also spelled Romania & Roumania

Kingdom 1881-1947

The Kingdom of Rumania in its short history has had the distinction of being the only country with a communist dominated government under a monarchy. When King Michael overthrew Marshal Antonescu, his country's fascist dictator, in 1944, and joined the Allies Rumania came under Soviet control. For his services Michael was allowed to stay on the throne until 1947, and then permitted to leave the country. In the meantime he had been awarded the rare Order of Victory of the U.S.S.R.!

In World War I Rumania joined the Allies, and many of her awards were made accordingly to citizens of friendly countries. During World War II Rumania was allied to Germany, and thus many awards were made to people on that side of the conflict.

Awards of the country are somewhat complicated and confusing to the collector. There are two types of some Orders, and several of the others may look similar. The makeup of Rumanian Orders reflects both German and French influences. German, because of the proliferation of classes, and the use of swords, as well as the existance of the Rumanian Hohenzollern House Order, as the Rumanian royal house was an offshoot of the Prussian. French, in the use of rosettes to designate the officer class of Orders, and the use of the term Grand Officer to indicate the II Class of an Order.

The high quality of many of the earlier issues can be attributed to their manufacture in Austria by the major jewelers, although those made by Resch of Bucharest were also very nicely done. The Orders of this country have an impressive appearance, and are worth collecting by the person who wants to have a handsome collection without having to pay very high prices.

With the exception of the World War II issues of the Order of Michael the Brave, there does not seem to be a problem with copies.

Order of King Carol-1906-1947

1.Collar	rare
2.Grand Cross badge with diamonds	rare
3.Grand Cross badge	3500.00
4.Grand Cross breast star with diamonds	rare
5.Grand Cross breast star	2500.00
6.Grand Officer badge	2500.00
7.Grand Officer breast star	2500.00
8.Commander	2500.00

Order of Michael the Brave-1916-1947
Type I-1916-1941-initial F and date 1916

9.I Class large pinback badge	1750.00
10.I Class with swords	1750.00
11.II Class neck badge	1250.00
12.II Class with swords	1000.00
13.III Class breast badge	600.00
14.III Class with swords	600.00

Type II-initial M and dated 1941; 1941-1944
15.I Class   1000.00
16.II Class   750.00
17.III Class   600.00
(Type II is of considerable interest to III Reich collectors, as this Order was awarded to a number of officers in the German armed forces in World War II.

Type III-initial M and dated 1944; 1944-1947
18.I Class   1250.00
19.II Class   900.00
20.III Class   600.00

Order of King Ferdinand I-1929-1947
21.Collar   rare
22.Grand Cross badge   rare
23.Grand Cross breast star   rare
24.Grand Officer badge   750.00
25.Grand Officer breast star   750.00
26.Commander   750.00
27.Officer   500.00
28.Knight   450.00

Order of St George-1940-1947
29.I Class-pinback cross with crown   700.00
30.I Class with swords   800.00
31.II Class neck badge   600.00
32.II Class with swords   650.00
33.III Class pinback cross   500.00
34.II Class with swords   550.00
35.IV Class-gilt breast cross   300.00
36.IV Class with swords   400.00
37.V Class-silver breast cross   350.00
38.V Class with swords   300.00
39.VI Class-bronze breast cross   250.00
40.VI Class with swords   300.00

Order of Merit-1931-1947
41.Grand Cross-breast star   700.00
42.Grand Cross-breast star with swords   800.00
43.Commander   550.00
44.Commander with swords   600.00
45.Officer-pinback cross   400.00
46.Officer with swords   450.00
47.Knight   350.00
48.Knight with swords   375.00
49.Merit Cross   250.00
50.Merit Cross with swords   300.00

Honor Cross for Merit-1937-1947
51.I Class-neck badge   350.00
52.I Class with swords   400.00

RUMANIA

53.I Class for ladies-on a bow ribbon	350.00
54.II Class	200.00
55.II Class with swords	250.00

Faithful Service Order-1932-1947
56.Collar	rare
57.Grand Cross badge	450.00
58.Grand Cross badge with swords	500.00
59.Grand Cross breast star-type I-8 points-1932-1935	800.00
60.Grand Cross breast star-type II-4 points-1935-1947-gilt	450.00
61.Grand Cross breast star with swords	500.00
62.Grand Officer badge	350.00
63.Grand Officer badge with swords	400.00
64.Grand Officer breast star-type I-pinback cross-1932-35	600.00
65.Grand Officer breast star-type II-4 points-1935-1947	350.00
66.Grand Officer breast star with swords	425.00
67.Commander	350.00
68.Commander with swords	400.00
69.Officer	250.00
70.Officer with swords	300.00

Order of the Star of Rumania-1864-1947
Type I-eagle obverse centre-rays between arms
71.Grand Cross badge	400.00
72.Grand Cross badge with swords	450.00
73.Grand Cross badge with swords on ring	450.00
74.Grand Cross badge with swords and swords on ring	500.00
75.Grand Cross breast star	350.00
76.Grand Cross breast star with swords	400.00
77.Grand Officer badge	250.00
78.Grand Officer badge with swords	300.00
79.Grand Officer badge with swords on ring	300.00
80.Grand Officer badge with swords and swords on ring	350.00
81.Grand Officer breast star	300.00
82.Grand Officer breast star with swords	350.00
83.Commander	250.00
84.Commander with swords	300.00
85.Commander with swords on ring	300.00
86.Commander with swords and swords on ring	350.00
87.Officer	100.00
88.Officer with swords	125.00
89.Officer with swords on ring	175.00
90.Officer with swords and swords on ring	200.00
91.Knight	100.00
92.Knight with swords	125.00
93.Knight with swords on ring	150.00
94.Knight with swords and swords on ring	200.00

Type II-1932-1947-eagle between arms-cipher CI on obverse
95.Grand Cross badge	300.00
96.Grand Cross badge with swords	350.00

97.Grand Cross badge with swords on ring	350.00
98.Grand Cross badge with swords and swords on ring	400.00
99.Grand Cross breast star	250.00
100.Grand Cross breast star with swords	300.00
101.I Class badge	250.00
102.I Class badge with swords	250.00
103.I Class badge with swords on ring	300.00
104.I Class badge with swords & swords on ring	350.00
105.I Class breast star	250.00
106.I Class breast star with swords	300.00
107.Grand Officer badge	200.00
108.Grand Officer badge with swords	250.00
109.Grand Officer badge with swords on ring	300.00
110.Grand Officer badge with swords & swords on ring	350.00
111.Grand Officer breast star	200.00
112.Grand Officer breast star with swords	250.00
113.Commander	200.00
114.Commander with swords	250.00
115.Commander with swords on ring	250.00
116.Commander with swords & swords on ring	300.00
117.Officer	100.00
118.Officer with swords	150.00
119.Officer with swords on ring	200.00
120.Officer with swords & swords on ring	250.00
121.Knight	85.00
122.Knight with swords	125.00
123.Knight with swords on ring	150.00
124.Knight with swords & swords on ring	200.00

Order of the Crown-1881-1947
Type I-crown on obverse centre-cipher between arms-1881-1932
Type II-cipher in centre-crowns between arms-1932-1947
Values are similar for both types.

125.Grand Cross badge	350.00
126.Grand Cross badge with swords	400.00
127.Grand Cross breast star	300.00
128.Grand Cross breast star with swords	350.00
129.Grand Officer	250.00
130.Grand Officer with swords	300.00
131.Grand Officer breast star	250.00
132.Grand Officer breast star with swords	300.00
133.Commander	250.00
134.Commander with swords	300.00
135.Officer	125.00
136.Officer with swords	150.00
137.Knight	100.00
138.Knight with swords	125.00
139.Ladies' Cross of the Order-type II	200.00

RUMANIA

Royal Household Order-1935-1947 (Sometimes referred to as the Hohenzollern House Order of Rumania; see also Prussia & Hohenzollern under Germany.)
140.Honor Cross I Class-large pinback cross	500.00
141.Honor Cross I Class with swords	550.00
142.Honor Commander Cross-neck badge	400.00
143.Honor Commander Cross with swords	450.00
144.Honor Commander Cross breast star	500.00
145.Honor Commander Cross breast star with swords	550.00
146.Honor Cross II Class-gilt	300.00
147.Honor Cross II Class with swords	325.00
148.Honor Cross III Class	225.00
149.Honor Cross III Class with swords	250.00
150.Honor Cross III Class with oakleaves	275.00
151.Honor Cross III Class with oakleaves & swords	325.00
152.Merit Cross I Class-gilt	200.00
153.Merit Cross I Class with swords	175.00
154.Merit Cross II Class	100.00
155.Merit Cross II Class with swords	125.00
156.Golden Medal	75.00
157.Golden Medal with swords	85.00
158.Golden Medal with crown	100.00
159.Golden Medal with crown & swords	125.00
160.Silver Medal	50.00
161.Silver Medal with swords	60.00
162.Silver Medal with crown	75.00
163.Silver Medal with crown & swords	85.00

Bene Merenti Order of the Royal House-1935-1940
164.I Class-men-neck badge with crown	500.00
165.I Class-ladies-badge with rays	400.00
166.II Class-men-neck badge	350.00
167.II Class-ladies-badge without rays	300.00
168.III Class-men-pinback cross	300.00
169.III Class-ladies-badge unenameled	275.00
170.IV Class-men-breast badge	200.00
171.Medal I Class-gilt	85.00
172.Medal II Class-silvered	65.00
173.Medal III Class-bronze	50.00

Agricultural Merit Order-1932-1947
Type I-cipher of Carol II-1932-1940; type II-cipher M-1940-1947
174.Grand Officerbadge	350.00
175.Grand Officer breast star	450.00
176.Commander	350.00
177.Officer	200.00
178.Knight	175.00

Cultural Merit Order-1931-1944
Type I-head of Carol 1931-1940; type II-head of Michael 1940-1944
179.Commander	225.00
180.Officer	100.00

181. Knight I Class with crown	75.00
182. Knight II Class	60.00
183. Medal I Class-gilt	50.00
184. Medal II Class-silvered	40.00

Air Force Bravery Order-1930-1947
Type I-cipher Carol-1930-1940; type II-cipher of Michael-1940-1947

185. Commander	300.00
186. Commander with swords	325.00
187. Officer	250.00
188. Officer with swords	275.00
189. Knight	150.00
190. Knight with swords	175.00
191. Merit Cross-gilt	75.00
192. Merit Cross with swords	100.00

(Note: Additional award bars are worn on the ribbon.)

Honor Decoration of the Rumanian Eagle-1933-1947

193. Grand Officer badge	300.00
194. Grand Officer breast star	500.00
195. Commander I Class-gilt	300.00
196. Commander II Class-silver	275.00
197. Officer	225.00
198. Knight-silvered	100.00

Bravery Decorations
Military Bravery (Army)

199. I Class-silver/gilt-type I-straight arms-wreath	300.00
200. I Class-gilt/bronze-type II-curved arms to cross	175.00
201. II Class-type I-silver	100.00
202. II Class-type II-silvered bronze	75.00

Air Force Bravery

203. I Class-gilt	200.00
204. II Class-silver	175.00
205. III Class-bronze	160.00
206. I Class with swords	225.00
207. II Class with swords	200.00
208. III Class with swords	175.00

Naval Bravery

209. I Class-gilt	200.00
210. I Class with crown	225.00
211. I Class with crown & swords	225.00
212. II Class-silver	175.00
213. II Class with crown	185.00
214. II Class with crown & swords	200.00
215. III Class-bronze	125.00
216. III Class-with crown	85.00
217. III Class with crown & swords	60.00

218. Elizabeth Cross-1878-silver/gilt	300.00

RUMANIA

Queen Marie Cross-1917
219.I Class-neck badge-silver/gilt & enamels | 400.00
220.II Class-silver/gilt | 100.00
221.III Class-bronze | 75.00

Civil Guard Order-1934-1940
222.I Class | 200.00
223.II Class | 150.00
224.III Class | 100.00
225.IV Class | 75.00

Civil Guard Merit Decoration-1937-1940
226.I Class-silver/gilt/enamel-pinback | 150.00
227.II Class-silver/enamel-pinback | 95.00
228.III Class-silver-pinback | 50.00
229."Pro Virtute" Cross of the Civil Guard | 85.00

Civil Guard Merit Medal-1934-1940
230.I Class-gilt | 60.00
231.II Class-silvered | 40.00
232.III Class-bronze | 25.00

Faithful Service Cross-1906-1947
Type I-1906-1932-rays between the arms
233.I Class-gilt | 50.00
234.II Class-silvered | 30.00
Type II-no rays between the arms-1932-1947
235.I Class-gilt | 50.00
236.I Class-with swords | 45.00
237.II Class-silvered | 40.00
238.II Class with swords | 35.00
239.III Class-bronze | 25.00
240.III Class with swords | 20.00

Faithful Service Medal-1878-1947
Type I-1878-1932
241.I Class-gilt | 30.00
242.II Class-silvered | 20.00
Type II-1932-1947
243.I Class-gilt | 30.00
244.I Class with swords | 30.00
245.II Class-silvered | 25.00
246.II Class with swords | 25.00
247.III Class-bronze | 20.00
248.III Class with swords | 20.00

Medal for Steadfastness & Loyalty-1903-1947
249.I Class-gilt | 40.00
250.I Class with swords | 45.00
251.II Class-silvered | 30.00
252.II Class with swords | 35.00

253.III Class-bronze	20.00
254.III Class with swords	25.00
255.bar 1913 to above-for the Balkan War	rare

Cross of Merit for Medical Personnel-1913-1947
256.I Class-bronze/gilt/enamel	150.00
257.II Class-silvered bronze/enamel	85.00
258.III Class-red enameled cross	75.00

Agricultural Merit Medal-1932-1947
259.I Class-bronze/gilt	35.00
260.II Class-silvered	20.00

Medal for Merit in Commerce & Industry-1912-1947
261.I Class-bronze/gilt	30.00
262.II Class-silvered	20.00
263.III Class-bronze	15.00

National Recognition Medal for Rumania-1943-1944
264.I Class	rare
265.II Class	rare
266.III Class	rare
267.Recognition Plaque for Factories	rare

268.Medal of Military Virtue-1848-1866	rare

269.Medal for Devotion & Courage-1864-1866	rare

Trans-Danube Cross-Turkish War 1877-1878
270.Cross for Military Personnel	300.00
271.with bar Traditie for "next of kin"	rare

(Copies of this decoration may exist.)

Medal for the Defense of Freedom-1877-1878
272.Bronze	250.00
273.Bronze/gilt	250.00

Jubilee of Carol I-1906-40th Anniversary
274.Civil Version-reverse coat of arms and dated	50.00
275.Military Version-reverse legend and dated	75.00

276.Balkan Wars Commemorative Medal-1913	75.00

World War I Commemorative Crosses
277.dated 1916-1918-standard issue	35.00
278.dated 1916-1919	200.00

(With dated battle bars add $40.00. With campaign or next of kin bars add $75.00. Bars for Russian Civil War add $100.00. Rumanians who served in Russia after the revolution were eligible for number 278.)

RUMANIA

World War I Victory Medal-1921
279.Original issue-reverse designer Kristesko   300.00

280.Pelesch Castle Medal-1923   rare

281.Independence Anniversary Medal-1877-1927   75.00

Carol I Centennial Medal-1939
282.Bronze Medal   75.00
283.with bar Pro Patria   100.00

Anti-Communist Campaign Medal-1942-1944
284.without bar for merit on the home front   25.00
285.with one campaign bar   45.00
286.with two campaign bars   60.00
287.with three campaign bars   85.00
288.with four campaign bars   120.00
(Eleven bars were awarded with this medal for service in Russia.)

270 144 250, 252, 254

5

138 (Type I)   16   19

207

108 & 113

137 (Type II)   284   93

182   256 - 258

149   200 & 202

RUSSIA

Empire till 1917
Provisional Government March-November 1917
Civil War Governments 1917-1921
Soviet Russia-later U.S.S.R. 1917

The Orders, decorations and medals of Imperial Russia can offer the collector a great deal of satisfaction. The Orders of Russia, except for a brief period in World War I, were of the highest quality of workmanship, being fashioned of gold and enamels. They represented quality which is no longer found today. When the collector has the chance to examine foreign Orders made in Russia, such as the Greek Order of the Redeemer, or the Persian Order of the Lion and Sun, the difference in quality compared to the items made in Paris or Switzerland is readily apparent in favor of the Russian made pieces.

Since the badges of Imperial Orders, except for the period 1916-1917, were made in gold any silver/gilt ones are copies. Bronze/gilt ones from World War I can be accepted with caution. The St Stanislas badges appear to be hallmarked, but not the other bronze/gilt examples.

The campaign medals of Imperial Russia are particularly interesting as they go back to the early 18th century, preceding those of Great Britain by a hundred years. However, the early ones are rather crude as the facilities for striking medals as we know them today did not exist,

The listing of Russia's campaign medals are a reflection of the struggles against Sweden, Prussia, France, Britain, and Japan, in the country's efforts to become and remain a great power. The expansion into Asia in the 19th century is testified to by the medals for the Caucasus, Central Asia and the Boxer Rebellion. Unlike Great Britain, Russia did not shrink from awarding medals to its troops despite defeats suffered, such as in the Crimean and Russo-Japanese Wars. Tragically, the enormous suffering of the Russian armed forces in the First World War was never to receive official recognition by any government, either Russian or Allied.

Copies of Imperial Russian awards do exist. One may see for example a silver/gilt double sided enameling on a St Stanislas badge. There have appeared insignia of the Order of St George marked by Faberge, although such has never been authenticated as being genuine. Copies of the I & II Classes of the St George Order have been made for collectors. They are silver/gilt and usually hallmarked by Rothe of Vienna. Copies in combination of gold and silver/gilt exist of the IV Class of St George also. In recent years there have also appeared copy breast stars of Russian Imperial Orders marked by Keibel.

Although outside of the scope of this book some mention should be made of Imperial Russian badges. Recently, some of these have been turning up with fake silver marks and other hallmarks. To the experienced collector they should be present no problem. However, to the novice it is a great problem. The Russian hallmark of 84 means silver. If the badge is not silver then the hallmark is meaningless.

Finally, a few words with regard to hallmarks on Imperial Russian items. Gold orders are normally marked with the number 56 (equivalent to 14 karat gold) on the suspension, plus other marks, such as an anchor or a head. The reverse of the badge may have the initials of the manufacturer, and possibly the Imperial eagle. Some silver medals, and the reverses of most breast stars are marked 84, which is slightly below the sterling standard of 925. The Russian gold mark of 56 represents 56 parts out of 96; and the silver mark of 84 represents 84 parts out of 96.

The Civil War issues of the White Armies are very elusive to come by. Fortunately for the collector the standard work on the subject has been translated into English by members of the Russian Numismatic Society. Copies of the awards exist, but many of these may have not been made to deceive the collector, but by exiles to replace other insignia. The Civil Wars issues do not include the awards established in exile, but only those of political or military formations which were generally accorded some form of recognition by other Russians or by the World War I allies of Russia.

The awards of the Grand Duke Kiril, Pretender to the Russian Throne, and self-styled Emperor, are included since they do show up in some collections. Their rarity is hard to judge since it is known that some were sold as a revenue producing measure. It would also be difficult to tell whether items are copies or not.

The enormous change in the values of the awards of the Soviet Union has come about as a completely unforeseen result of the total collapse of that country and the emergence of the Russian Republic. What has happened since the publication of VERNON'S COLLECTORS' GUIDE, 2nd edition, is that a flood of Soviet awards has come on the market in the West. This has had beneficial results in that prices have come down. However, some material has been dumped in huge quantities, making some rare items only scarce, and some scarce items very commonplace.

The awards of Soviet Russia and the U.S.S.R. were first very sparse, as that country regarded the imperial system of decorating military and government officers as one of the particular evils of the past, and in cartoons ridiculed the recipients of such awards. However, as time has passed the Soviet Union has gone much further than old Russia in its awards system. In the U.S.S.R. civilians on even the most trivial occasions wore their decorations. The high military, government and Communist Party officials were drenched with awards of various types. The Soviet Union also followed the practice of multi-awards of the same decoration, with the actual piece being awarded and worn at the same time. This is quite in contrast the practice of the last Emperor, Nicholas II, who before World War I wore only the Order of St Vladimir IV Class on his colonel's tunic for most occasions.

There are several types of problems with Soviet awards. The World War II campaign medals were not of high quality, and some have a stippled appearance. Copies of some of them are of better quality, although cast copies exist also.

There are copies of the Order of the Patriotic War II Class marked 800 (for silver content) on the reverse. These cannot be genuine, because no Soviet decoration was identified in that way, and it is an indication of its being German or Austrian made.

Some time ago a bronze/gilt/enameled Order of Lenin appeared, in a red case, apparently made in Great Britain. These pieces have been sold from $75.00 to

$750.00! The Order of Lenin is a gold, platinum and enameled award, numbered on the reverse, and with the Moscow or Leningrad mint mark.

Occasionally, the collector will come across a Soviet award where the serial number has been erased. While this item is still genuine it is up to you to decide whether it is as desirable as one not tampered with. However, I know some collectors feel that an erased number may be sign of authenticity. The number being ground off to protect the identity of the recipient from the authorities. After the collapse of communism this last point is no longer pertinent.

I want to emphasize that the collector must be much more beware of buying Soviet material. This applies to the whole range from "rare" to "common". The words rare and common are in quotation marks as rarity for Soviet awards is very much harder to define than it used to be. This is for three reasons. First, there is much more material available. Second, there are many more fakes than before. Third, there were some official reissues of some awards, such as the Patriotic War I & II Classes; and most of the World War II campaign medals.

Where possible I shall try to indicate the reissues, and indicate appropriate values.

Regarding fakes, copies, reproductions or whatever else one might call them, the following remarks may be of assistance.
1. Order of Lenin-I have seen bronze/gilt and silver/gilt pieces. The genuine pieces were made of gold/platinum/enamels, and were hallmarked in Russian with either House of the Mint and numbered, for Moscow; or Leningrad-House of the Mint and numbered.
2. Order of Suvorov-gilt/bronze-not made like this.
3. Hero of the Soviet Union-not gold, and not numbered. Should be gold, and numbered
4. Hero of Socialist Labor-see 3. above.
5. Order of Kutuzov-III Class-on standard type ribbon. This award should be a screwback piece.
6. Order of the Patriotic War-marked 800. This is a non-Russian hallmark. Never used in Russia/U.S.S.R.
7. Order of Glory I Class-silver/gilt. Should be gold.
8. Screwback awards converted to ribbon awards. For a number of Soviet Orders and Decorations the first type was suspended from a small horizontally red ribbon, which was soldered or attached to the top of the award in some way. These pieces, if original are still quite rare. However, they are being faked by their screwbacks being ground off, and the ribbon attachment being added. Great care should be taken with these items. Use a good magnifier.

A final comment is in order regarding documents. Sometimes one may see a little red book with the decoration(s) listed inside, with the number(s) corresponding to those on the award(s). Some people see this as a good sign. Perhaps! However, one might also consider that it is now much easier to forge Soviet documents! Most people would be none the wiser. This doesn't mean that a document is a bad sign; just that caution should be exercised always.

Since the U.S.S.R. no longer exists, it is likely that the rarity of high Soviet awards on the collector market will change. Thus, it might be expected that for a period of time values will go down. However, that seems to have promoted more interest in these items, so that eventually the value curve may go the other way. It must be emphasized that there can be considerable fluctuation in values.

There is also a question as to whether a lower numbered, therefore earlier issued piece is worth more than a higher numbered, later issued one. The assumption has been made that the earlier awards were made more sparingly than the later ones. However, absent an award document or order book I wonder whether it really matters. This is not an unimportant concern as there would be a three tier value system; I for the low numbers, II for the medium numbers, and III for the high numbers. The question then becomes where do these categories start and end? Thus, the values listed are for genuine, properly numbered and marked pieces. The basic principle still holds good, namely, an item is worth what someone is willing to pay for it on any given day!

RUSSIA-Imperial

Order of St Andrew
1.Collar	25,000.00
2.Badge of the Order	15,000.00
3.Badge of the Order with diamonds	rare
4.Breast Star	10,000.00
5.Breast Star with diamonds	rare

Order of St Catherine-for ladies
6.Grand Cross badge	25,000.00
7.Grand Cross breast star	20,000.00
8.Badge of the Lesser Cross-II Class	15,000.00

(Note: The insignia of this Order are set with real diamonds.)

Order of St Alexander Nevsky-(see also U.S.S.R.)
9.Badge of the Order	8500.00
10.Badge of the Order with swords	13,500.00
11.Badge of the Order with diamonds	rare
12.Breast Star	3500.00
13.Breast Star with swords	7500.00
14.Breast Star with diamonds	rare

Order of the White Eagle-see also Poland
15.Badge of the Order	7500.00
16.Badge of the Order with swords	10,000.00
17.Badge of the Order with diamonds	rare
18.Breast Star	3000.00
19.Breast Star with swords	3500.00
20.Breast Star with diamonds	rare

Order of St George-military-for officers
21.First Class Cross	rare
22.Breast Star of the First Class	rare
23.Second Class neck badge	rare
24.Breast Star of the Second Class (same as 22)	rare
25.Third Class neck badge	8500.00

26.Fourth Class breast badge	3500.00
27.Fourth Class breast badge-bronze/gilt-World War I	2000.00
28.Fourth Class breast badge for 25 years	7000.00

(Examples of number 27 exist which were made in emigration; their value would be about 25% of an original.)

St George Cross (Insignia of Distinction of the Military Order of St George-for Enlisted Men for bravery.)

29.Silver Cross-pre-1856-only one class	600.00
30.I Class-gold	rare
31.I Class-gilt-World War I	1500.00
32.II Class-gold	rare
33.II Class-gilt-World War I	1000.00
34.III Class-silver	275.00
35.III Class-white metal-World War I	350.00
36.IV Class-silver	175.00
37.IV Class-white metal-World War I	275.00
38.Kulm Cross (awarded to Prussians for the Napoleonic Wars battle of 1813)	1200.00

(Note: There is a non-Christian type of the above where the imperial eagle replaces St George on the obverse. Triple the above values. However, it is hard to tell copies from the originals. The IV Class St George Cross was also awarded to some British officers assisting the White Armies against the Communists during the Civil War 1917-1921. Values listed above are for World War I issues.)

St George Medal for Bravery-for enlisted men

39.I Class-gold(copies exist-unnumbered)	2500.00
40.II Class-gold	1750.00
41.III Class-silver	150.00
42.IV Class-silver	75.00

(Note: Some of the I & II Class medals were awarded to British troops, and are found named. To collectors of British items these medals may have considerably more worth. Values for the above reflect World War I issues.)

Order of St Vladimir

43.I Class badge	3500.00
44.I Class badge with swords	4500.00
45.I Class breast star	2200.00
46.I Class breast star with swords	3000.00
47.II Class neck badge-50mm	1500.00
48.II Class badge with swords	1750.00
49.III Class neck badge-45mm	1250.00
50.III Class badge with swords	1750.00
51.IV Class breast badge-35mm	850.00
52.IV Class breast badge with swords	1200.00

Order of St Anne

53.I Class badge	1750.00
54.I Class badge with swords	2500.00
55.I Class badge with crown	3500.00
56.I Class badge with diamonds	rare
57.I Class breast star (reverse gilt)	1500.00

58. I Class breast star with swords	1800.00
59. I Class breast star with crown	2500.00
60. II Class neck badge	900.00
61. II Class neck badge with swords	1250.00
62. II Class neck badge with crown	1750.00
63. II Class breast star (reverse shows silver)	1100.00
64. II Class breast star with swords	1350.00
65. III Class breast badge	650.00
66. III Class breast badge with swords	750.00
67. III Class breast badge with swords-bronze/gilt	550.00
68. IV Class	500.00
69. Insignia of Distinction of the Order	450.00

Order of St Stanislas-see also Poland

70. I Class badge	1750.00
71. I Class badge with swords	2000.00
72. I Class badge with crown	3500.00
73. I Class badge with crown & swords	4500.00
74. I Class badge-non-Christian	3000.00
75. I Class badge with swords-non-Christian	3500.00
76. I Class breast star (identical with II Class star)	1000.00
77. I Class breast star with swords	1500.00
78. I Class breast star with crown	3500.00
79. I Class breast star with crown & swords	4500.00
80. I Class breast star-non-Christian	1500.00
81. I Class breast star with swords-non-Christian	2500.00
82. II Class neck badge	850.00
83. II Class neck badge with swords	1100.00
84. II Class neck badge-bronze/gilt-1916-1917	600.00
85. II Class neck badge with swords-bronze/gilt-1916-1917	700.00
86. III Class breast badge	550.00
87. III Class breast badge with swords	650.00
88. III Class breast badge-bronze/gilt-1916-1917	400.00
89. III Class breast badge with swords-bronze/gilt 1916-17	550.00

(Note: More non-Christian items have appeared since the downfall of the Soviet Union. It is difficult to tell whether these are genuine pieces coming on the market, or clever fakes. Caution should be exercised in buying these items. There are also genuine breast stars with fake swords.)

90. Order of Merit in Agriculture-breast badge	rare

Order of St John of Jerusalem-Knights of Malta

91. I Class badge	rare
92. I Class breast star	rare
93. II Class badge	rare

Order of Noble Bokhara

94. I Class badge	rare
95. I Class star	1250.00
96. II Class badge	1500.00

97.II Class star   1500.00
98.III Class-VIII Class   rare
(Note: According to Werlich this Order was awarded liberally. However, only breast stars seem to appear periodically. Some may have Russian hallmarks.)

Order of the Crown of Bokhara
99.I Class badge   1500.00
100.I Class star   950.00
101.II-VIII Classes   rare
(See remarks regarding Noble Bokhara Order.)

Bokharan Medals for Loyal & Meritorious Service
102.Gold Medal   1500.00
103.Silver Medal   950.00
104.Bronze Medal   600.00

VARIOUS AWARDS OF THE RUSSIAN EMPIRE

Medals for Bravery
105.Catherine the Great-silver-1789   4000.00
106.Large Gold neck medal-50mm   3500.00
107.Small Gold breast medal-30mm   2500.00
108.Large Silver neck medal-50mm   1000.00
109.Small Silver breast medal-30mm   550.00
(Established in 1878-values given for Nicholas II-earlier ones are worth much more.)

Lifesaving Medals & Rescue from Drowning-1834
110.Nicholas I-gold   2000.00
111.Nicholas I-silver   650.00
112.Alexander II-gold   2000.00
113.Alexander II-silver   650.00
114.Alexander III-gold   2000.00
115.Alexander III-silver   650.00
116.Nicholas II-gold   1500.00
117.Nicholas II-silver   450.00
(Werlich indicates that Polish issues exist; much rarer than above.)

Medals for Zeal
118.Alexander I-large bronze/gilt neck medal   750.00
119.Nicholas I-large gold neck medal   2500.00
120.Nicholas I-small gold breast medal   1250.00
121.Nicholas I-large silver neck medal   750.00
122.Nicholas I-small silver breast medal   350.00
123.Nicholas I-For Zealous Service   750.00
124.Alexander II-large gold neck medal   2500.00
125.Alexander II-small gold breast medal   1100.00
126.Alexander II-large silver neck medal   750.00
127.Alexander II-small silver breast medal   250.00
(Note: There are three different issues for Alexander II-young head; middle-aged, and old heads. Values roughly same for all.)

128.Alexander III-large gold neck medal	3000.00
129.Alexander III-large silver/gilt neck medal	850.00
130.Alexander III-small gold medal	1100.00
131.Alexander III-large silver neck medal	650.00
132.Alexander III-small silver medal	250.00
133.Nicholas II-large gold neck medal	3000.00
134.Nicholas II-large silver/gilt neck medal	750.00
135.Nicholas II-small gold medal	850.00
136.Nicholas II-large silver neck medal	450.00
137.Nicholas II-small silver medal	125.00
138.same-but named on rim to British Sailor-World War I	250.00

Exemplary (Blameless) Police Service-1876

139.Alexander II	450.00
140.Alexander III-types I & II	350.00
141.Nicholas II	250.00

Exemplary Service in the Prison Guard

142.Alexander II	rare
143.Alexander III	1500.00
144.Nicholas II	1500.00

Long Service & Good Conduct Badges (Roman Numerals)

145.15 years	250.00
146.25 years	300.00
147.30 years	400.00
148.35 years	500.00
149.40 years	600.00
150.50 years	750.00

Campaign & Commemorative Medals

151.Capture of Kalish-Poland-Peter I-1706	2000.00
152.Victory of Poltava-gold-1709	rare
153.Victory of Poltava-silver	2000.00
154.Battle of Gangut (Hango)-naval officers-1714	2000.00
155.Capture of Four Swedish Frigates-1720	rare
156.Peace of Nystad-for Officers-1721	rare
157.Battle of Kunersdorf-(Seven Years War)-Elizabeth-1759	1100.00
158.Battle of Kagul-Catherine II-1770	2000.00
159.Battle Tchesme-naval-1770	2000.00
160.Peace with Turkey-officers-circular-1774	1100.00
161.same-but diamond shaped	rare
162.Battle of Kinburn-1787	2000.00
163.Ochakov Cross-officers-gold	5000.00
164.Ochakov Medal-enlisted men-silver	1100.00
165.Victory over Sweden in Finnish Waters-1789	1100.00
166.Peace with Sweden-1790	1100.00
167.Peace with Turkey-1791	3500.00
168.same-but oval variation	rare
169.Ismail Cross-officers-gold-1791	5000.00
170.Ismail Medal-enlisted men	3000.00
171.Praga Cross-officers-gold-Poland-1795	5000.00

172.Praga Medal-enlisted men-silver	2500.00
173.Medal for Generosity-Alexander I-gold	rare
174.Medal for Generosity-silver	2000.00
175.Medal of Imperial Favor-Nicholas I-gold	rare
176.Medal of Imperial Favor-silver	1100.00
177.Medal of Gandzha-1804	2000.00
178.Georgian Liberation Medal-bronze to Persians-1805	1100.00
179.Loyalty & Zeal Medal to Persians for Georgia	1100.00
180.Re-enlistment Medal-to enlisted men-1806	850.00
181.First Circumnavigation of the World-1806	7500.00
182.Militia Service Medal-gold-1807	rare
183.Militia Service-silver	1100.00
184.Battle of Preussische-Eylau-Officers Gold Cross	3000.00
185.Crossing of the Swedish Coast-1809	1200.00
186.Battle of Torneo-1809	1200.00
187.Bazardjik Cross-Officers' gold cross-1810	5000.00
188.Bazardjik Medal-silver-enlisted men	850.00
189.War of 1812-silver	450.00
190.War of 1812-bronze	350.00
191.Chaplains' Cross for the War of 1812-bronze	850.00
(Copies exist of number 191.)	
192.Capture of Paris-silver-1814	300.00
193.Polar Expedition Medal-bronze-1821	rare
194.Persian War Medal-1826-1828	600.00
195.Suppression of Polish Rebellion-1831-I Class in gold	rare
196.same-II Class-general officers	1500.00
197.III Class-Colonels & Lt Colonels	950.00
198.IV Class-other officers	600.00
199.V Class-enlisted men-bronze	450.00
200.Capture of Warsaw-1831	350.00
201.Mouraviev Medal-Egyptian Campaign-1833	550.00
202.Turkish Medal for the Mouraviev Campaign	650.00
203.Russo-Prussian Maneuvers-1835	rare
204.Capture of Akhulgo (Caucasus)-1839	1500.00
205.Jubilee Medal for the 6th Prussian Cuirassiers	750.00
206.Jubilee Medal for the 5th Kaluga Infantry-gold	rare
207.same-bronze/gilt for enlisted men	500.00
(most of 207 issued without suspension)	
208.Pacification of Hungary-1849	155.00
209.Defense of Sevastopol-1855	175.00
210.Crimean War Campaign Medal-bronze-1856	110.00
211.Chaplains' Cross for the Crimean War-bronze	250.00
(Copies exist of number 211.)	
212.Conquest of the Chechen & Daghestan (Caucasus)	250.00
213.Serf Emancipation Medal-gold	2000.00
214.Serf Emancipation Medal-silver	750.00
216.Alexander II Liberation Medal-1861	7750.00
217.Cross for Service in the Caucasus-bronze-1864	450.00
218.Conquest of the Western Caucasus-1864	300.00
219.Polish Rebellion-1865-light bronze-combatants	250.00
220.same-dark bronze-for non-combatants	150.00
221.Agrarian Reforms in Poland-gold-1866	1500.00

RUSSIA

222.Agrarian Reforms in Poland-silver   550.00
223.For Efficiency in Military Factories-1867   550.00
224.Caucasus-Imperial Personal Service-1871   600.00
225.Khiva Campaign-1873   650.00
226.Conquest of Kokhand Khanate-bronze-1876   400.00
227.Liberation of Bulgaria-bronze-1878   400.00
228.Russo-Turkish War-silver-1877-8   250.00
229.same-light bronze-combatants   95.00
230.same-dark bronze-non-combatants   95.00
231.Geok-Teppe Campaign Medal-silver-1881   400.00
232.Geok-Teppe Campaign Medal-bronze   350.00
233.In Memory of Alexander II-1881   250.00
234.Coronation of Alexander III-bronze   250.00
235.Commemorating the Reign of Nicholas I-1825-1855-silver   rare
236.same-bronze to lower ranks   150.00
237.Commemorating Reign of Alexander III-silver-1881-1894   75.00
238.Coronation of Nicholas II-silver-1895   125.00
(There are several variations of number 238 both in silver and bronze which are presumably unofficial.)
239.Campaigns in Central Asia-silver-1896   450.00
240.Campaigns in Central Asia-bronze   350.00
241.Census Medal-bronze-1896   95.00
242.China 1900-01-Boxer Rebellion-silver   450.00
243.same-in bronze   300.00
244.50th Anniversary of Defense of Sevastopol   200.00
245.Battle of Chemulpo Commemorative-1904   1000.00
246.Russo-Japanese War Medal-1904-05-silver-1906   300.00
247.same-light bronze-combatants   125.00
248.same-dark bronze-non-combatants   125.00
249.Red Cross Medal for Russo-Japanese War   250.00
250.Admiral Rozhestvensky Expedition-silver-1907   rare
251.same-in bronze-this medal is not listed in Werlich's book, but one came up for sale in London, England in a Glendining's Auction- so   ?
252.Teachers' Merit Medal-silver-1909   200.00
253.200th Anniversary of Poltava-1709-1909   95.00
254.100th Anniversary of the War of 1812   75.00
255.300th Anniversary of the Romanovs-1613-1913   50.00
(According to Werlich at least 10 variations exist of number 255, as well as copies.)
256.100th Anniversary of Battle of Leipzig-1813-1913   175.00
257.200th Anniversary of Battle of Gangut-1714-1814   125.00
258.Distinguished Service in the Mobilization of 1914   125.00
(Number 258 was the only official Imperial Russian award specifically established in relation to World War I.)

PROVISIONAL GOVERNMENT-March-November 1917

Order of Alexander Nevsky
259.Badge of the Order-uncrowned eagles   rare
260.Badge with swords   rare
261.Breast Star   rare
262.Breast Star with swords   rare

Order of St Stanislas
263.I Class badge-uncrowned eagles	2000.00
264.I Class badge with swords	2250.00
265.I & II Class breast star	1000.00
266.II Class badge	450.00
267.II Class badge with swords	600.00
268.III Class badge	350.00
269.III Class badge with swords	450.00

(Note: It has been suggested that only the military badges were officially awarded.)

St George Medal (St George & Dragon on obverse)
270.I Class-gilt	700.00
271.II Class-gilt	500.00
272.III Class-white metal	350.00
273.IV Class-white metal	200.00

GEORGIAN REPUBLIC-1918-1921

Order of Queen Tamara-founded by the Georgian Legion of the German Army in 1915.
274.I Class breast star	600.00
275.II Class breast star	450.00
276.III Class breast star	250.00
277.IV Class breast star-silver	200.00

(The values listed above are for locally made pieces. Some stars were made by the famous German court jeweler Godet. These pieces would bring a premium on the above.)

RUSSIAN CIVIL WAR-1917-1921

The various anti-Communist governments besides issuing their own decorations also continued to award some of the Imperial Orders (mainly St Anne & St Stanislas, and some St George Crosses and Medals.) For the most part it may be safely assumed that they were struck in base metals, except where stocks of original items were available.)

SOUTH RUSSIA

278.First Kuban Campaign 1917-sometimes referred to as the "Crown of Thorns " Decoration	550.00
279.Badge of the Kornilov Shock Regiment	700.00
280.General Markov's 1st Infantry Officers' Regiment Cross	rare
281.General Markov's Artillery Company Cross	rare
282.Alexeiev Infantry Regiment Badge	rare
283.Alexeiev Artillery Company Badge	rare
284.I Mounted General Alexeiev Mounted Regiment	rare
285.Medal for Colonel Drozdov's Contingent-silver	rare
(Cast copies of this medal exist.)	
286.Cross of the II General Drozdov Officers' Sharpshooters Regiment	700.00
287.Badge of the II General Drozdov Officers' Mounted Regiment	rare

RUSSIA

288.Colonel Chernetsov Partisan Detachment Cross   950.00
289.Cross for the Steppes Campaign   700.00
290.Cross for the Deliverance of the Kuban-I Class   rare
291.same-II Class   950.00
292.Kuban Liberation Medal-I Class   rare
293.Kuban Liberation Medal-II Class   rare
294.Cross of the Ekaterinoslav Campaign   750.00
295.General Bredov Campaign Cross-1920   rare
296.Order of St Nicholas the Miracle Worker-I Class   rare
297.same-II Class   rare
(Werlich states that about fifty of this Order were given, but does not indicate what class, and illustrates a type given to a Muslim.)
298.Badge for the Deliverance of the Crimea-1919-1920-
    instituted by General Wrangel.   rare

BATUM REGION

299.Medal for Bravery   rare
(This medal, in a private collection, appears to have been made from a Nicholas II Medal for Zeal IV Class. The obverse has been ground down to remove Nicholas's face and titles, and is replaced by a circle with a palm tree, bearing the legend Batum Oblast (Batum Region). The reverse has a half wreath with the Russian words equivalent to "For Bravery". Likely to be unique or extremely rare.)

WEST & NORTHWEST RUSSIA

300.The General Keller Cross   rare
301.Badge of the General Bermont-Avalov Volunteer Army   400.00
302.Medal of the General Bermont-Avalov Volunteer Army   400.00
303.Cross I Class of General Bermont-Avalov   rare
304.Cross II Class of General Bermont-Avalov   700.00
305.Cross of the Baltic Landwehr   85.00
(Also known as the Baltic Cross. German reference books consider this as a German award, and it was allowed to be worn during the Nazi period.)

General Yudenich Army Awards
306.Commemorative Cross-1919   rare
307.Northwest Union Badge (lapel)   rare
308.Prince Lieven Badge (lapel)   rare
309.Valor Cross of General Bulak-Bulakovich   375.00
(Three references show this as a breast cross, but one German auction catalogue also shows a breast star.)

NORTH RUSSIA

310.Commemorative Medal of General Miller   rare
311.Archangel/Murmansk Cross (lapel)   rare

EASTERN SIBERIA

311A.Ural Cossacks-Cross of Archangel Michael	rare
312.Order of Liberation of Siberia	rare
313.Military Order of the Siberian Campaign-I Class-	
St George ribbon-similar to item 268, except that	
the diagonal sword is "gold"	rare
314.same-II Class on the St Vladimir ribbon	rare
315.Cross of the Achinsky Mounted Partisans	rare
316.Valor Cross of General Semenov	950.00
317.Commemorative Badges of the Special Manchurian	
Company of General Semenov	700.00
318.XX Anniversary Badge-1937	rare

COMMEMORATIVE CROSSES OF GENERAL WRANGEL'S ARMY IN VARIOUS INTERNMENT CAMPS (After leaving Russia November 1920.)

319.Gallipoli	250.00
320.Lemnos	250.00
321.Bizerta	250.00
322.Cross with dates 1920-1921	rare
323.Undated & unnamed crosses	rare

(Copies of these crosses undoubtedly exist. I have seen a German made Lemnos Cross. The best ones to buy are those that bear the name of a Zagreb [Yugoslavia] maker.)

Decorations of the Grand Duke Kiril-Pretender to the Throne, and self-styled Emperor Kiril I.

324.Order of St Nicholas	225.00
325.Order of St Nicholas for Medical Personnel	200.00
326.Order of St Nicholas for non-Christians	275.00
327.Medal for Loyalty and Personal Service	95.00

Russian Veterans Society of the Great War

328.Order of the Compassionate Heart	250.00

SOVIET RUSSIA-U.S.S.R. (SOVIET UNION)

329.Hero of the Soviet Union (Gold Star Medal)	1000.00
330.Hero of Socialist Labor	700.00

(Copies of both of the above exist.)

Order of Lenin

331.Type I-screwback-1930-1931	rare
332.Type II-screwback-1931	750.00
333.Type III-on ribbon	550.00

(Copies of the above exist.)

334.Order of the October Revolution-1967	175.00

335.Order of Victory-1945 (various copies exist)   rare

Order of the Red Banner-1924
336.Type I-screwback   200.00
337.Type II-on ribbon-World War II   75.00
338.same-with number 2 for two awards   200.00
339.same-with number 3 for three awards   300.00
340.same-with number 4 for four awards   600.00
341.same-with number 5 for five awards   rare
342.Order of the Red Banner of the R.S.F.S.R.-1918   rare
343.Order of the Red Banner of Azerbaijan-1920   rare
344.Order of the Red Banner of Georgia-1920   rare
345.Order of the Red Banner of Armenia-1922   rare
346.Order of the Red Banner of Bohkara-1922   rare
347.Order of the Red Banner of Khorezm-1923   rare
(Note: Items 342-347 were replaced by item 336 in 1924.)

Order of Suvorov-Army-1942
348.I Class-platinum   8000.00
348.II Class-gold   2500.00
350.III Class-silver   1000.00
(Copies exist of the above.)

Order of Ushakov-Navy-1944
351.I Class-platinum   8000.00
352.II Class-gold   3000.00

Order of Kutuzov-Army-1942-1943
353.I Class-gold   6000.00
354.II Class-silver/enamels   1500.00
355.III Class-silver   400.00
(Copies exist of the above.)

Order of Nakhimov-Navy-1944
356.I Class-silver & gold   4500.00
357.II Class-silver   3500.00
(Copies exist of the above.)

Order of Bohdan Khmelnitsky-1943
358.I Class-gold & silver   3000.00
359.II Class   2000.00
360.III Class   800.00
(Copies exist of the above.)

361.Order of Alexander Nevsky-1942   500.00
(Note: Collectors appear willing to pay more for a low numbered piece, indicating
original World War II issue. Copies exist.)

Order of the Patriotic War-1942
362.I Class-silver/gold & enamels-original issue   300.00
363.same-but 1970's reissue-silver/gilt/enamels   75.00

364.II Class-silver/gilt/enamels-original issue   150.00
365.same-but 1970's reissue   50.00
(Note: The originals and reissues are easy to confuse from the obverse. The reverses are quite different. Original issues are smooth. Reissues have a stippled look to them which makes for a poor quality appearance.)

Order of the Red Star-1918-1922 & 1930
366.I Class-1918   rare
367.II Class-1918-worn on ribbon   3000.00
368.Screwback type-1930   40.00
(Note: Item 366 came to light in an auction in London, England in 1987. Very little is known about it.)

Order of Glory-1943
369.I Class-gold/enamel   1000.00
(Note: The collector must be aware and beware of silver/gilt examples of this award. Originals were gold; silver/gilt ones are gold plated III Class badges; possibly with one or more digits of the serial number ground off.)
370.II Class-silver/gilt/enamel   175.00
371.III Class-silver   45.00

Order of Honor-1935-(Previously known as the Badge of Honor)
372.Type I-screwback   150.00
373.Type II-ribbon   35.00

Order of the Red Banner of Labor-1928
374.I type-screwback   500.00
375.II type-on ribbon   40.00
(Note: There are two variations of number 375. They differ slightly in size and appearance. However, they have no real difference in value.)
376.Red Banner of Labor of the R.S.F.S.R.-1920   rare
377.Red Banner of Labor of Armenia-1923   rare
378.Red Banner of Labor of Khorezm-1923   rare
379.Red Banner of Labor of Byelo-Russia-1924   rare
380.Red Banner of Labor of Azerbaijan-1925   rare
381.Red Banner of Labor of Ukraine-1925   rare
382.Red Banner of Labor of Uzbekistan-1925   rare
(Note: Items 376-382 were replaced by item 374 in 1928.)

Order for Service to the Motherland in the Armed Forces
383.I Class   rare
384.II Class   rare
385.III Class   800.00

Motherhood Orders & Medals
386.Order of Mother Heroine-for 10 or more children   200.00
387.Order of Motherhood Glory-I Class-9 children   100.00
388.Order of Motherhood Glory-II Class-8 children   75.00
389.Order of Motherhood Glory-III Class-7 children   50.00
390.Motherhood Medal-I Class-6 children   25.00
391.Motherhood Medal-II Class-5 children   20.00

Decorations, Campaign & Commemorative Medals

392. Marshal's Star	rare
393. Medal for Valor-1st issue-on small red ribbon	200.00
394. Medal for Valor-standard ribbon-type I-numbered	50.00
395. same-but the unnumbered issue for Afghan War	50.00
396. Meritorious Service in Battle-1st issue-on small red ribbon	150.00
397. Meritorious Service in Battle-rifle/sabre on obverse-type I-numbered	50.00
398. same-but the unnumbered issue for Afghan War	50.00
399. Ushakov Medal-silver	300.00
400. Nakhimov Medal-bronze	225.00
401. Storming the Winter Palace-1920	1000.00
402. XX Anniversary of the Red Army-1938	175.00
403. XXX Anniversary of the Army & Navy-1948	10.00
404. 40th Anniversary of the Armed Forces-1958	10.00
405. 50th Anniversary of the Armed Forces-1968	10.00
406. 60th Anniversary of the Armed Forces-1978	10.00
407. 70th Anniversary of the Armed Forces-1988	10.00
408. Partisan Warfare Medal-I Class-silver-World War II	200.00
409. Partisan Warfare Medal-II Class-brass	125.00
410. Heroic Labor During World War II-1945	15.00
411. Defense of the Soviet Arctic	40.00
412. Defense of Leningrad	25.00
413. Defense of Moscow	25.00
414. Defense of Odessa	150.00
415. Defense of Sevastopol	200.00
416. Defense of Stalingrad	25.00
417. Defense of the Caucasus	40.00
418. Defense of Kiev	125.00
419. Victory over Germany	10.00
420. Victory over Japan	40.00
421. Capture of Budapest	100.00
422. Capture of Koenigsberg	35.00
423. Capture of Vienna	75.00
424. Capture of Berlin	25.00
425. Liberation of Prague	45.00
426. Liberation of Belgrade	250.00
427. Liberation of Warsaw	25.00

(Note: The values for World War II Campaign Medals are for original issues. The reissues are fairly easy to tell as they are "bright and shiny" in appearance, and not well struck. Their ribbons are usually mint.)

428. Valiant Labor-silver/enamel-1938	20.00
429. Distinguished Labor Service-1938	25.00
430. Good Conduct Medal-I Class-20 years	25.00
431. Good Conduct Medal-II Class-15 years	20.00
432. Good Conduct Medal-III Class-10 years	15.00

(430-432-to the Armed Forces-for the MVD-Interior Police-double the above values;for the KGB-triple the above values.)

433. Restoration of the Donets Mines-1947	125.00
434. Frontier Defense Medal-1950	200.00
435. Distinguished Service Preservation of Public Order	200.00

436.	Reclaiming Virgin Lands-1956	75.00
437.	Restoration of Heavy Industry-1956	85.00
438.	Fireman's Valor Medal-1957	50.00
439.	Lifesaving from Drowning-1957	125.00
440.	800th Anniversary of the founding of Moscow	30.00
441.	250th Anniversary of the founding of Leningrad	15.00
442.	1500th Anniversary of the founding of Kiev	50.00
443.	20th Anniversary of World War II-1965	10.00
444.	30th Anniversary of World War II-military-1975	10.00
445.	30th Anniversary of World War II-civil	10.00
446.	40th Anniversary of World War II-1985	10.00
447.	50th Anniversary of the Militia-1967	50.00
448.	Order of Friendship of Nations	850.00
449.	Order for Fame in Labor-I Class	500.00
450.	same-II Class	375.00
451.	same-III Class	150.00
452.	Armed Forces Service to the Motherland-I Class	rare
453.	same-II Class	rare
454.	same-III Class	150.00
455.	Centennial Medal of Lenin's Birth-military-1970	25.00
456.	Centennial Medal of Lenin's Birth-civil	15.00
457.	same-but on standard size ribbon	15.00
458.	Veterans of Labor Medal-1974	20.00
459.	Distinction in the Armed Forces-I Class	275.00
460.	same-II Class	200.00
461.	Armed Forces Veterans' Medal-1976	75.00
462.	Baikal-Amur Railway Construction-1978	200.00
463.	Development of non-black earth zone of the U.S.S.R.	200.00
464.	Oil & Gas Development-Western Siberia-1978	200.00
465.	Combat Cooperation Medal-1979	350.00

26 76 86

47 & 49 65

177 & 188   212

225   238

332   329   333

330

348 - 350   358 - 360

336   361

399 402 400

402

413 412

414 416

417 415

411 422

427

423

424

421

SAN MARINO

Republic

This small republic wholly within the territory of Italy is another one of history's political curiosities. This area was alone in avoiding being swallowed up in the wars for Italian unification in the 19th century.

The Order of San Marino (St Marinus),after whom the country is named, presents a particularly handsome appearance. The Order of St Agatha, considering the size of the country awarding it, is quite commonly seen.

There does not seem to a problem with copies.

Order of San Marino
Type I-civil-"Merito Civile"
1.Grand Cross badge	650.00
2.Grand Cross breast star	650.00
3.Commander (Grand Officer) neck badge	450.00
4.Commander breast star	475.00
5.Officer	350.00
6.Knight	250.00

Type I-military-"Merito Militare"
7.Grand Cross badge	700.00
8.Grand Cross breast star	650.00
9.Commander neck badge	550.00
10.Commander breast star	500.00
11.Officer	350.00
12.Knight	300.00

Type II-civil & military-"Merito Civile e Militare"
13.Grand Cross badge	500.00
14.Grand Cross breast star	500.00
15.Commander neck badge	400.00
16.Commander breast star	400.00
17.Officer	225.00
18.Knight	175.00
19.Golden Merit Medal	100.00
20.Silver Merit Medal	75.00
21.Bronze Merit Medal	50.00

Order of St Agatha-1923
22.Grand Cross badge	400.00
23.Grand Cross breast star	350.00
24.Commander (Grand Officer) neck badge	275.00
25.Commander breast star	250.00
26.Officer	150.00
27.Knight	125.00

28.Volunteers' Medal for Hospital Service-World War I	200.00

6, 12, 18 3, 9, 15 27

19 & 20 21

SPAIN

Kingdom till 1931
Republic 1931-1939
Franco Regime-1939
Kingdom-1976

The Orders, decorations and medals of Spain are a clear reflection of that country's tumultuous history, and its religious faith. The Orders, all ready extensive under the monarchy, were greatly expanded under Franco's government. Franco's decorations system is also of interest to the collector of German World War II material because of awards being made to the German Armed Forces for the Spanish Civil War, and for participation in the fighting in Russia in World War II.

Because there have been so many variations of some of the Spanish Orders I have been forced to simplify things somewhat. The values listed are for the most common types of the various issues. The Spanish Order system is also complicated because they have used a reverse numbering system for some of the Orders. Thus, in the Merit Orders of the Army, Navy, and Air Force the I Class is the lowest rather than the highest. The Franco period also saw the issuance of breast stars about half-size of the royal period pieces. This can be seen in such as the Orders of Maria Christina, St Hermengildo, and the Army, Navy, and Air Force Merit Orders.

Despite the great proliferation of awards, there does not seem to be a problem of copies, except for the Order of the Golden Fleece.

The medals of Spain are particularly interesting as they cover from the Napoleonic period to the present. There are also many items from the various civil wars, and the colonial campaigns of the 19th and 20th centuries. The medals for the Cuban and Philippine campaigns prior to the Spanish American War are also of some interest to the American collector.

The items of the Franco period have not appreciated in value. Except as noted, all royal items date from pre 1931.

KINGDOM

Order of the Golden Fleece-1429-1931;1976
1.Collar-early	rare
2.Badge on neck ribbon-early	4000.00
3.Collar-1976	2500.00
4.Badge on neck ribbon	2000.00
(Note: There are many variations of this Order.)

Order of Charles III-1771
5.Collar	3000.00
6.Grand Cross badge	500.00
7.Grand Cross breast star	500.00
8.Commander I Class	400.00
9.Commander I Class breast star	400.00

10.Commander II Class	400.00
11.Knight	250.00

(Note: Values listed are for silver/gilt pieces; gold badges would command 50-100% more. There are several variations of this Order.)

Order of Isabella the Catholic-1815

12.Collar	3000.00
13.Grand Cross badge	500.00
14.Grand Cross breast star	500.00
15.Commander I Class	350.00
16.Commander I Class breast star	350.00
17.Commander II Class	350.00
18.Knight	175.00
19.Silver Cross	100.00
20.Silver Medal	75.00
21.Bronze Medal	50.00

(Note: There are several variations of this Order.)

Order of St Ferdinand-1811

22.V Class badge (Grand Cross)	500.00
23.V Class breast star	550.00
24.IV Class (Officer with star)	300.00
25.IV Class breast star	450.00
26.III Class badge	250.00
27.III Class breast star	250.00
28.II Class (Officer)	200.00
29.I Class (Knight)	150.00

(Note: This Order illustrates the Spanish reverse style of numbering its Orders. There are several variations of this Order.)

Order of St Hermengildo-1814

30.Grand Cross badge	450.00
31.Grand Cross breast star	450.00
32.Commander	300.00
33.Knight	200.00

(Note: There are several variations of this Order.)

Military Merit Order-1864
Red Enamel for War Merit

35.IV Class badge (Grand Cross)	400.00
36.IV Class breast star-gilt;silver lilies	350.00
37.III Class breast star-as above	350.00
38.II Class breast star-silver; gold lilies	250.00
39.I Class breast badge (Knight)	75.00
40.Silver Merit Cross	40.00

Red Enamel-with white bars for pension award

41.IV Class	425.00
42.IV Class breast star	375.00
43.III Class	375.00
44.II Class	300.00
45.I Class	100.00

White Enamel for Peacetime Merit
46.IV Class		300.00
47.IV Class breast star		300.00
48.III Class		250.00
49.II Class		200.00
50.I Class		75.00
51.Silver Merit Cross		35.00

White Enamel-with red bars for pension award
52.IV Class		325.00
53.IV Class breast star		300.00
54.III Class		275.00
55.II Class		225.00
56.I Class		95.00

Naval Merit Order-1866
Red Enamel for War Merit
57.IV Class		350.00
58.IV Class breast star-gilt; silver lilies		350.00
59.III Class breast star-as above		350.00
60.II Class breast star-silver; gold lilies		250.00
61.I Class-knight-breast badge		75.00
62.Silver Merit Cross		45.00

Red Enamel-with gold bars for pension award
63.IV Class		375.00
64.IV Class breast star		375.00
65.III Class		375.00
66.II Class		275.00
67.I Class		100.00

White Enamel for Peacetime Merit
68.IV Class		350.00
69.IV Class breast star		350.00
70.III Class		350.00
71.II Class		250.00
72.I Class		100.00
73.Silver Merit Cross		50.00

White Enamel-blue bars for pension award
74.IV Class		375.00
75.IV Class breast star		375.00
76.III Class		375.00
77.II Class		275.00
78.I Class		100.00

Military Order of Maria Christina-1890
Military Division-lilies between the arms of cross
79.III Class (Grand Cross)		350.00
80.III Class breast star		350.00
81.II Class breast star-silver cross		250.00
82.I Class breast star-bronze cross		225.00
83.Knight-breast badge		100.00

Naval Division-anchors between arms of cross
84.III Class		375.00
85.III Class breast star		400.00

86.II Class 350.00
87.I Class 275.00
88.Knight 200.00

Order of Alfonso XII-1902-1931
89.Grand Cross badge 350.00
90.Grand Cross breast star 350.00
91.Commander I Class 275.00
92.Commander I Class breast star 350.00
93.Commander II Class 275.00
94.Knight 125.00

Civil Merit Order-1926
Type I-1926-1931
95.Grand Cross badge 300.00
96.Grand Cross breast star 300.00
97.Grand Officer badge 250.00
98.Grand Officer breast star 250.00
99.Commander 250.00
100.Officer 100.00
101.Knight 75.00

Order of Charity-1856
Type I-1856-1910
102.I Class-breast star rare
103.II Class-neck badge 850.00
104.III Class-breast badge 350.00
Type II-1910-1931
105.Grand Cross badge 300.00
106.Grand Cross breast star 300.00
107.I Class-breast star 300.00
108.II Class-neck badge 175.00
109.III Class-breast badge 75.00

Agricultural Merit Order-1905
Type I-1905-1931
110.Grand Cross badge 275.00
111.Grand Cross breast star 275.00
112.Commander I Class 250.00
113.Commander I Class breast star 250.00
114.Commander II Class 250.00
115.Knight 100.00

Red Cross Merit Order-1864
Type I-1864-1931
116.I Class breast star 400.00
117.I Class decoration-neck badge 250.00
118.II Class breast star-silver 275.00
119.II Class decoration-breast badge 75.00
120.Bronze Merit Medal 25.00

SPAIN

Maria Louisa Ladies' Order-1792-1931
121.Badge of the Order   1000.00

REPUBLIC-1931-1939

Order of Isabella the Catholic-type II
122.Grand Cross badge   450.00
123.Grand Cross breast star   450.00
124.Grand Officer   350.00
125.Grand Officer breast star   350.00
126.Commander   350.00
127.Knight   150.00
128.Silver Merit Cross   100.00
129.Silver Medal   75.00
130.Bronze Medal   50.00

Republic Merit Order
131.Grand Cross badge   750.00
132.Grand Cross breast star   750.00
133.Grand Officer badge   450.00
134.Grand Officer breast star   450.00
135.Commander   450.00
136.Officer   350.00
137.Knight   250.00

Franco Dictatorship

Order of Charles III
138.Collar   1600.00
139.Grand Cross badge   275.00
140.Grand Cross breast star   275.00
141.Commander I Class   175.00
142.Commander I Class breast star   175.00
143.Commander   175.00
144.Knight   75.00

Order of Isabella the Catholic
145.Collar   1800.00
146.Grand Cross badge   250.00
147.Grand Cross breast star   250.00
148.Commander I Class   150.00
149.Commander I Class breast star   150.00
150.Commander   150.00
151.Knight   65.00
152.Silver Merit Cross   50.00
153.Silver Medal   40.00
154.Bronze Medal   25.00

Order of St Ferdinand
155.Grand Cross badge   250.00
156.Grand Cross breast star   250.00
157.Sword Cross with wreath   125.00
158.Knight   85.00

Order of St Hermengildo
159.III Class (Grand Cross)   250.00
160.III Class breast star-with crown   250.00
161.II Class breast star-without crown   150.00
162.Knight   75.00
(Note: There are many variations of this Order.)

Order of the Yoke and Arrows
163.Collar   2000.00
164.Grand Cross badge   250.00
165.Grand Cross breast star   250.00
166.Grand Officer   150.00
167.Grand Officer breast star   150.00
168.Commander   150.00
169.Golden Medal   125.00

Order of Alfonso X (The Wise)
170.Collar   2000.00
171.Grand Cross badge   250.00
172.Grand Cross breast star   250.00
173.Grand Officer   150.00
174.Grand Officer breast star   150.00
175.Commander   150.00
176.Knight   75.00
177.Golden Medal   50.00

Order of Cisneros-1944
178.Collar   2000.00
179.Grand Cross badge   250.00
180.Grand Cross breast star   250.00
181.Grand Officer   150.00
182.Grand Officer breast star   150.00
183.Commander   150.00
184.Knight   65.00
185.Golden Medal   40.00

Military Merit Order
Red Enamel for War Merit
186.IV Class (Grand Cross)   250.00
187.IV Class breast star (gilt-silver lilies)   250.00
188.III Class-breast star-as 187 but smaller   85.00
189.II Class-breast star-as 188-silver-gold lilies   65.00
190.I Class breast badge   35.00
191.Silver Merit Cross   35.00

Red Enamel-white bars for pension award
192.	IV Class	250.00
193.	IV Class breast star	250.00
194.	III Class	175.00
195.	II Class	85.00
196.	I Class	40.00

White Enamel for Peacetime Merit
197.	IV Class	200.00
198.	IV Class breast star	200.00
199.	III Class	125.00
200.	II Class	50.00
201.	I Class	35.00
202.	Silver Merit Cross	25.00

White Enamel-red bars for pension award
203.	IV Class	250.00
204.	IV Class breast star	250.00
205.	III Class	175.00
206.	II Class	85.00
207.	I Class	40.00

Naval Merit Order
Red Enamel for War Merit
208.	IV Class (Grand Cross)	225.00
209.	IV Class breast star-gilt	225.00
210.	III Class breast star-gilt-silver lilies	85.00
211.	II Class-as 210-silver-golden lilies	65.00
212.	I Class	35.00
213.	Silver Merit Cross	35.00

(Note: The breast stars for the III & II Classes are much smaller than that of the IV Class.)

Red Enamel-gold bars for pension award
214.	IV Class	250.00
215.	IV Class breast star	250.00
216.	III Class	175.00
217.	II Class	85.00
218.	I Class	40.00

White Enamel for Peacetime Merit
219.	IV Class	200.00
220.	IV Class breast star	200.00
221.	III Class	125.00
222.	II Class	50.00
223.	I Class	35.00
224.	Silver Merit Cross	25.00

White Enamel-blue bars for pension award
225.	IV Class	225.00
226.	IV Class breast star	225.00
227.	III Class	150.00
228.	II Class	85.00
229.	I Class	40.00

Air Force Merit Order-1945
Red Enamel for War Merit

230.III Class badge (Grand Cross)	175.00
231.III Class breast star-gilt	175.00
232.II Class breast star-silver	75.00
233.I Class breast badge	35.00
234.Silver Merit Cross	35.00

Red Enamel-white bars for pension award

235.III Class	200.00
236.III Class breast star	200.00
237.II Class	85.00
238.I Class	45.00

White Enamel for Peacetime Merit

239.III Class	175.00
240.III Class breast star	175.00
241.II Class	65.00
242.I Class	35.00
243.Silver Merit Cross	35.00

White Enamel-red bars for pension award

244.III Class	175.00
245.III Class breast star	175.00
246.II Class	75.00
247.I Class	35.00

Order of Maria Christina
Military Division-lilies between arms of cross

248.III Class (Grand Cross)	175.00
249.III Class breast star	175.00
250.II Class breast star-silver with silver cross	125.00
251.I Class breast star-silver with bronze cross	100.00
252.Knight	75.00

Naval Division-anchors between arms of cross

253.III Class	250.00
254.III Class breast star	250.00
255.II Class	175.00
256.I Class	150.00
257.Knight	100.00

Civil Merit Order-1942

258.Collar	2000.00
259.Grand Cross badge	250.00
260.Grand Cross breast star	250.00
261.Grand Officer	150.00
262.Grand Officer breast star-silver	150.00
263.Commander	150.00
264.Officer	75.00
265.Knight	50.00
266.Silver Merit Cross	35.00

SPAIN

Order of Charity
267.Grand Cross badge — 200.00
268.Grand Cross breast star — 200.00
269.I Class breast star — 200.00
270.II Class neck badge — 110.00
271.III Class breast badge — 50.00

Order of St Raymond of Penafort-1944
272.Collar of the Grand Cross-gilt — 2250.00
273.Collar of the Honor Cross-half silver & half gilt — 900.00
274.Grand Cross badge — 225.00
275.Grand Cross breast star — 225.00
276.Honor Cross — 150.00
277.Honor Cross breast star — 150.00
278.Commander — 125.00
279.Commander breast star — 125.00
280.Commander — 125.00
281.Knight — 60.00
282.Gold Medal with enamel — 40.00
283.Silver Medal with enamel — 30.00
284.Bronze Medal with silver — 25.00
285.Bronze Medal — 20.00

Order of Africa
286.Grand Cross badge — 225.00
287.Grand Cross breast star-gilt — 225.00
288.Grand Officer — 125.00
289.Grand Officer breast star-silver — 125.00
290.Commander — 125.00
291.Officer — 75.00
292.Silver Honor Badge — 50.00

Civil Order of Health
293.Grand Cross badge — 200.00
294.Grand Cross breast star — 200.00
295.Grand Officer — 125.00
296.Grand Officer breast star — 125.00
297.Commander — 125.00
298.Knight — 65.00

Agricultural Merit Order
299.Grand Cross badge — 175.00
300.Grand Cross breast star — 175.00
301.Commander I Class — 125.00
302.Commander I Class breast star — 125.00
303.Commander II Class — 125.00
304.Knight — 65.00
305.Bronze Merit Decoration — 45.00

Red Cross Merit Order
306.I Class breast star — 225.00
307.I Class Medal — 125.00

308. II Class breast star	150.00
309. II Class Medal	50.00
310. III Class Medal	25.00

Order of the War Cross

311. Grand Cross badge	250.00
312. Grand Cross breast star-gilt	250.00
313. II Class breast star-silver	200.00
314. III Class breast star-bronze	125.00
315. IV Class-breast cross on ribbon	75.00

(Note: This Order may be found with palms on the insignia; add 20%. To compound the confusion the badges of this Order bear no resemblance to the breast stars. The breast stars are very similar to the Order of Maria Christina.)

316. War Cross-1936-1939-bestowed as a bravery award in 1940- similar in appearance to the War Cross badges above	50.00

Various Campaign Medals & Decorations

317. Cross for Sappers at Alcala de Henares-1808	rare
318. Cross for Valencay (For Faithful Service)-1808	700.00
319. Cross for Adherents of the King-1814	500.00
320. Medal for Captured Troops-gilt	75.00
321. Medal for Captured Troops-silver	50.00

(Note: The last two items were originally established in 1814. The medals were reinstituted in 1900 [for the Spanish American War], and in 1921 for future use. Awarded to troops captured or wounded in action. Values given for the most recent issues.)

322. Cross for Deported Civilians in France-1815	450.00
323. Medal for the Victims of May 1808;-1815	450.00
324. Cross for Cabinet Couriers-1815	rare
325. Cross for Alcolea 1808;-1815-gold	rare
326. Cross for Alcolea-silver	500.00
327. Cross for Saragossa-1808-1809	400.00
328. Cross for the Defense of Lerin-Officers	rare
329. Medal for the defense of Lerin-Enlisted Men	500.00
330. Cross for Menjibar 1808;-1816	500.00
331. Cross for Portugal 1808;-1815	500.00
332. Cross for Bubierca 1808;-1816	500.00
333. Cross for Rosas 1808;-1821	rare
334. Cross for Madrid 1808; 1817	500.00
335. Cross for the Asturian Army-1808;-1815	550.00
336. Medal for Taracon 1808;-Officers-gold-1815	rare
337. Medal for Taracon-junior officers-silver	500.00
338. Medal for Taracon-enlisted ranks-bronze	400.00
339. Naval War Cross 1808; 1816	450.00
340. Cross for the Provincial Juntas 1808;-1818	500.00
341. Northern Campaign Cross-1809	rare
342. Defense of Gerona-1809	rare
343. Cross of Castello de Ampurias-1809; 1817	rare
344. Cross for Vallis in Catalonia-1809; 1815	rare
345. Cross for Mora and Consuegra	rare

346.Cross for Lugo and Villafranca-1809;-gold-1817   rare
347.Cross for Lugo and Villafranca-privates-bronze   450.00
348.Cross for Alcaniz 1809;-1815   500.00
349.Cross for Talavera-1809;-officers-gold-1810   rare
(Note: See also Great Britain-Military General Service Medal with campaign bar for Talavera.)
350.Cross for Almonacid-1809;-1816   500.00
351.Cross for Aranjuez-1809;-1816   500.00
352.Medal for Tamames-1809;-1815   450.00
353.Medal for Medina del Campo-1809;-1815   450.00
354.Cross for Ciudad Rodrigo-1810;-officers-gold-1814   rare
355.Cross for Ciudad Rodrigo-silver-enlisted men   450.00
(Note: See also Great Britain-Military General Service Medal with campaign bar for Ciudad Rodrigo.)
356.Cross for Abisbal, San Feliu, and Palmos-1810;-1817   rare
357.Medal for Bagur & Palamos-gold-1910   6000.00
358.Medal for Bagur & Palamos-silver   750.00
359.Defense of Astorga Cross-1810;gold-1815   rare
360.Defense of Astorga Cross-silver   500.00
361.Cross of the Estremadura-1810;-1815   500.00
362.Cross for Albuhuera-1811;-1815   500.00
363.same-but in gold as awarded to British Officers   rare
(See note after 349.)
364.Cross for Chiclana-1811;-1815   500.00
365.Cross for Arroyo-Molinos-1811;-1817   500.00
366.Defense of Tarifa-1811-Officers-gold;-1815   rare
367.Defense of Tarifa-silver-Enlisted Men   500.00
368.Cross for Taragona-1811;-1815   500.00
369.Medal for the 1st Army-1811   500.00
370.Medal for the 1st Army-1813-1814   500.00
371.2nd Army Cross-1815   500.00
372.7th Army Cross-1810-1812;-1815   500.00
373.7th Army Cross-1815   500.00
374.Utiel Cross-1812;-1815   rare
375.Cross for the Recovery of Seville-1812-gold;-1815   rare
376.same-bronze   500.00
377.Army of Andalusia Cross-1814   500.00
378.Castella Cross-1813;-1816   rare
379.Cross for the Sieges of Pamplona & Bayonne-1815   1000.00
380.Cross for Vittoria-1813;-1815   500.00
(See note after 349.)
381.San Marcial Cross-1813;-1814   500.00
382.Ordal Cross-1813;-1815   rare
383.Cartagena Cross (Colombia)-1814-gold;-1816   rare
384.Cartagena Cross-silver   500.00
385.Cross of Merit for San Lorenzo del Puntal-1815   rare
386.Tolosa Cross-1814   500.00
(See note after 349; British medal-bar Toulouse.)
387.Council of Mesta Decoration-1816   rare
388.Majorca Division Cross-1816   500.00
389.Madrid Cross-1818   500.00

390. Shield of Fidelity	rare
391. Military Cross of Fidelity-gold-1824	rare
392. Military Cross of Fidelity-silver	500.00
393. Military Cross of Fidelity-bronze	300.00
394. Cross for Epidemics-1829	rare
395. Cross for Cuenca-1823;-1837	rare
396. Cross for Valencia-1823 & 1826	500.00
397. Cross for Cadiz-1823;-1836	rare
398. Prisoners' Cross-1823;-1840	rare
399. Cross for Vargas-1833;-1838	rare
400. Cross for Saragossa-1833-35;-1842	rare
401. Defense of Vergara-1834	rare
402. Cross for Mendigorra-1835	500.00
403. Cross for St Maria del Hort-1836;-1842	500.00
404. Cross for Chiva-1836;-1840	500.00
405. Medal for St Sebastian-to British Volunteers	500.00
406. Shield for Lodosa-1836;-1837	500.00
407. Cross for Cattavieja-1836;-1837	500.00
408. Cross for Bilbao-1835	500.00
409. Cross for Liberators of Bilbao-1836;-1837	500.00
410. Cross for Defenders of Bilbao-1836;-1837	500.00
411. Medal for Chiva-gold-1837	rare
412. Medal for Chiva-silver	500.00
413. Medal for Segovia-1837;-1842	500.00
414. Cross for Andalusia-1838	500.00
415. Cross for Saragossa-1838	500.00
416. Cross for Penacerrada-1838	500.00
417. Cross for the Siege of Solsona-gold-1838	rare
418. Cross for the Siege of Solsona-silver	500.00
419. Cross for Cheste-1838;-1841	rare
420. Cross for Iniesta-1838	rare
421. Cross for Tales-1839;-1843	rare
422. Medal for Peracamps-gold for Officers-1840	rare
423. Medal for Peracamps-bronze	500.00
424. Cross for Morella-1840	500.00
425. Cross for Olmedilla-1840;-1843	500.00
426. Cross of September 1 1840-1841	350.00
427. Cross for the Civil War-1841	375.00
428. Medal for cadiz-1841;-1842	350.00
429. Medal for Madrid-1841	350.00
430. Medal for Pamplona-1841	350.00
431. Cross for Castile-1841	350.00
432. Cross for Aragon-1841	350.00
433. Cross for Guipuzcoa-1841	375.00
434. Morocco 1860-African Campaigns	75.00
435. Cuban Volunteers Medal-1872	rare
436. Puerto Rican Volunteers Medal	rare
437. Civil Guard Cross-1870-1873	rare
438. Medal for Carraca-1873	rare
439. Medal of Alfonso XII	100.00
440. Civil War Medal-silver-1873-1874;-1876	200.00
441. Civil War Medal-bronze	125.00

442. Medal for Bilbao-silver-1874   75.00
443. Medal for Bilbao-bronze   50.00
444. Medal of the City of Bilbao-1874   50.00
445. Medal for Puigcerda-1874   75.00
446. Medal for Teruel-1874   75.00
447. Medal of Cervera-1875   75.00
448. Medal of Madrid-1876   50.00
449. Medal for Cuba-1868-1878;-1873   100.00
(Note: The Cuban Medal of 1873 was awarded with campaign bars. Add $25.00 per bar.)
450. Cuban Volunteers Medal-1868-1878 & 1882   125.00
451. Medal for Jolo-1876   125.00
452. Medal for Mindanao-1895   125.00
453. Medal for Luzon-1896-1897;-1898   125.00
454. Medal for the Philippines 1896-1898;-1898   125.00
455. Cuban Campaign Medal 1895-1898;-1899   125.00
456. Cuban Volunteers Medal 1895-1898   150.00
457. Filipino Volunteers Medal-1898   150.00
458. Medal of Alfonso XIII-silver-1902   50.00
459. Medal of Alfonso XIII-bronze   35.00
460. Medal of Maria Christina-silver-1903   50.00
461. Medal of Maria Christina-bronze   35.00
462. Medal for Melilla-1909-1912;-1910   25.00
(Add $10.00 per campaign bar.)
463. Medal for Africa 1911;-1912   25.00
464. Medal for Morocco-1916   25.00
(Similar to 462 above, except undated; add $5.00 per bar.)
465. Military Medal for Meritorious Service-1918   25.00
466. Peace in Morocco-1926   35.00
467. Ifni-Sahara Medal-gilt & enameled-officers   35.00
468. Ifni-Sahara Medal-bronze   25.00
469. Victory in the Civil War-1939   15.00
470. Volunteers Medal for the Spanish Blue Division in
     Russia-1941-beware of copies   150.00
471. German Medal for Spanish Volunteers   75.00
(Note: For the campaign and commemorative medals two sets of dates are often shown. The first is for the period covered by the medal, the second is the date it was founded. In most cases, where one date appears it may be assumed that it is the date of founding.)

36 23 47

180 118

449 456

466 462 & 464 469

SWEDEN

Kingdom

This country was once one of the great powers of Europe. However, this was before the time of issuing awards as we know them today. Thus, Sweden, unlike most European countries, has not been involved in military activity in modern times, and as a consequence its Orders, Medals and Decorations are not numerous in number. The breast stars of Swedish Orders are very different in appearance to most in that properly speaking they are not stars, but massive silver crosses, with little or no enamel. The breast stars are also similar in appearance which may confuse the collector.

The Royal Order of the Sword is certainly one of the most beautiful ever awarded, and its insignia very distinctive. The badges of Swedish Orders are often found in gold, especially in the higher grades.

There does not seem to be a problem with copies.

Order of the Seraphim-1748
1.Collar	rare
2.Badge	3500.00
3.Breast Star	3000.00

Order of the Sword-1748
4.Collar	rare
5.Grand Cross badge	2000.00
6.Grand Cross breast star	1500.00
7.Commander I Class	1250.00
8.Commander I Class breast star	900.00
9.Knight I Class	450.00
10.Knight II Class	350.00
11.Silver Merit Medal	275.00
12.War Cross I Class-silver/gilt	350.00
13.War Cross II Class-silver	300.00
14.War Cross III Class-bronze	250.00

Order of the North Star-1748
15.Collar	rare
16.Grand Cross badge	1000.00
17.Grand Cross breast star	550.00
18.Commander I Class	550.00
19.Commander I Class breast star	450.00
20.Commander II Class	550.00
21.Knight-gold	450.00
22.Knight-silver/gilt	300.00

Order of Vasa-1772
23.Collar	rare
24.Grand Cross badge	1000.00
25.Grand Cross breast star	550.00
26.Commander I Class	550.00
27.Commander I Class breast star	350.00

SWEDEN

28.Knight I Class-gold	350.00
29.Knight I Class-silver/gilt	250.00
30.Knight II Class	225.00
31.Silver Merit Cross	225.00
32.Gold Medal	200.00
33.Silver Medal	175.00
34.Bronze Medal	100.00

Other Awards

35.Medal for Valor-gold	rare
36.Medal for Valor-silver	rare
37.Long Service in the Naval Dockyard-silver	75.00
38.Lifesaving Medal-gold	2000.00
39.Lifesaving Medal-silver	500.00
40.Crown Prince Gustav's Wedding Medal-1906	100.00
41.Oscar II's Golden Wedding Medal-1907	100.00
42.Medal for the 1912 Olympics	750.00
43.Patriotic Society Medal-gold	500.00
44.Patriotic Society Medal-silver	50.00
45.50th Anniversary of Postal Union-1926	25.00
46.Militia Long Service Medal-I Class-silver/gilt	75.00
47.Militia Long Service Medal-II Class-silver	45.00

21 & 22   9 & 10

28 - 30

TURKEY

Ottoman Empire till 1921

The Orders of this country are much more familiar to collectors than one might expect. The reason is that many of them were awarded to officials, military and civil of friendly countries. In particular British Officers were the recipients of those from the Turkish and Egyptian governments before World War I. During that war many were awarded to Officers of the German Army; and the collector may come across German made insignia of the Medjidie Order with scimitars, which are avidly sought by German collectors of the World War I period. Strictly speaking these German made pieces should be regarded as copies, but the collectors seem to ignore this matter.

One Turkish award which causes confusion is the 1915 Campaign Star or Medal. In the U.S.A. it commonly referred to as the "Gallipoli Star", although it was granted for other campaigns also. In Germany it is known as the "Iron Halfmoon or Crescent." This piece has been extensively copied, as the original Turkish struck piece was of poor quality. German Officers had better quality items struck by Godet of Berlin. Again, these pieces are accepted by collectors. However, there are others which are marked B.B. Co. on the reverse, which do not appear to be German made, and should be regarded with caution.

The main problem collecting Turkish awards is that their inscriptions are in Turkish using Arabic letters, making it very difficult for the collector to find out exactly what these pieces are. This is a pity because the Turkish campaign medals of the 19th century are a chronicle of the decline of their empire.

Order of Nishan-Imtiaz-1879-1921
1.Badge	rare
2.Breast star	rare

Osmanli Order-(Order of Osmania)-1862-1921
3.I Class badge	550.00
4.I Class	500.00
5.II Class neck badge	375.00
6.II Class breast star	350.00
7.III Class neck badge	375.00
8.IV Class-Officer	175.00
9.V Class	150.00

(Note: This Order was awarded frequently to British Officers by the Khedive of Egypt, nominally the Sultan's Viceroy in Egypt. For insignia with scimitars add 50%.)

Order of the Medjidie-1852-1921
10.I Class badge	550.00
11.I Class breast star	500.00
12.II Class neck badge	350.00
13.II Class breast star	350.00

14. III Class neck badge 350.00
15. IV Class-Officer 175.00
16. V Class 150.00
(Note: This Order was awarded to British Officers for the Crimean War. Insignia from this time period are sought after by the British collector, and command a higher price. The insignia are of a cruder make than later made pieces. Also awarded by the Khedive of Egypt. For pieces with scimitars add 50%.)

Order of Nishani-Shefkat (Order of Charity or Chastity)-1878-1921
17. I Class badge-gold and diamonds 5000.00
18. I Class badge-gold & enamels 1000.00
19. I Class breast star-gold and diamonds 5000.00
20. II Class neck badge-gold and diamonds 3500.00
21. II Class neck badge-bronze/gilt and diamonds 2500.00
22. III Class breast badge-gold/enamel 850.00

Imtiaz Medal
23. Gold 1500.00
24. Silver 500.00

Liakat Medal
25. Gold 500.00
26. Silver 250.00

Campaign Medals
27. Syria-1840-gold 1500.00
28. Syria-silver/gilt 450.00
29. Syria-silver 150.00
30. Syria-bronze 100.00
(Also awarded to British naval personnel, according to rank.)
31. Crimea-British type-unnamed-CRIMEA 75.00
32. Crimea-British type-named 100.00
33. Crimea-French type-unnamed-LA CRIMEE 110.00
34. Crimea-French type-named to British recipient 200.00
35. Crimea-French type-named to a French recipient 200.00
36. Crimea-Sardinian type-unnamed-LA CRIMEA 50.00
37. Crimea-Sardinian type-named to a British recipient 85.00
(The Crimean War Medals were awarded by the Sultan of Turkey to his allies in the War against Russia 1854-1856. The most common type is the Sardinian.)
38. Danube Campaign Medal-1855 .... 500.00
39. Defense of Kars-1855 .... 450.00
40. Cretan Campaign-1895 .... 450.00
41. 1915 Campaign Star-original issue 100.00
42. 1915 Campaign Star-superior German type 200.00
43. Red Crescent Medal-I Class-gold & enamels 350.00
44. Red Crescent Medal-II Class-silver & enamel 300.00
45. Red Crscent Medal-III Class-bronze and enamel 200.00
46. Army Pilot and Observer Badge-copies exist 650.00
47. Navy Pilot and Observer Badge-copies exist 750.00

5 & 7

6

UNITED STATES OF AMERICA

Of all the major powers of the world, the United States in distinction to all the others was alone in not having a system of awards for its armed forces until the early 20th century. With the notable exceptions of the Army and Navy Medals of Honor, which were established during the Civil War, it was not until after the Spanish American War of 1898 that any strong movement for an awards program appeared.

In order to emphasize the democratic nature of U.S. awards there are no multi-class Orders that can be awarded to the U.S. Armed Forces. However, there does exist the curious Legion of Merit in four grades, Chief Commander, Commander, Officer, and Legionnaire. Only the fourth grade, Legionnaire, can be awarded to U.S. military recipients, and then is known simply as the Legion of Merit. The other grades are reserved for award to foreign military personnel. The Presidential Medal of Freedom, in several grades, as a civilian award can be presented without the restrictions of the Legion of Merit.

Identifying copies and fakes is a serious problem for American medal collectors, and has only become worse in recent years. The latest fakes to appear are named Army Civil War and Indian Wars medal pairs. These are recent strikes with ring suspensions which have been artificially aged. Then they are engraved with a number and the supposed name of the recipient. The same is also being done with USMC Civil War medals. While these fakes have what appear to be old ribbons, they are all missing their brooches. Often they are matched with a military fob engraved with the same name as the medals. Copies of the Specially Meritorious Cross present some difficulty. However, they are usually darker than the originals which are a light chocolate in color. While copies may be unnamed there are also genuine unnamed specimens. Fake 1919-20 bars for the Haiti 1915 are common, as is the WAKE ISLAND bar for the Navy and Marine Corps Expeditionary Medal. Thus far, it appears that faking of U.S. awards is confined to the military items.

One of the best sources of information on United States medals is the series of reference works edited by the late Albert F. Gleim and published by Planchet Press (see bibliography). Another excellent source is **THE CALL OF DUTY** which contains information and photos of American medals never before presented.

MILITARY AWARDS

(Under current US law it is illegal to sell the Medal of Honor, so "values" are theoretical and are for information purposes only. Some have appeared in European auctions.)

Medal of Honor-United States Army
1.Civil War-awarded medal   7500.00
2.Civil War-awared to the 27th Maine   3000.00
3.Civil War-awarded medal-1904 type   5000.00
4.Awarded medal for any action after the Civil War   rare
(This includes the Indian Wars, Spanish American War era, WWI, WWII, Korea and Vietnam.)

5.Civil War-specimen	2500.00
6.Civil War type with 1896 ribbon-specimen	2500.00
7.1904 type-on breast ribbon-specimen	1500.00
8.World War II-1944 type on neck ribbon with small pad-specimen	1000.00
9.same-marked BB Co or Bastian Bros-specimen	1200.00
10.Vietnam War era-large pad on cravat-specimen	500.00

Medal of Honor-United States Navy, USMC, Coast Guard

11.All awarded examples from the Civil War through Vietnam War	rare
12.Civil War type 1862-1904 with r,w&b ribbon-specimen	3000.00
13.1904-1913 type with light blue ribbon and white stars-specimen	2500.00
14.1913-1943 type on neck ribbon without pad-specimen	2500.00
15.Tiffany Gold Cross-gold specimen	rare
16.same-but a bronze/gilt specimen	2000.00
17.World War II-1944 type on neck ribbon with small pad-specimen	1000.00
18.Vietnam War era-large pad on cravat-specimen	500.00

Medal of Honor-U.S.A.F.

19.All awarded examples	rare
20.Vietnam War era-marked HLP-specimen	750.00
21.same-unmarked-specimen	500.00

The collector must be particularly careful of copies of the Army and Navy Civil War Medals of Honor. Usually, they can be detected by their color which is much darker than the originals. The designer's name should be clear as Paquet F. If the Paquet appears as a P followed by some vertical lines of varying length then it is a fake. If the designer's name does not appear at all then the piece is a fake. Use a strong magnifier! I have seen a fake Army Civil War named to an entitled member of the 27th Maine Regt. The collector must also be on guard for the naming of a recent specimen to an earlier known recipient. I have seen at least two fake Korean War Army Awards, and two fake World War II Air Corps awards.

Named Medals of Honor, except for the Army Civil War and a few Indian Wars awards, are rare primarily because so many are in museums, or have been retained by the families. Moreover, after the Civil War they were much more sparingly awarded.

DECORATIONS-The values given for the decorations listed below are for unnamed or unattributed awards, unless other wise noted. Named or attributed awards will command a premium of 10% to ten times, depending upon details of the citation.

Since the late 1980's large quantities of recently manufactured decorations and medals have come onto the market. These items are generally of poorer quality and should be avoided by the collector. **Values for items listed here as "later strike" do not apply to these medals.**

Distinguished Service Cross
22.exchange for Certificate of Merit (only 75 awarded)	rare
23.World War I-first type-numbered	rare
24.World War I-first type-French restrike	200.00
25.World War I-second type-numbered-attributed	from 1200.00
26.World War I-second type-numbered-unattributed	500.00
27.World War I-second type-French restrike	150.00
28.World War II-numbered-unattributed	250.00
29.World War II-unnumbered-black slot brooch	125.00

Navy Cross
30.World War I issue	650.00
31."Black widow" (beware of copies)	750.00
32.World War II	350.00
33.Vietnam War era	125.00

Air Force Cross
34.First issue-hallmarked HLP	150.00
35.Second issue-not hallmarked	65.00

Marine Corps Brevet Medal
36.original strike	rare
37.numbered specimen-marked "Display" or "Exhibition"	3500.00

(Note: There are many types of copies; use extreme caution.)

Specially Meritorious Cross-1898
38.named award	6500.00
39.specimen (some are marked "Display" or "Exhibition")	1750.00

(Note: Copies of this decoration exist. Usually a darker bronze than originals.)

Cardenas Medal of Honor-1898
40.Table medal (gold, silver & bronze)	rare
41.Wearable medal (gold, silver & bronze)	rare

(Awarded to the officers and crew of the Revenue Cutter Hudson for towing the disabled U.S.S. Winslow to safety during the battle at Cardenas.)

Defense Department Awards
42.Distinguished Service Medal	125.00
43.Superior Service Medal	85.00
44.Meritorious Service Medal	25.00

Certificate of Merit
45.paper document	1800.00
46.Medal-numbered-attributed	3250.00
47.Medal-numbered-unattributed/exhibition	1700.00
48.Medal-unnumbered specimen-US Mint strike	750.00
49.Medal-unnumbered specimen	450.00

(Note: Could be exchanged for the Army Distinguished Service Medal after 1919 or the Distinguished Service Cross after 1934. See appropriate section. Awards for combat will command a premium.)

UNITED STATES

Distinguished Service Medal

50. Army-exchange for Certificate of Merit	rare
51. same-World War I-numbered-attributed	750.00
52. same-World War I-numbered-unattributed	400.00
53. same-World War I-French restrike	250.00

(The French made copy of the Army Distinguished Service Medal is easily discernible because it does not swivel at the suspension.)

54. same-World War II-numbered	250.00
55. same-World War II-unnumbered	125.00
56. same-post World War II-unnumbered	60.00
57. Navy-World War I issue-type I	5000.00

(A few of the Navy D.S.M. type I-struck, but not issued, have appeared over the years, and named to Japanese admirals.)

58. Navy-World War I-standard issue	750.00
59. same-World War II	375.00
60. same-post-World War II	125.00
61. Air Force-HLP on brooch	85.00
62. Coast Guard-original strike	rare
63. same-later strike	65.00

Silver Star

Created in 1932, retroactive to Civil War, this decoration originated as the "Silver Citation Star" on the World War I Victory Medal ribbon.

64. Army-World War I-Bailey Banks & Biddle Co.-numbered-unnamed	225.00
65. same-World War I-numbered-named	from 350.00
66. same-World War I-with large oak leaf cluster*	from 675.00
67. same-World War II-numbered-wrap brooch	95.00
68. same-World War II-numbered-slot brooch	85.00
69. same-World War II-unnumbered-Bastian Bros.	125.00
70. same-World War II-unnumbered-slot brooch	50.00
71. Navy-World War II-"frosted"-wrap brooch-unnumbered-in red case	200.00

(*Numerous fakes of the original large oak leaf cluster are being manufactured. The collector should exercise extreme caution.)

Legion of Merit

72. Chief Commander Breast Star-I issue-World War II- numbered-silver/gilt/enamels by Bailey Banks & Biddle	2000.00
73. same-unnumbered	750.00
74. same-bronze/gilt reverse marked "12C"	300.00
75. same-reverse dull gilt	175.00
76. Commander-neck badge-I issue-World War II-numbered	850.00
77. same-unnumbered	350.00
78. same-later strike	175.00
79. Officer-World War II-numbered wrap brooch	200.00
80. same-unnumbered wrap brooch	125.00
81. same-Vietnam War era	35.00
82. Legionnaire-World War II-numbered wrap brooch	185.00
83. same-unnumbered wrap brooch	125.00
84. same-slot brooch	85.00

85.same-Navy type-wrap brooch-short drape   200.00
86.Legionnaire-pierced planchet-enameled on reverse   800.00
87.Legionnaire-Vietnam War era   25.00
(Note: Only the grade of Legionnaire can normally be awarded to U.S. servicemen. The award when for combat may be worn with a "V" on the ribbon.)

Distinguished Flying Cross
88.Pre World War II-numbered-marked "BB&B" or "Aug. Frank"   650.00
89.same-named/attributed   rare
90.World War II-Army-numbered-slot brooch   185.00
91.World War II-Army-unnumbered-slot brooch   75.00
92.World War II-Army-"frosted"-slot brooch   85.00
93.World War II-Navy-"frosted"-wrap brooch   140.00
94.later strike   40.00

Soldiers' Medal
95.Pre-World War II-numbered and named/attributed   850.00
96.Pre-World War II-numbered-unattributed   300.00
97.World War II-numbered   110.00
98.World War II-unnumbered   50.00
99.Vietnam War era strike   30.00

Navy & Marine Corps Medal
100.original WWII strike   175.00   101.Vietnam War era strike   65.00

Airman's Medal
102.original Vietnam War era strike   35.00

Coast Guard Medal
103.original US Mint strike   350.00   104.VietnamWar era strike   40.00

Bronze Star (can be worn with "V" for valor)
105.World War II-Army-slot brooch   25.00
106.World War II-Navy-wrap brooch-thick planchet   125.00
107.Vietnam War era strike   20.00

Air Medal
108.World War II-Army-numbered wrap brooch   75.00
109.World War II-Army-unnumbered wrap brooch   45.00
110.World War II-slot brooch   30.00
111.World War II-Navy-wrap brooch   100.00
112.Vietnam War era strike   20.00

113.Meritorious Service Medal   10.00

Lifesaving Medals
114.Gold-large size   6500.00
115.Gold-small size-post 1949   3500.00

116.Silver-large size	2250.00
117.Silver-small size-post 1949	1500.00

(Note: The above values are based on named, traceable awards to the armed services with a good citation. Civilian awards are perhaps 60-75% of above values. In recent years it has been the practice to award medals like the Soldiers' Medal etc. to members of the armed forces instead of lifesaving medals. There are known to be a few specimens of the large gold medal, some of which may be bronze/gilt. Specimens of the large silver medal exist also. In the last few years a large quantity of the small version of the Gold and Silver medals have come on the market.)

Commendation Medals

118.Army-original 1950s strike 25.00	119.same-1960s strike	20.00
120.Navy-original 190s strike 25.00	121.same-1960s strike	20.00
122.Air Force		20.00
123.Coast Guard-type I-Treasury Dept		450.00
124.Coast Guard-type I-Treasury Dept 3-ring suspension		400.00
125.Coast Guard-type II-Transportation Dept		40.00
126.Joint Service		25.00

Achievement Medals

127.Army	10.00	128.Navy	20.00
129.Air Force	20.00	130.Coast Guard	25.00
131.Joint Service	25.00		

Purple Heart (created 1932, retroactive to the Civil War)
Army-World War I and earlier-always issued named
(flat enamel heart-5 digit number on edge-split wrap brooch-always named)

132.Pre World War I award-named and attributed	rare
133.World War I award-named and attributed	150.00
134.same-with large oak leaf cluster (beware of fakes)	275.00

Army-World War II*

135.Type I-flat enamel or painted heart-6 digit number-slot brooch	65.00
136.Type II-raised plastic heart-edge numbered-slot brooch	50.00
137.Type III-raised plastic heart-unnumbered-slot brooch	35.00

Navy-World War II*

138.Type I-silver/gilt planchet-gilt split wrap brooch-frequently found in a small purple case	100.00
139.Type II-gilt full wrap brooch	75.00

(*These types were produced during World War II but issued as late as the Vietnam War.)

Good Conduct Medals

140.Army-ring suspension-numbered-wrap brooch	rare
141.same-knob suspension-numbered-wrap brooch	55.00
142.same-knob suspension-unnumbered-slot brooch	15.00
143.Navy-type I-Nickel Cross-1869-1884 (copies exist)	1000.00
144.Navy-type II-bar suspension-reverse engraved with name, ship or station and date (pre 1932)*	from 65.00

145.same-engraved with name and year (1932-1941)   40.00
146.same-impressed with name and year (1942-1953)   30.00
147.same-unnamed   25.00
148.same-knob suspension   10.00
(*With additional service bars or to an unusual ship or station values can be considerably higher, especially for earlier issues. With so many variations values can vary greatly.)
149.Marine Corps-reverse engraved with name and date*   from 85.00
150.same-unnamed-numbered on edge-World War I   55.00
151.same-reverse impressed with name and year (WWII-1953)   45.00
152.same-no number or name   25.00
153.no USMC top bar   15.00
(*A variety of engraving styles and date/year formats used through WWII, early issues worth more. Additional "Enlistment" bars worth minimum $20.00 extra.)
154.Air Force   10.00
155.Coast Guard-type I-reverse named*   165.00
156.same-type I-unnamed   85.00
157.same-type II-knob suspension   20.00
(*Early issues worth more; especially with extra service bars.)
158.Coast Guard Reserve   15.00

Armed Forces Reserve Medals-medals have common obverse & ribbon with different reverses reflecting the respective services. Values are for original strikes.

159.Army	15.00	160.Navy	20.00
161.Air Force	15.00	162.Marine Corps	35.00
163.National Guard	15.00	164.Coast Guard	35.00

Other Reserve Medals
165.Naval Reserve-type I-ring suspension-wrap brooch   60.00
166.Naval Reserve-type II-knob suspension   15.00
167.Naval Reserve Meritorious Service   20.00
168.Air Force Reserve Meritorious Service   20.00
169.Fleet Marine Corps Reserve   850.00
170.Marine Corps Reserve-ring suspension-wrap brooch   125.00
171.same-ring suspension-later strike   45.00
172.same-but type II-knob suspension   15.00
173.Army Reserve Components Achievement   10.00
174.National Guard Achievement   10.00

Miscellaneous Other Awards
175.Typhus Commission Medal   1200.00
176.Peary Polar Expedition-1908-1909   rare
177.NC-4 Medal-wearing type "miniature"   2000.00
178.Byrd Antarctic Expedition-1928-1930   rare
179.Second Byrd Antarctic Expedition-1933-1935   rare
180.Antarctic Expedition-1939-1941-bronze   350.00
181.Antarctic Expedition-1939-1941-silver   rare
182.Antarctic Expedition-1939-1941-gold   rare
(Beware of recent strikes of 176-182, which have no significant collector value.)

183.Aerial Achievement Medal	15.00
184.Prisoner of War Medal	15.00
185.Air Force Combat Readiness Medal	15.00
186.Outstanding Volunteer Service Medal	15.00
187.Bailey Medal-awarded piece	rare
188.Bailey Medal-specimen	2000.00
189.Navy Sharpshooter Badge (predecessor to 190 & 192)	275.00
190.Navy Expert Pistol Shot Medal-early strike	65.00
191.Navy Expert Pistol Shot Medal-later shiny strike	20.00
192.Navy Expert Rifleman Medal-early strike	65.00
193.Navy Expert Rifleman Medal-later shiny strike	20.00
194.Coast Guard Expert Rifleman Medal-original strike	85.00
195.Coast Guard Expert Rifleman Medal-later strike	35.00
196.Coast Guard Expert Pistol Shot Medal-original strike	85.00
197.Coast Guard Expert Pistol Shot Medal-later strike	35.00
198.Short Range Battle Practice Medal "Great Guns Medal"	1000.00
199.Admiral Trenchard Section Navy League Turret Gunpointer Medal	850.00
200.Knox Trophy Medal-Army Light Artillery reverse	850.00
201.Knox Trophy Medal-Navy Gunpointing reverse	850.00
202.American Spirit Honor Medal (non-wearable)	100.00

(Note: There are many marksmanship medals and badges for the armed forces. These are too complicated to go into here.)

CAMPAIGN AND SERVICE MEDALS

Not unlike the award of the British Military and Naval General Service Medals of 1848, the institution of the Army Civil War Campaign Medal in 1905 saw only a small number of eligible recipients who were alive to claim it. The Civil War Campaign Medal was issued in three types, Army, Navy and Marine Corps. This pattern was followed wherever all three services were involved together in a campaign. The Navy and Marine Corps issues had the same obverse, with the reverse stating the particular service involved.

With the exception of the Manila Bay Medal (Dewey Medal), and the West Indies Naval Campaign Medal (Sampson Medal), American campaign medals were not officially named. However, most of the early awards were issued with a number on the rim. There were three basic styles of numbering: with a prefix "No."; with a prefix "M.No."; plain number without prefix. The plain numbers appear in several different sizes and styles as applied by the various commercial firms which produced medals on contract for the Armed Forces. The only thing they have in common is the lack of "No." and "M.No." prefixes used by the U.S. Mint in its uniform numbering style.

The three charts that follow outline the numbering system of U.S. campaign medals. They reflect the ranges of numbered medals believed to have been produced, however, no one has any idea what the survival rate of these series has been. Should your medal have a number which is not listed in the range included in the chart it does not mean that your medal is spurious as a few isolated numbers have been reported outside these limits. In some cases these "strays" could be genuine medals which were not numbered as part of a continuous sequence. Others, however, are the result of faking. Therefore, a number in the correct sequence does not guarantee that your medal is genuine.

While numbered campaign medals are of particular interest due to the possibility of researching the recipient, the unnumbered ones are also of interest to the collector because they are cheaper, and easier to obtain. However, it is here that the collector is presented with the very serious problem of faking.

Some of these fakes are very obvious, many of them made in Taiwan. They are poorly struck, thick, and have a little knob on top rather than the proper ring. Some swindler has even replaced the knobs with rings! Confusing the situation even more is the fact that there are genuine restrikes, made for late claims, and issued unnumbered. Some of these genuine unnumbered medals have been later been spuriously numbered, turning them into fakes. The only way to tell the difference is to compare it with a known genuine medal.

Unnumbered campaign medals have been struck by such firms as Davison, Medallic Art, E.H. Simon and Vanguard to name a few. In recent years a main supplier for all types of awards has been HLP (His Lordship Products) later known as Lordship Industries.

In the past there was the practice of providing both decorations and campaign medals, some even numbered, to veterans' posts and museums for display. Some, but not all, of the items have been marked "DISPLAY", "FOR DISPLAY" or "FOR EXHIBITION PURPOSES ONLY". These display medals, marked as such, or when revealed by the relevant issue roll to be such, will generally lose about 25% or more of their value.

The French copy of the U.S. World War I Victory Medal has the French type ball suspension. However, American collectors have come to regard this item as an acceptable variation. Bars for the Victory Medal stamped Made in France have come to the same acceptance. However, there are many fake bars to the World War I Victory Medal, especially the navy types. Again, the best way to be sure of one of these is to compare with a known original.

Medals privately engraved on the rim with the recipient's name, or otherwise attributed, will command a premium.

UNITED STATES ARMY CAMPAIGN MEDALS 1861-1939

Campaign	Prefix No.	Plain Numbers	Prefix M.No.
Civil War	1-600	601-3700+	1-6000
Indian Wars	1-2000	2001-2250	1-1750
War with Spain	1-8500	8300-12500	1-6400
Spanish War Service	none	1-31200	none
Cuban Occupation	1-5000	5001-9200	1-4600
Porto Rico		1-200	
Occupation	201-400	401-2000+	1-2000+

Army Campaign Medals continued

Campaign	Prefix No.	Plain Numbers	Prefix M.No.
Philippine Campaign	1-25000	23001-33000	1-9200+
Philippine Congressional	1-11500	none	none

(Note: Philippine Campaign & Congressional both state Philippine Insurrection on the obverse. The Congressional has the soldiers on the obverse, the other has a palm tree.)

China Relief	1-1700	1701-1800	1-600
Cuban Pacification	1-6500	6501-7000	1-300
Mexico 1911-1917	1-10000	10001-15000	1-300
" Border Service	none	1-41300+	none

(Note: + indicates that the range extends beyond this number but the exact cut off is unknown.)

203. Civil War-numbered No.	1750.00
204. Civil War-numbered M.No.	425.00
205. Civil War-plain numbered	350.00
206. Civil War-unnumbered early strike	150.00
207. Indian Wars-numbered No.	1500.00
208. Indian Wars-numbered M.No.	750.00
209. Indian Wars-plain numbered	900.00
210. Indian Wars-unnumbered early strike	200.00
211. Indian Wars-later Medallic Art Co-unnumbered strike	125.00
212. Spanish Campaign-numbered No.	150.00
213. Spanish Campaign-numbered M.No.	100.00
214. Spanish Campaign-plain numbered	85.00
215. Spanish Campaign-early unnumbered strike	50.00
216. Spanish War Service-1898-plain numbered	75.00
217. Spanish War Service-1898-unnumbered early strike	45.00
218. Porto Rico Occupation-numbered No.	1000.00
219. Porto Rico Occupation-numbered M.No.	500.00
220. Porto Rico Occupation-plain numbered 1-200	1000.00
221. Porto Rico Occupation-plain numbered 401-2000	325.00
222. Porto Rico Occupation-unnumbered early strike	100.00
223. Cuban Occupation-numbered No.	200.00
224. Cuban Occupation-numbered M.No.	125.00
225. Cuban Occupation-plain numbered	100.00
226. Cuban Occupation-unnumbered early strike	75.00
227. Philippine Campaign-numbered No.	150.00
228. Philippine Campaign-numbered M.No.	95.00
229. Philippine Campaign-plain numbered	75.00
230. Philippine Campaign-unnumbered early strike	50.00

231.Philippine Congressional-numbered No.(below 6180)   175.00
232.Philippine Congressional-numbered No.(above 6179)   100.00
233.Philippine Congressional-unnumbered   40.00
(Note: Both the Philippine Campaign-Army and the Philippine Congressional state "Philippine Insurrection" on the obverse. The Philippine Campaign has a palm tree on the obverse, while the Congressional has three soldiers.)

234.China Relief Expedition-numbered No.   1000.00
235.China Relief Expedition-numbered M.No.   500.00
236.China Relief Expedition-plain numbered   800.00
237.China Relief Expedition-unnumbered early strike   125.00

238.Cuban Pacification-numbered No.   200.00
239.Cuban Pacification-numbered M.No.   600.00
240.Cuban Pacification-plain numbered   150.00
241.Cuban Pacification-unnumbered early strike   75.00

242.Mexican Service 1911-1917-numbered No.   150.00
243.Mexican Service 1911-1917-plain numbered   110.00
244.Mexican Service 1911-1917-numbered M.No.   600.00
245.Mexican Service 1911-1917-unnumbered early strike   75.00

246.Mexican Border Service-plain numbered   85.00
247.Mexican Border Service-unnumbered early strike   40.00

248.Victory Medal-World War I-with no bars-standard issue   20.00
249.Victory Medal-numbered with "U.S.M." prefix   rare
250.Victory Medal-ring type-no bars   50.00
251.Victory Medal-ball type-French copy   25.00
252.Victory Medal-three ring type-El Oro, Philippines-copy   75.00
World War I Victory Medal-Army bars-with medal

253.Defensive Sector			20.00
254.England	75.00	255.France	30.00
256.Italy	85.00	257.Russia	150.00
258.Siberia	200.00	259.Cambrai	200.00
260.Somme, Defensive	100.00	261.Lys	350.00
262.Aisne	25.00	263.Montdidier-Noyon	45.00
264.Champagne-Marne	25.00	265.Aisne-Marne	25.00
266.Somme, Offensive	60.00	267.Oise-Aisne	25.00
268.Ypres-Lys	25.00	269.St Mihiel	25.00
270.Meuse-Argonne	25.00	271.Vittorio-Veneto	250.00
272.two bars	40.00	273.three bars	45.00
274.four bars	55.00	275.five bars	65.00
276.six bars (maximum to any one unit)			85.00

(Note: Values of multi-bar medals are based on combination of common bars, not the combined value. There are many copies of the Army bars, especially of Russia and Siberia. There are also army type bars which are pure inventions, such as Army of Occupation. A Silver Citation Star was authorized for wear on the ribbon of individuals cited for heroism. This star is quite scarce in its original form, however the abundance of later versions make values on this items difficult to access. See Silver Star section.)

277.Army of Occupation-World War I-type I ribbon-wavy edges	80.00
278.Army of Occupation-World War I-type II ribbon	75.00

UNITED STATES NAVY CAMPAIGN MEDALS 1861-1939

Campaign	Plain Numbers	Prefix M.No
Civil War	1-2900+	none
Spanish Campaign	1-6050*	none
West Indies	1-4033*	none
Philippine	1-4192#	4193-4392##
China 1901	1-500	none
China 1900	501-1150	none
Cuban Pacification	1-2500	none
Nicaragua 1912	1-1600	none
Haiti 1915	1-5300**	none
Dominican 1916	1-3800	none
Mexico 1911-17	1-15500#	15501-16674##
Haiti 1919-20	all unnumbered as issued	
II Nicaragua	none	1-10500
Yangtze Service	none	1-13500

+ The range extends beyond this number but the exact cut off is unknown
* These two medals were intertwined in a single numbering sequence through number 2700. Thus, if there was a Spanish Campaign 1550 there was no corresponding West Indies 1550.
** Medals in the 3000 and 5000 range were issued to the USMC.
#-curved "For Service" on reverse.
##-straight "For Service" on reverse.

279.Navy Expeditionary-original US Mint type-wrap brooch	225.00
280.Navy Expeditionary-with bar "Wake Island"	900.00
281.Navy Expeditionary-later ring type by HLP	25.00
282.Navy Expeditionary-later knob type	15.00
283.Civil War-plain numbered	850.00
284.Civil War-unnumbered early strike	200.00
285.Spanish Campaign-plain numbered	550.00
286.Spanish Campaign-unnumbered 3 ring type	150.00

(This medal with engraved numbers 851-1350 were issued to the Marine Corps.)

287.Spanish Campaign-usual type-unnumbered	75.00
288.West Indies Campaign-numbered	750.00
289.Manila Bay Medal (Dewey Medal)-named to enlisted man	2000.00
290.Manila Bay Medal (Dewey Medal)-named to officer	3000.00

West Indies Naval Campaign Medal (Sampson Medal)
(Admiral Sampson on obverse-not to be confused with item 288 above.)
The "Sampson Medal" is very complex, appearing with a variety of ship and engagement bars. Many are officially named on the rim in one of three styles. It is not possible to give values for all ships and possible engagement bar combinations in the space available. The main factor in determining value, however, is the ship. Medals to the crew of small ships or those engaged in significant battles can be worth many times the values given below. Another factor in determining value is the recipient's rank as medals to officers are worth a minimum 50% premium. A number of original unnamed medals are also available which are worth generally 25-50% less than named medals. The reader is advised to consult a superb reference work on this medal entitled: **THE WEST INDIES NAVAL CAMPAIGN OF 1898, THE SAMPSON MEDAL, THE SHIPS AND THE MEN** (see bibliography).
The values below are for the most common ships and bar combinations.

291. Ship bar-no campaign bars-named	450.00
292. Ship bar-no campaign bars-unnamed	225.00
293. Ship bar-multiple campaign bars-named	550.00
294. Ship bar-multiple campaign bars-unnamed	300.00
295. Chain link type-with one or more bars-named	1200.00
296. Chain link type-unnamed	600.00

(There are numerous fakes of this medal, as well as fake bars. The book previously mentioned can be of great assistance in identifying these.)

297. Philippine Campaign-plain numbered	375.00
298. Philippine Campaign-numbered M.No.	rare
299. Philippine Campaign-unnumbered early strike	125.00
300. China Relief Expedition-plain numbered-1900 date	950.00
301. China Relief Expedition-plain numbered-1901 date	1200.00
302. China Relief Expedition-unnumbered early strike	100.00
303. Cuban Pacification-plain numbered	375.00
304. Cuban Pacification-unnumbered early strike	125.00
305. Nicaraguan Campaign 1912-plain numbered	750.00
306. Nicaraguan Campaign 1912-unnumbered early strike	100.00
307. Mexican Service 1911-1917-plain numbered	165.00
308. Mexican Service 1911-1917-numbered M.No.	450.00
309. Mexican Service 1911-1917-unnumbered early strike	75.00
310. Haitian Campaign 1915-plain numbered below 3000	350.00
311. bar 1919-20 for above	500.00

(Bars should be checked very carefully. Many copies exist.)

312. Haitian Campaign 1915-unnumbered early strike	75.00
313. Dominican Campaign 1916-plain numbered	350.00
314. Dominican Campaign 1916-unnumbered early strike	75.00

315.Victory Medal-World War I-with no bars-standard issue			20.00
316.Victory Medal-ring type-no bars			50.00
317.Victory Medal-ball type-French copy			25.00
318.Victory Medal-three ring type-El Oro, Philippines-copy			75.00

World War I Victory Medal-Navy bars-with medal

319.Overseas	40.00	320.Armed Guard	55.00
321.Asiatic	250.00	322.Atlantic Fleet	45.00
323.Aviation	250.00	324.Destroyer	55.00
325.Escort	50.00	326.Grand Fleet	50.00
327.Mine Laying	165.00	328.Mobile Base	225.00
329.Mine Sweeping	165.00	330.Naval Battery	350.00
331.Patrol	85.00	332.Salvage	350.00
333.Subchaser	175.00	334.Submarine	200.00
335.Transport	40.00	336.West Indies	200.00
337.White Sea	350.00	338."Maltese Cross"	75.00

(Note: There are several different types of copies of the navy bars, some of which are easy to tell because of the "pebbled" rather than smooth background on the front, and the peculiar "aging" which they have. Also, fakes of the Maltese Cross exist. There are French copies of navy bars made like the army ones, some of which are stamped MADE IN FRANCE on the reverse. These seem to find favor with collectors.)

339.Army of Occupation-World War I-type I ribbon-wavy edges	80.00
340.Army of Occupation-World War I-type II ribbon	75.00

341.Haitian Campaign 1919-20-unnumbered as issued	250.00
342.Haitian Campaign 1919-20-same-"Whitehead & Hoag" brooch	300.00

343.Second Nicaraguan Campaign 1926-numbered M.No.	175.00
344.Second Nicaraguan Campaign 1926-unnumbered early strike	60.00

345.Yangtze Service-numbered M.No.	175.00
346.Yangtze Service-unnumbered early strike	60.00

347.China Service-type I 1937-1939-ring suspension-unnumbered	185.00

UNITED STATES MARINE CORPS CAMPAIGN MEDALS 1861-1939

Campaign	Plain Numbers	Prefix M. No.
Civil War	1-175	none
West Indies	1-400	none
Spanish Campaign	401-850	none

(Navy 3-ring type with engraved numbers 851-1350 were issued to the Marine Corps. See listing under USN.)

Philippine	1-1525	none
China 1900	1-625	none
Cuban Pacification	1-1575	none
Nicaragua 1912	1-1100	none
Mexico 1911-17	1-2499	none

Marine Corps Campaign Medals continued

Campaign	Plain Numbers	Prefix M. No.
Haiti 1915 (See under USN for the Haiti 1915)		
Dominican 1916	1-2800	none
Haiti 1919-20	1-3500	none
II Nicaragua	none	1-6000
Yangtze Service	none	1-6300
China Service	1-3800	none
Expeditionary	none	1-10000

348.USMC Expeditionary Medal-ring type-numbered M.No.		225.00
349.USMC Expeditionary Medal-with bar "Wake Island"		900.00
350.USMC Expeditionary Medal-ring type-unnumbered		85.00
351.USMC Expeditionary Medal-later knob type		25.00
352.Civil War-plain numbered		6500.00
353.Civil War-unnumbered early strike		200.00
354.Spanish Campaign-plain numbered		1500.00
355.Spanish Campaign-USN 3 ring type- engraved #s 851-1350		1250.00
356.Spanish Campaign-early unnumbered strike		150.00
357.West Indies Campaign-numbered		1750.00
358.Manila Bay Medal (Dewey Medal)-named to enlisted man		3500.00
359.Manila Bay Medal (Dewey Medal)-named to officer		rare

West Indies Naval Campaign Medal (see commentary in US Navy section)
The values below are for the most common ships and bar combinations.

360.Chain link type-with one or more bars-named	1500.00
361.Ship bar-no campaign bars-named	750.00
362.Ship bar-multiple campaign bars-named	950.00
363.Blank Ship bar-to Huntington's Battalion	1750.00
364.Philippine Campaign-plain numbered	650.00
365.Philippine Campaign-unnumbered early strike	200.00
366.China Relief Expedition-plain numbered	1500.00
367.China Relief Expedition-early unnumbered strike	200.00
368.Cuban Pacification-plain numbered	650.00
369.Cuban Pacification-unnumbered early strike	150.00
370.Nicaraguan Campaign 1912-plain numbered	1350.00
371.Nicaraguan Campaign 1912-unnumbered early strike	150.00
372.Mexican Service 1911-1917-plain numbered	350.00
373.Mexican Service 1911-1917-unnumbered early strike	100.00

374. Haitian Campaign 1915-USN reverse, 3000 and 5000 number range 450.00
375. bar 1919-20 for above   500.00
(Note: No 1915 Haitian Campaign with a USMC reverse was authorized, although there seem to have been a few trial strikes. The majority of USMC versions encountered, however, are copies made for collectors. Marines were issued the Navy medal with numbers in the 3000 and 5000 range. Bars for 374 should be checked very carefully. Many copies exist.)

376. Dominican Campaign 1916-plain numbered   450.00
377. Dominican Campaign 1916-unnumbered early strike   85.00

378. Victory Medal-World War I-with no bars-standard issue   20.00
379. Victory Medal-ring type-no bars   50.00
380. Victory Medal-ball type-French copy   25.00
381. Victory Medal-three ring type-El Oro, Philippines-copy   75.00
(Marines could receive the Victory Medal with Army or Navy bars. See Army or Navy section for bar values and commentary.)

382. Army of Occupation-World War I-type I ribbon-wavy edges   80.00
383. Army of Occupation-World War I-type II ribbon   75.00

384. Haitian Campaign 1919-20-plain numbered   375.00
385. Haitian Campaign 1919-20-unnumbered strike   75.00

386. Second Nicaraguan Campaign 1926-numbered M.No.   200.00
387. Second Nicaraguan Campaign 1926-unnumbered   75.00

388. Yangtze Service-numbered M.No.   200.00
389. Yangtze Service-unnumbered   75.00

390. China Service-type I 1937-1939-ring suspension-plain number   475.00

ARMED FORCES CAMPAIGN AND SERVICE MEDALS 1939-1991

391. American Defense Service Medal-type I-ring suspension   35.00
392. American Defense Service Medal-type II-knob suspension   15.00
393. American Defense-bar Foreign Service-Army   25.00
394. American Defense-bar Fleet-USN, USMC, USCG   20.00
395. American Defense-bar Base-USN, USMC, USCG   30.00
396. American Defense-bar Sea-USCG   75.00
397. American Campaign Medal   15.00
398. European-African-Middle Eastern Campaign Medal   15.00
399. Asiatic Pacific Campaign Medal   15.00
400. World War II Victory Medal   10.00
401. Women's Army Corps Medal-1st issue-dull type   50.00
402. Women's Army Corps Medal-2nd issue-shiny type   25.00
403. Army of Occupation World War II   15.00
404. same-bar Germany   20.00   405. same-bar Japan   20.00

406. Navy Occupation-World War II		20.00
407. same-bar Asia 25.00	408. same-bar Europe	30.00
409. USMC Occupation-World War II		25.00
410. same-bar Asia 30.00	411. same-bar Europe	35.00
412. China Service-USN-type II-knob suspension		40.00
413. China Service-USMC-type II-knob suspension		40.00
414. Medal for Humane Action (Berlin Airlift)		15.00
415. National Defense Service Medal-type I-1950's		15.00
416. National Defense Service Medal-type II-1960's & 1970's		10.00
417. Korean Service Medal		15.00
418. United Nations Korean Service Medal		25.00
419. United Nations Observers' Medal for the Congo		35.00
420. Antarctica Service Medal		15.00
421. same-gold bar Wintered Over		30.00
422. same-silver bar Wintered Over		25.00
423. same-bronze bar Wintered Over		20.00
424. Coast Guard Arctic Service Medal		35.00
425. Armed Forces Expeditionary Medal		10.00
426. Vietnam Service Medal		15.00
427. Armed Forces Humanitarian Service Medal		15.00
428. South West Asia Service (Gulf War)		15.00

MERCHANT MARINE
429. Distinguished Service Medal	1500.00
430. Meritorious Service Medal-numbered	250.00
431. Meritorious Service Medal-named & numbered	350.00
432. Mariners's Medal	175.00
433. Defense Medal	25.00
434. Atlantic War Zone Medal	25.00
435. Mediterranean Middle East War Zone Medal	25.00
436. Pacific War Zone Medal	25.00
437. World War II Victory-original strike	75.00
438. Expeditionary Medal	25.00
439. Korean War Service Medal	25.00
440. Vietnam War Service Medal	25.00

(Note: Collectors should beware of "later strikes" of all Merchant Marine decorations and the World War II Victory Medal. They are unauthorized and as such are fakes.)

CIVILIAN AWARDS
441. Congressional Space Medal of Honor	rare
442. Presidential Medal of Freedom	rare
443. Medal for Merit-large stars-initials on rim	300.00
444. Medal for Merit-small stars-initials on rim	300.00
445. Medal of Freedom-gold palm	150.00
446. Medal of Freedom-silver palm	100.00
447. Medal of Freedom-bronze palm	85.00
448. Medal of Freedom-without palm	65.00

449.National Security Medal-woven ribbon	1000.00
450.National Security Medal-"painted" ribbon	950.00
451.Department of State Vietnam Service Medal-original strike	150.00
452.Department of State Vietnam Service Medal-current strike	50.00
453.Gulf War Civilian Service	25.00

(Note: Values for most of the above listed civilian award are for unnamed pieces. Named awards to persons of distinction or with documentation would be worth more.)

STATE CAMPAIGN AND SERVICE MEDALS

Many state medals for war service proceeded federal issues, and some of them were issued at the time of service. An excellent reference is STATE MEDALS FOR WAR SERVICE by Douglas Boyce. A selection is presented below.

454.California-Spanish American War Volunteers Medal 1898-1899	150.00
455.Colorado-Spanish American War Medal 1898-1899	250.00
456.Colorado-Mexican Border Service 1915-various ribbons	45.00
457.Colorado-Active Service Medal	25.00

(The following bars were authorized: Utes 1879, Utes 1887, 1917-1919, Berlin Crisis, Vietnam. All are rare.)

458.Connecticut-Civil War Campaign Medal	350.00
459.Connecticut-Spanish American War	50.00
460.Connecticut-World War I Service	25.00
461.Delaware-Mexican Border Service	200.00
462.Massachusetts-Minute Man-Civil War	250.00
463.Missouri-Spanish American War	50.00
464.Missouri-Mexican Border Service	35.00
465.Missouri-World War I Service	20.00
466.Montana-Spanish American War Volunteers	250.00
467.Nebraska-Sioux War	1250.00
468.New Hampshire-World War I Service	25.00
469.New Jersey-First Defenders' Medal-Civil War	rare
470.New Jersey-Spanish American War Cross	65.00
471.New Jersey-Mexican Border Service	45.00
472.New Jersey-World War I Service	20.00
473.New Mexico Bataan Medal-WWII	200.00
474.New York-Mexican War 1845	1500.00
475.New York-Civil War-large or small type	rare
476.New York-City of Brooklyn-Army	175.00
477.New York-City of Brooklyn-Navy	350.00
478.New York-Spanish AmericanWar/Philippines/Boxer Rebellion	50.00
479.New York-Mexican Border Service	35.00
480.New York-World War I-overseas service	15.00
481.New York-World War I-home service	20.00
482.New York-Conspicuous Service Cross-WWI	75.00
483.New York-Conspicuous Service Cross-WWII	50.00
484.New York-Conspicuous Service Cross-post WWII	25.00
485.Ohio-Civil War	50.00
486.Ohio-Mexican Border Service	50.00

487.Pennsylvania-First Defenders-Civil War-five types   rare
488.Pennsylvania-Spanish American War Marksman's Medal   35.00
489.Pennsylvania-Malate Cross for 10th Infantry-Spanish American War 200.00
490.Pennsylvania-Mexican Border Service   35.00
491.Pennsylvania-WWI Service-Federal   25.00
492.Pennsylvania-WWI Service-National Guard   25.00
493.Rhode Island-WWI Service   200.00
494.Utah-Indian Wars Medal   1200.00
495.West Virginia-Civil War-Killed in Battle   1500.00
496.West Virginia-Civil War-Died in Service   600.00
497.West Virginia-Civil War-Honorably Discharged   250.00
498.Wisconsin-Spanish American War Medal   125.00
499.Wisconsin-Mexican Border Service Medal   50.00

AMERICAN SOCIETY MEDALS

Since the recent publication of AMERICAN SOCIETY MEDALS by Lee Bishop & J.Robert Elliott, the interest in this material has grown. Since much of it is beautifully made and quite rare it was decided to include some items. In a sense, many of these were the precursors to campaign medals. Values listed are for original or earlier insignia, later strikes are worth considerably less.

500.Order of the Cincinnati-many varieties   from 600.00
501.Society of Colonial Wars   175.00
502.Sons of the Revolution   250.00
503.Sons of the American Revolution   125.00
504.Aztec Club   750.00
505.Military order of the Loyal Legion   from 175.00
506.Grand Army of the Republic   65.00
507.Army of the Potomac   500.00
508.United Daughters of the Confederacy (UDC) Civil War Cross from 350.00
(Beware of copies of the above.)
509.UDC Spanish American War Service Cross   rare
510.UDC World War I Service Cross   175.00
511.UDC World War II Service Cross   275.00
512.UDC Vietnam War Service Cross   275.00
513.Society of the Army of Santiago-gold/enamel or bronze-named   650.00
514.same-unnamed   400.00
515.Order of the Carabao-type I   1200.00
516.same-type II   750.00
517.Military Order of the Serpent   35.00
518.Military Order of the Dragon-U.S. recipient   1750.00
519.Imperial Order of the Dragon   800.00
520.United Spanish War Veterans Cross-type I   125.00
521.same-type II   65.00
522.Military Order of the World War   from 75.00
523.Military Order of the World Wars   50.00

8   17

21

56
84

117
103

71 100

95-96 136-137

203-204 207

212 228

283, 352   297, 364

305, 370   341-342, 384

293-294, 362   295-296, 360

291-292, 361   289-290, 358-359

219   223

216   246

48   231-232

242   234

38-39 198

308 280

149   348

347, 390   170

144
192

180
274

297, 303, 307, 320

106, 111, 343, 392, 397

485   462

491   480

470

479

468

504 500 507

513-514 522

508   511

516   517

505 506

518 519

VATICAN

(Papal States until 1870)

Until 1870 the head of the Roman Catholic Church was a ruler of territory in his own right, and thus was a political figure as well as a religious one. In that capacity a number of Orders were established to reward those who earned recognition for some type of service. Between 1870, when Rome became the capital of a United Italy, and 1929, when the Church signed an agreement with Mussolini's government, the political authority of the Pope ceased to exist. After this agreement the Vatican State was established, and its awards reflected once again political and religious authority.

Papal Orders are handsome in appearance, and have been made by a variety of manufacturers in several countries. The Order of Christ is also a Portuguese one.

There does not seem to be a problem with copies.

Order of the Holy Sepulchre-1496
1.Civil Grand Cross badge		500.00
2.Military Grand Cross badge		550.00
3.Grand Cross breast star		400.00
4.Civil Commander		450.00
5.Military Commander		475.00
6.Civil Knight		250.00
7.Military Knight		275.00

(The military version of this Order is suspended from a "trophy of arms.)

Order of the Golden Spur-1559-1841; 1905
8.Collar		rare
9.Badge		3000.00
10.Breast Star		1750.00

Order of St Sylvester and the Golden Spur-1841-1905
11.Collar		rare
12.Commander		500.00
13.Knight		400.00

Order of St Sylvester-1905
14.Collar		rare
15.Grand Cross badge		500.00
16.Grand Cross breast star		450.00
17.Commander		325.00
18.Commander breast star		325.00
19.Knight		200.00

VATICAN

Order of Christ-1319 (See also Portugal.)
20.Collar	rare
21.Badge	3000.00
22.Breast star	1750.00

Order of St Gregory-1831
23.Civil Grand Cross badge	400.00
24.Military Grand Cross badge	450.00
25.Grand Cross breast star	400.00
26.Civil Commander	325.00
27.Military Commander	350.00
28.Civil Knight	250.00
29.Military Knight	300.00

(Military badges of this Order are suspended from a "trophy of arms", civil badges from a wreath.)

Order of Pius-1847
30.Collar	rare
31.Grand Cross badge	500.00
32.Grand Cross breast star	450.00
33.Commander	325.00
34.Commander breast star	325.00
35.Knight	250.00

Lateran Cross-1903
36.Gold	150.00
37.Silver	100.00
38.Bronze	75.00

Cross "Pro Ecclesia et Pontifice"-1888 & 1908
39.Gold-only class since 1908	150.00
40.Silver-obsolete since 1908	100.00
41.Bronze-obsolete since 1908	75.00

Campaign Awards
42.Cross of Mentana	350.00
43.Decoration for the Battle of Castelfiardo	350.00

(These last two items were awarded to French and other foreign troops who defended the papacy against nationalist forces attempting to unify Italy.)

33

6   19   6

26

29 27 28

REPUBLIC OF VIETNAM (South)

After 1954, Vietnam, formerly a French colony, was effectively split into two countries; the north a Communist state, and the south a pro-Western one. South Vietnam, as it is commonly referred to, established an extensive system of decorations and medals.

In the earliest period some of these awards were made in France. For example, on the reverse of the suspension of the Army Gallantry Cross can be seen the word "FRANCE". Early issues of the Military Merit Medal bear the head of the former Emperor of Annam (Vietnam) Bao Dai.

Most awards seen however, are of Vietnamese or U.S. manufacture. Neither are of exceptionally high quality, but the Vietnamese ones generally have a poor looking appearance, and the ribbons are of a coarse material. It should be pointed out that for the most part U.S. made versions of South Vietnamese awards were made on contract to the U.S. Armed Forces, and thus do not fall into the usual category of copies.

Values listed below are for the Vietnamese made pieces except where noted. Values for U.S. made pieces are approximately 25%-50%.

National Order of Vietnam-1950-1973
1.Grand Cross badge (I Class)	500.00
2.Grand Cross breast star	600.00
3.Grand Officer breast star (II Class)	600.00
4.Commander (III Class)	350.00
5.Officer (IV Class)	250.00
6.Knight (V Class)	200.00

Civilian Decorations
7.Chuong My Merit Medal I Class	150.00
8.Chuong My Merit Medal II Class	140.00
9.Administrative Service Medal I Class	100.00
10.Administrative Service Medal II Class	95.00
11.Dedicated Service Medal I Class	75.00
12.Dedicated Service Medal II Class	70.00
13.Justice Medal I Class	75.00
14.Justice Medal II Class	70.00
15.Cultural and Educational Service Medal I Class	75.00
16.Cultural and Educational Service Medal II Class	70.00
17.Public Health Service Medal I Class	75.00
18.Public Health Service Medal II Class	70.00
19.Social Service Medal I Class	75.00
20.Social Service Medal II Class	70.00
21.Economic Service Medal I Class	75.00
22.Economic Service Medal II Class	70.00
23.Finance Service Medal I Class	75.00
24.Finance Service Medal II Class	70.00

25.Psychological Warfare Medal I Class	65.00
26.Psychological Warfare Medal II Class	60.00
27.Agricultural Service Medal I Class	65.00
28.Agricultural Service Medal II Class	60.00
29.Public Works, Communications & Transport Medal I Class	65.00
30.Public Works, Communications & Transport Medal II Class	60.00
31.Labor Medal I Class	65.00
32.Labor Medal II Class	60.00
33.Rural Revolutionary Development Medal I Class	65.00
34.Rural Revolutionary Development Medal II Class	60.00
35.Ethnic Development Service Medal I Class	70.00
36.Ethnic Development Service Medal II Class	65.00
37.Veterans' Medal I Class	70.00
38.Veterans' Medal II Class	65.00
39.Police Merit Medal I Class	70.00
40.Police Merit Medal II Class	65.00
41.Police Merit Medal III Class	50.00
42.Police Honor Medal-I Class-25 year service	60.00
43.Police Honor Medal-II Class 20 year service	50.00
44.Police Honor Medal-III Class-15 year service	40.00
45.Self Defense Medal I Class	60.00
46.Self Defense Medal II Class	50.00
47.Youth & Sports Service Medal I Class	50.00
48.Youth & Sports Service Medal II Class	45.00

Military Decorations

49.Military Merit Medal-type I-Bao Dai on obverse	350.00
50.Military Merit Medal-type II-Republic	200.00
51.Army Distinguished Service Order I Class	200.00
52.Army Distinguished Service Order II Class	200.00
53.Navy Distinguished Service Order I Class	200.00
54.Navy Distinguished Service Order II Class	200.00
55.Air Force Distinguished Service Order I Class	200.00
56.Air Force Distinguished Service Order II Class	200.00
57.Army Meritorious Service Medal	75.00
58.Navy Meritorious Service Medal	75.00
59.Air Force Meritorious Service Medal	75.00
60.Special Service Medal	60.00
61.Army Gallantry Cross-with star or palm-French made	125.00
62.Army Gallantry Cross-with palm or star	75.00
63.Navy Gallantry Cross	75.00
64.Air Force Gallantry Cross	75.00
65.Hazardous Service Medal	60.00
66.Lifesaving Medal	75.00
67.Wound Medal	50.00
68.Leadership Medal	50.00

69. Armed Forces Honor Medal I Class	65.00
70. Armed Forces Honor Medal II Class	60.00
71. Staff Service Medal-I Class-officers	65.00
72. Staff Service Medal-II Class-enlisted men	60.00
73. Technical Service Medal I Class-officers	65.00
74. Technical Service Medal II Class-enlisted men	60.00
75. Training Service Medal I Class	50.00
76. Training Service Medal II Class	45.00
77. Civic Action Medal I Class-officers	65.00
78. Civic Action Medal II Class-enlisted men	60.00
79. Loyalty Medal	60.00
80. Military Service Medal I Class	75.00
81. Military Service Medal II Class	60.00
82. Military Service Medal III Class	55.00
83. Military Service Medal IV Class	50.00
84. Military Service Medal V Class	45.00
85. Navy Service Medal I Class	75.00
86. Navy Service Medal II Class	70.00
87. Navy Service Medal III Class	65.00
88. Navy Service Medal IV Class	60.00
89. Air Service Medal I Class	75.00
90. Air Service Medal II Class	70.00
91. Air Service Medal III Class	65.00
92. Air Service Medal IV Class	60.00
93. Good Conduct Medal I Class	60.00
94. Good Conduct Medal II Class	55.00
95. Good Conduct Medal III Class	50.00
96 Good Conduct Medal IV Class	45.00
97. Good Conduct Medal V Class	40.00
98. National Sacrifice Medal	50.00
99. Unity Medal	50.00
100. Campaign Star-with pre 1960 bar	125.00
101. Campaign Star-with two pre 1960 bars	150.00
102. Campaign Star bar 1960-	60.00

(Note: The above values are for original, Vietnamese made items. Official U.S. made items on government contract are valued at about 25%-50% of above. There is currently in circulation a fake of the Campaign Star-bar 1960, which has a fixed suspension.)

61 & 62

50   69   53

WORLD WAR I VICTORY MEDALS-1914-1918

This is a particularly interesting series for the collector. Besides the theme, the Great War for Civilization, it is the only other series besides the United Nations Korea Medal, to use the same ribbon design, regardless of the issuing country. Furthermore, especially of benefit to the collector is the appearance of an excellent book on the subject **THE INTERALLIED VICTORY MEDALS OF WORLD WAR I** by Alexander J. Laslo, which provides much material, hitherto unknown, and which is now reflected in the values of these medals.

Several of these medals are rare. Those of Brazil and Siam are especially seldom seen, so much so that copies are not run across frequently.

Many Victory Medals were copied in France after World War I, and show a typical French ball type suspension. However, there are also genuine Victory Medals with the French type suspension. A Japanese Victory with such a suspension is a copy, but not necessarily a Portuguese. Most of the medals have a designer's name on the obverse or reverse, or on both. The Portuguese seems to have gone through the most copies, including the most recent which have a chocolate color, and others from a cracked die. There are also many copy bars for the U.S. Medal, especially for the Naval issue. Some bars must even be described as fake, since they don't exist in the original.

1.Belgium-by Paul DuBois-Over 300,000 issued   20.00
(Laslo states there are 3 unofficial issues, and a French copy.)

2.Brazil-by Jorge Soubre-approximately 2500 issued   2500.00
(Laslo states official type has CASA DA MOEDA - RIO impressed on rim; unofficial type-unmarked; others are copies.)

3.Cuba-by Charles (obverse)-6,000-7000 issued   1500.00
(Laslo states official type has Chobillon hallmark and BRONZE impressed on rim; copy has MADE IN FRANCE & BRONZE-cast?)

4.Czechoslovakia-by Otakar Spaniel-about 90,000 issued   125.00
(Laslo states that there are 2 reissues after World War II without Spaniel's name;four unofficial types, and one copy-French made.)

5.France-by Alexandre Morlon-approximately 2,000,000   20.00
6.France-rejected design by Charles-unofficial type I   175.00
7.France-by M.Pautot-unofficial type II   300.00
(According to Laslo there are five other unofficial types.)

8.Great Britain-by William McMillan-over 6,000,000   10.00
(According to Laslo two copy types have been seen. However, the originals are so plentiful, and most are named.)

9.Greece-by Henry Nocq-approximately 200,000 issued   150.00
(According to Laslo there are three unofficial types.)

10.Italy-by G.Orsolini-various makers   25.00
(According to Laslo there are five official types;two official reissues, and three unofficial types. Cast copies exist.)

11.Japan-approximately 700,000 issued   350.00
(Original type has barrel suspension;copies have a ball suspension-and may or may not have MADE IN FRANCE on rim.)

12.Portugal-by Joao da Silva-type I-small ball or 2 ring   rare
13.same-but no designer named with ball suspension-100,000   250.00
(Laslo states there are two unofficial types, and two copies. I believe that there are more than such.)

14.Rumania-by Kristesko-approximately 300,000 issued   300.00
(Laslo states there are three unofficial types; I have seen a cast copy.)

15.Siam-approximately 1500 issued   3000.00
(Laslo states there are two copy types. I have seen a cast copy.)

16.Union of South Africa-approximately 75,000-obverse is
the same as the British version; reverse is bilingual   75.00

17.United States of America-approximately 2,500,000-type
I-standard issue-knob suspension   20.00
18.U.S.A.-type II-wire loop or ring suspension   75.00
19.U.S.A.-type III-as II-stamped U.S.M. with 1 or 2 digits   rare
20.U.S.A.-recent strike by HLP or Lordship Industries   10.00
(Laslo refers to five copy types.)

See United States section for the various Army & Navy bars.

The Cuban Victory Medal used the obverse of the rejected French Charles version for its obverse.

The numbers listed as being issued are taken from Laslo's book.

1   12   4

9   10

7   16   6

14   17

YUGOSLAVIA

Serbia 1804-1882-Principality
Serbia 1882-1919-Kingdom
Montenegro 1852-1910-Principality
Montenegro 1910-1919-Kingdom
Kingdom of Yugoslavia 1919-1945
Croatia 1941-1945-Nazi puppet state

The Orders, decorations and medals of Yugoslavia can be divided into the constituent parts as shown by the political units above.

Serbia was the basis of the unified South Slav state, and as such absorbed several territories after the end of World War I and the break up of the Austro-Hungarian Empire, to form the Kingdom of the Serbs, Croats and Slovenes (Yugoslavia), which was then disrupted by World War II, and replaced by the later Communist state.

The awards of Serbia, as a longer lived state, and the nucleus of Yugoslavia, are necessarily wider in scope, and more common. The collector may be confused by the fact that both Serbia and Montenegro honored the hero Milosh Oblitch, although the two medals are completely different in appearance. The campaign medals of Serbia are a clear reflection of its struggle to maintain its independence, and its expansion.

The Orders and decorations of Montenegro were of short duration but of lasting beauty, especially of the Danilo Order in its varieties.

The awards of Croatia are of some interest to the collector of German World War II items, as Croatian decorations were frequently given to members of the German Armed Forces. Since many of the awards were made in Germany it is likely that the collector must be careful about copies.

As a final note, it should be pointed out that before World War I Serbian and Montenegrin Orders were generally made in Vienna, Austria. After the war Serbian/Yugoslavian Orders were made in Switzerland by the firm of Huegenin.

CROATIA
Nazi puppet state-1941-1945

Order of the Crown of Zvonimir-1941

1.Grand Cross badge	700.00
2.Grand Cross badge with swords	750.00
3.Grand Cross badge with oakleaves	800.00
4.Grand Cross breast star	650.00
5.Grand Cross breast star with swords	700.00
6.Grand Cross breast star with oakleaves	750.00
7.I Class neck badge (with star)	600.00
8.I Class neck badge with swords (with star)	650.00

9.I Class neck badge with oakleaves (with star)	600.00
10.I Class breast star	600.00
11.I Class breast star with swords	650.00
12.I Class breast star with oakleaves	500.00
13.I Class neck badge (without star)	500.00
14.I Class neck badge with swords (without star)	550.00
15.I Class neck badge with oakleaves (without star)	500.00
16.II Class-pin back cross	350.00
17.II Class with swords	400.00
18.II Class with oakleaves	425.00
19.III Class-breast badge	300.00
20.III Class with swords	325.00
21.III Class with oakleaves	350.00
22.Silver Medal	200.00
23.Silver Medal with oakleaves	225.00
24.Bronze Medal	150.00
25.Bronze Medal with oakleaves	175.00
26.Iron Medal	100.00
27.Iron Medal with oakleaves	125.00

Order of the Iron Trefoil-1941

28.I Class-neck badge	600.00
29.I Class with oakleaves	650.00
30.II Class-pin back cross	500.00
31.II Class with oakleaves	550.00
32.III Class-worn from 2nd buttonhole of tunic	325.00
33.III Class with oakleaves	375.00
34.IV Class-breast badge	225.00
35.IV Class with oakleaves	275.00

Croatian Order of Merit-1942

36.Grand Cross badge-for Christians	550.00
37.Grand Cross badge-for Muslims	1000.00
38.Grand Cross breast star-for Christians	550.00
39.Grand Cross breast star-for Muslims	1000.00
40.I Class badge-for Christians (with star)	350.00
41.I Class badge-for Muslims (with star)	750.00
42.I Class breast star-for Christians	350.00
43.I Class breast star-for Muslims	750.00
44.I Class badge-for Christians	350.00
45.I Class badge-for Muslims	750.00
46.II Class badge-for Christians	250.00
47.II Class badge-for Muslims	500.00
48.III Class badge-for Christians	225.00
49.III Class badge-for Muslims	400.00

Medal for Bravery-1941
50.Gold Medal	350.00
51.Large Silver Medal	225.00
52.Small Silver Medal (to next of kin-officers)	175.00
53.Small Bronze Medal (to next of kin-Enlisted Men)	100.00

Wound Medal-1943
54.Gold Medal	125.00
55.Iron (zinc)	75.00

56.Independence Commemorative-1918;-1943	175.00

57.Incorporation of Dalmatia Medal-1943	rare

Various Badges of the Croat State-beware of copies
58.Labor Service Sports Badge	175.00
59.Army Legion Badge	300.00
60.Naval Legion Badge	350.00
61.Air Force Legion Badge	350.00
62.Pilot's Badge	350.00
63.Air Crew-Radio Operator Badge	350.00
64.Croat Legion Badge-Italian Army	350.00

MONTENEGRO
Principality 1852-1910
Kingdom 1910-1919-then absorbed into Yugoslavia

Royal Family Order of St Peter-1852-1918
65.Badge of the Order	5000.00

Order of Danilo-1852-1918
66.Grand Cross badge-50mm	750.00
67.Grand Cross breast star-83mm	650.00
68.Grand Officer badge-47mm	550.00
69.Grand Officer breast star-70mm	500.00
70.Commander badge-50mm	550.00
71.Knight	400.00
72.Silver Merit Cross (enameled)	450.00

(Note: There are several versions of this Order. The values listed are for the most common insignia.)

Milosh Oblitch Medal for Bravery
73.Type I-reverse dated 1847-gold or silver/gilt	rare
74.Type II-reverse dated 1851-gold or silver/gilt	850.00

(Note: The above should not be confused with the Serbian medal of the same name, which is far more common.)

YUGOSLAVIA

Bravery Medal
75.Type I-cylindrical suspension on medal   450.00
76.Type II-with ball suspension   350.00
(Note: There several variations of number 76.)

77.Battle of Grahovo Medal-1858   rare

78.Medal for Heroism-1862-silver   rare

79.Independence Medal-1875-1878   200.00

Medal for Zeal-1895
80.I Class-gold or silver/gilt   750.00
81.II Class-silver   200.00
(Note: There are two variations of this medal distinguished only by the type of
suspension.)

82.Prince Danilo's Wedding Medal-1899   100.00

Fortieth Anniversary Medal-Prince Nicholas-1860-1900
83.Gold   rare
84.Silver   300.00
85.Bronze   200.00

Fiftieth Anniversary Medal-Nicholas I-1860-1910
86.Gold (gilt)   150.00
87.Silver   rare

Red Cross Order-1912-1919
88.Type I-reverse dated 1912   400.00
89.Type II-reverse dated 1912-1913   300.00
90.Type III-reverse undated for World War I   400.00

Red Cross Medal-1913-1919
91.I Class-gilt   275.00
92.Silvered   225.00

93.Balkan Wars Commemorative Medal-1913   500.00

94.Order for the Freedom of Montenegro-1919   400.00

SERBIA
Principality 1804-1882; Kingdom 1882-1918

Order of Milosh the Great-1899-1903
95.I Class badge   2500.00
96.I Class breast star   2800.00

97.II Class neck badge	2000.00
98.II Class breast star	2800.00
99.III Class neck badge	2000.00
100.IV Class breast badge	1250.00

Order of the White Eagle-1882-1915
Type I-cipher on reverse-1882-1903

101.Grand Cross badge	1000.00
102.Grand Cross badge with swords	1200.00
103.Grand Cross breast star	700.00
104.Grand Cross breast star with swords	850.00
105.Grand Officer badge	600.00
106.Grand Officer badge with swords	650.00
107.Grand Officer breast star	550.00
108.Grand Officer breast star with swords	600.00
109.Commander	600.00
110.Commander with swords	650.00
111.Officer	400.00
112.Officer with swords	450.00
113.Knight	350.00
114.Knight with swords	400.00

Type II-dated 1882 on reverse-1903-1915

115.Grand Cross badge	800.00
116.Grand Cross badge with swords	850.00
117.Grand Cross breast star	650.00
118.Grand Cross breast star with swords	700.00
119.Grand Officer badge	550.00
120.Grand Officer badge with swords	600.00
121.Grand Officer breast star	500.00
122.Grand Officer breast star with swords	550.00
123.Commander	550.00
124.Commander with swords	600.00
125.Officer	350.00
126.Officer with swords	400.00
127.Knight	300.00
128.Knight with swords	350.00

Order of Takovo-1865-1903 (The badges bear several ciphers)

129.Grand Cross badge	650.00
130.Grand Cross badge with swords	700.00
131.Grand Cross breast star	600.00
132.Grand Cross breast star with swords	650.00
133.Grand Officer badge	550.00
134.Grand Officer badge with swords	600.00
135.Grand Officer breast star	500.00
136.Grand Officer breast star with swords	550.00

137.Commander	550.00
138.Commander with swords	600.00
139.Officer	375.00
140.Officer with swords	400.00
141.Knight	200.00
142.Knight with swords	250.00

Order of St Sava-1883-1945
Type I-red robes-reverse cipher "M"-1883-1903

143.Grand Cross badge	700.00
144.Grand Cross breast star	650.00
145.Grand Officer badge	550.00
146.Grand Officer breast star	500.00
147.Commander	550.00
148.Officer	375.00
149.Knight	275.00

Type II-red robes-reverse date 1883

150.Grand Cross badge	450.00
151.Grand Cross breast star	450.00
152.Grand Officer badge	325.00
153.Grand Officer breast star	325.00
154.Commander	325.00
155.Officer	250.00
156.Knight	150.00

Type III-green/yellow robes-reverse date 1883

157.Grand Cross badge	400.00
158.Grand Cross breast star	400.00
159.Grand Officer badge	275.00
160.Grand Officer breast star	275.00
161.Commander	275.00
162.Officer	150.00
163.Knight	100.00

Order of Karageorge-1904-1915

164.Grand Cross badge	800.00
165.Grand Cross badge with swords	850.00
166.Grand Cross breast star	750.00
167.Grand Cross breast star with swords	800.00
168.Grand Officer badge	650.00
169.Grand Officer badge with swords	700.00
170.Grand Officer breast star	600.00
171.Grand Officer breast star with swords	650.00
172.Commander	650.00
173.Commander with swords	700.00

174.Knight	500.00
175.Knight with swords	550.00
176.Merit Cross	400.00
177.Merit Cross with swords	450.00

Natalie Order-1878-1903
Type I-cipher "H"

178.I Class-gilt	550.00
179.II Class-silver	450.00

Type II-cipher "N"

180.I Class	550.00
181.II Class	450.00
182.Red Cross Order-1876	250.00
183.Medal of St Andrew-1858	300.00
184.Medal for Bravery-silver-1876	400.00
185.Medal for Bravery-bronze/gilt-Milosh IV-1877	350.00
186.Campaign Service Medals-1876-1878	125.00
187.Devoted Service Medal-1877-1878	150.00
188.Military Merit Medal-gilt-1883	50.00
189.Medal for Bravery-Milan I-King-1885-1886	350.00
190.Bulgarian War Campaign Medal-1885-1886	125.00

Marksmanship and Proficiency Medals

191.Military Sharpshooting Medal	35.00
192.Machine Gun Proficiency Medal	50.00
193.Artillery Proficiency Medal	50.00
194.Civil Merit Medal-1902-gilt	40.00

Coronation Medal-Peter I-1903

195.Gold Medal (gilt)	300.00
196.Silver Medal	200.00
197.Bronze Medal	150.00
198.Insurrection & Coronation Commemorative-1804-1904	150.00

Medal for Bravery-1912

199.Gold (gilt)	350.00
200.Silver	175.00

YUGOSLAVIA

201.	Devoted Service Medal-1913	75.00

Milosh Oblitch Medal-1913 (For bravery-see also Montenegro)

202.	Gold Medal (genuine gold)	rare
203.	Gold Medal-gilt	400.00
204.	Silver	175.00

Balkan Wars Medals-1912-1913

205.	1st Balkan War Medal-1912	75.00
206.	2nd Balkan War Cross-1913	50.00
207.	Cross of Mercy-1912	75.00
208.	Red Cross Medal-1913	50.00

YUGOSLAVIA
Kingdom (first known as Kingdom of Serbs, Croats & Slovenes)

Order of St Sava (see previous listings-continued as a Yugoslav Order.)

Order of the Crown-1929-1945

209.	Grand Cross badge	450.00
210.	Grand Cross breast star	450.00
211.	Commander I Class	325.00
212.	Commander I Class breast star	375.00
213.	Commander II Class	325.00
214.	Officer	200.00
215.	Knight	175.00

216.	Albanian Campaign-(Retreat to Albania-1915)	100.00
217.	Commemorative Cross 1914-18	50.00
218.	Cross for War Invalids	75.00
219.	Devoted Service Medal-silver	50.00
220.	Commemorative Medal of the Liberation of Southern Serbia-1912-1937	50.00
221.	Commemorative Medal of the Liberation of the Northern Territories-1919-1939	50.00
222.	World War II Commemorative Cross-1941-1945	150.00

(Note: This last decoration was issued by King Peter II in exile after World War II. I do not know how many were struck or "awarded", making a value difficult to determine.)

29
40 50 & 51 46

8 &13

72   71   94

65

75   73 & 74

88 - 90

103, 107, 117, 121   166

137   131

175   114 & 128   177

149, 156, 163

217 211 & 213 222

210 & 212

NOTES

NOTES